THE GREAT

SCAM

One Shrink's Personal Journey

Colin A. Ross, M.D.

Manitou Communications, Inc.

1701 Gateway, Suite 349
Richardson, TX 75080
Phone: 1-800-572-9588, FAX: 972-918-9069

www.manitoucommunications.com
www.rossinst.com
rossinst@rossinst.com

ISBN-10: 0-9704525-2-7
ISBN-13: 978-0-9704525-2-8

Library of Congress Card Number: 2004108974

Ross, Colin A.

The Great Psychiatry Scam: One Shrink's Personal Journey

ISBN-10: 0-9704525-2-7
ISBN-13: 978-0-9704525-2-8

1. Psychiatry 2. Autobiography 3. Mental Illness

Also By The Author

Northern Studies (1975)

Portrait Of Norman Wells (1979)

Adenocarcinoma And Other Poems (1984)

The Osiris Complex: Case Studies In Multiple Personality Disorder (1994)

Satanic Ritual Abuse: Principles Of Treatment (1995)

Pseudoscience In Biological Psychiatry (1995)

Dissociative Identity Disorder: Diagnosis, Clinical Features, And Treatment Of Multiple Personality, Second Edition (1989/1997)

Spirit Power Drawings: The Foundation of a New Science (2004)

Songs For Two Children: On Dissociation and Human Energy Fields (2004)

Schizophrenia: Innovations in Diagnosis and Treatment (2004)

The CIA Doctors: Human Rights Violations By American Psychiatrists (200/2006)

The Trauma Model: A Solution To The Problem Of Comorbidity In Psychiatry (2000/2007)

Moon Shadows:Stories of Trauma & Recovery (2007)

TABLE OF CONTENTS

Dedicated to those who have been abused by psychiatrists.
Verbal, emotional, physical, sexual abuse. Neglect.
Political abuse. Mind control experimentation.
To all victims of The Great Psychiatry Scam.

PRODUCT WARNING LABEL

Notice. The Department of Agriculture has determined that certain materials in this book may be harmful to your mental health, your ego integrity, or your olfactory apparatus. The risk of such adverse reactions has been determined to be especially high for psychiatrists.

Certain paragraphs in this book may be mistaken for manure. Any resemblance to such material is purely coincidental. Other passages take the form of Dr. Seuss rhyming and quipping for adults. These passages should not be mistaken for signs of mental illness, mania, loose associations, poor judgment, or lousy writing skills on the part of the author. The author, who is a trained psychiatrist, certifies that his mental health and writing skills are fine.

This book contains a great deal of satire. The jokes might seem at times not to match the gravity of the subject matter. Humor has been an essential survival strategy for the author.

If the psychiatrists made fun of in this book are offended by the humor, they should consult a psychiatrist.

The U.S. Geological Service has certified that the strata and substrata of this book contain both gems and nuggets, in addition to pockets of gas.

The Department of Health and Human Services has certified that this book could be effective therapy for the field of psychiatry, if the psychiatrists agreed to participate in treatment. The Department of Energy has conducted extensive studies of the author and found his chakras to be in working order. Finally, the Central Intelligence Agency has reviewed the manuscript using the latest satellite technology and certified it to be intelligent.

The opinions expressed in this book are solely those of the author; they are not endorsed by and are not the responsibility of Manitou Communications. However, Manitou Communications agrees to make its opinions available should it formulate any such opinions at any time in the future. By virtue of reading this Product Warning Label, the reader has provided informed consent to the use of said Product. The reader should consult a Board Certified psychiatrist or other physician concerning any adverse reactions to the Product.

FOREWORD

"Into whatever houses I enter, I will go into them for the benefit of the sick and will abstain from every voluntary act of mischief and corruption, and further, from the seduction of females or males...

While I continue to keep this oath unviolated, may it be granted to me to enjoy life and practice of the art, respected by all men, in all times, but should I trespass and violate this oath, may the reverse be my lot."
(The Hippocratic Oath)

Colin A, Ross, M.D., a psychiatrist, has upheld the physician's oath to which he swore upon completion of medical school in 1981.

In fact, Dr. Ross has trod several steps further in his service to mankind. He has dedicated his medical practice as well as his personal life to education, quality care, and advocacy for his patients and all of those tens of millions of vulnerable, traumatized people who need psychiatric diagnosis and treatment.

In 1985, as a bright young student of psychiatry, Dr. Ross received the prestigious Laughlin Fellowship from the American College of Psychiatrists. This fellowship is awarded to only fifteen psychiatry residents throughout North America annually, based on academic achievements and publications. Colin Ross has authored over one hundred scientific and medical publications including six papers in *The American Journal of Psychiatry*, and to date has published ten books. Just two-and-a-half years after finishing his psychiatry residency, Colin A. Ross, M.D. authored a definitive psychiatric textbook on the diagnosis and treatment of multiple personality disorder.

I met Colin Ross just three-and-a-half years ago when my legal associates and I began a lengthy investigation into one of the most famous medical malpractice cases of the twentieth century. Our client, Chris Costner Sizemore, is the real Eve from the best-selling non-fiction book and Academy Award-winning motion picture, *The Three Faces of Eve*.

Through this joint investigation we have now proven and thoroughly documented that Corbett H. Thigpen, M.D., Chris Sizemore's psychiatrist and co-author of *The Three Faces of Eve*, financially exploited, sexually abused, and mentally controlled his patient for over four decades.

During his fifteen years of practice, Dr. Ross has become too familiar with the pain of running head on into one brick wall after another in his attempt to deliver quality medical care to his many patients.

Colin Ross has too often felt the sting of negative media attacks, fed by the good ole' boys of the old school of psychiatry. His character has even been battered by misguided bureaucrats from sensitive government positions in

America, Canada, and the United Kingdom because Dr. Ross stepped too close to revealing the untouchable truths of the abuses of psychiatry in the name of national and international security.

It would have been easy for this bright young doctor to join forces with those who would throw their Hippocratic Oath out the window in their desire to make money at any cost.

In one of our last interviews with Dr. Thigpen, just before his death in 1999, Corbett Thigpen revealed that, under government contract, he had performed over two hundred frontal lobotomies in one afternoon on various unwitting convicts at the Georgia State Penitentiary, in the name of psychiatric research.

Colin Ross could be doing government contracted psychiatric research and perhaps assisting other psychiatrists in the creation of the next group of mind controlled Manchurian Candidates, however, that is not the Colin Ross I know, and you will get to know through the pages of this book.

The Great Psychiatry Scam: One Shrink's Personal Journey might be very entertaining – perhaps a satirical look at psychiatry today – if it were not for the fact that the revelations within these pages are a tragic statement of the general state of affairs in patient care and the overall lack of quality in psychiatry.

If the reader finds my friend, Colin Ross, to be a bit cynical or suffering from a great deal of angst, well, that's because he speaks from his heart, asserting his deep feelings of disappointment in the medical career he loves.

Dr. Colin Ross states that the medical care most psychiatric hospitals are able to provide is no better than the frayed, stained carpets the patients walk on as they enter the facilities – if they do arrive at the clinics at all for care, or if the clinics are still open. The desire is there, but the funds for care from private insurance or from government medical payments are just not adequate for providing quality mental health care. Look at your personal family health insurance policy. How much does it pay towards mental health coverage – including drug and alcohol abuse? I hope neither you nor any member of your family ever has to use this outdated, primitive insurance program.

There are hundreds of voices in Washington, D.C., and throughout the nation calling for better health care for the mentally ill – quality care, not just warehousing. However, little is being done to guarantee that those who need these services are going to get better treatment anytime soon because of the multitude of problems Colin Ross has documented so well in this writing.

Dig deep and try to get to know Colin A. Ross, M.D., through this great expose. Then dig a lot deeper and help the mentally ill and mentally challenged get the quality care they so desperately deserve and need.

There is no voice which can articulate with such emotional sincerity and honesty the message in this book better than Colin Ross has done. There is no one who can speak of his personal feelings, draw from his personal experiences, and give the reader his personal insight with such enthusiasm and straight talk as Dr. Colin Ross.

Listen carefully to the voice of this book, Colin A. Ross, M.D., for you may never again have the opportunity to hear the voice of one with such authority and experience. You may never have the opportunity to peer inside the hallowed halls and dark crevices of psychiatry with such an insider's view of the real truth. Dr. Colin A. Ross has mustered the guts to "go out of bounds," break the old boys chain, and tell us all of the dirty little secrets of his psychiatric professional peers. Heed the voice, and know the truth.

The personal revelations Colin Ross makes within *The Great Psychiatry Scam: One Shrink's Personal Journey* are extraordinary for one in his position. You must take this opportunity to heart, and experience a personal journey of awakening you will never forget.

Jerry Naylor
Former White House Appointee
President Ronald Reagan Administration

INTRODUCTION: SOME TOP SCAMS IN PSYCHIATRY

The profession of psychiatry ran a big scam in the twentieth century. On the public, on patients, and on itself. The Great Psychiatry Scam. So far, nothing looks different in the twenty-first century.

I can't credit my profession with the brains or organization to run the Scam consciously. As a psychiatry resident, I was sucked into the machine, but I spat myself out. I wrote this book. I would be embarrassed to be a psychiatrist, without putting the truth on the record. Otherwise people might think I'm like the boys in charge.

There are good individual people in psychiatry. People who practice decent medicine. But the field as a whole is a mess. The standards of thinking, research and scholarship in psychiatry are pathetic. They're far, far below other departments in the university, like chemistry or philosophy. The amount of science in day-to-day clinical psychiatry is nil.

Unbelievable? What about medications and brain scans? Read on, read on. I will prove to you that over 90% of medication prescriptions for psychiatric inpatients have no scientific basis.

Then there is the mental health of psychiatrists. It's abysmal. What is stressful about working in a psychiatric hospital? Not the patients. It's the staff. The majority of my job stress, I would say over 90%, comes not from the patients, but from the hospital staff. Psychiatrists and nurses are the worst.

Like every profession, psychiatry markets itself to the public. The components of the marketing package are a scam. You will hear about them in this book.

The belief system and the propaganda of twenty-first century psychiatry are no more scientific than the beliefs and behavior of any other cult. Psychiatrists scoff at people who believe in alien abductions, but their own belief system is no more scientific or grounded in reality. Psychiatrists get brainwashed into a group delusional system that controls how they understand mental illness and treat patients. The delusional system is bad news for patients.

Individual psychiatrists can be decent people. But if they buy into the delusional system, they are in trouble. In trouble and causing trouble. Think of this book as therapy for psychiatry. The patient is self-destructive, dangerous, powerful, and highly resistant to treatment.

Ready for a quick guided tour through some top scams in psychiatry? More details to follow in later chapters.

LSD Is A Dangerous Drug

What does psychiatry have to say about LSD? Let's turn to the 1990-page textbook, *Psychiatry* published by Drs. Tasman, Kay and Lieberman in 1997. Check this out from page 941:

> *LSD produces some features of schizophrenia, including a profound psychotic state, distractibility, social withdrawal, referential thinking, and delusions.*

The doctors know that LSD is a dangerous drug. Makes you psychotic. Right? This is based on science. Right? Well, there's part of the story the doctors forgot to tell you.

One of the big drugs in psychiatry these days is Prozac, manufactured by Eli Lilly Company. Prozac is one of the most widely prescribed drugs in the world. It works on serotonin. So does LSD.

Who was the first major manufacturer and distributor of LSD in North America? Beatniks? Columbians? The Mafia? No. Eli Lilly Company. Your psychiatrist forgot to tell you part of the story. I will tell you.

In 1953, the CIA provided Eli Lilly with $400,000.00 through its secret mind control program, MKULTRA, to manufacture and supply LSD. The clearance status of this grant, MKULTRA Subproject 18, was TOP SECRET. Another TOP SECRET contract, MKULTRA Subproject 6, was for $5,000.00, also in 1953. Subproject 6 was to develop a secure supply of LSD, and Subproject 18 was for the manufacturing. I obtained all the MKULTRA documents from the CIA through the Freedom of Information Act.

The first acid heads in North America were psychiatrists and spies. This included Dr. Joel Elkes, Chairman of the Department of Psychiatry at Johns Hopkins University, who first took LSD in the late 1940's. He talked about his LSD trips in a 1970 newspaper interview.

The shrinks worked with the CIA and military to give LSD to thousands of citizens in the 1950's and 1960's, without informed consent. This included giving LSD daily to children as young as five years old for weeks and months at a time.

How do I know about that? I went to the medical school library and photocopied the published papers describing the experiments.

Was the doctor who gave LSD and psilocybin to hundreds of children age five to twelve, some mad scientist hidden in a basement somewhere? No. She was Dr. Lauretta Bender, a much revered child psychiatrist whose obituary appeared in a recent issue of *The American Journal of Psychiatry*. You have to be a real big shot in psychiatry to get a full-page obituary in *The American Journal of Psychiatry*, also called The Green Journal.

You won't get this history from your shrink. It is left out of the lecture series provided to doctors in training to become psychiatrists. Psychiatric history has been rewritten, glossed over, and forgotten by psychiatrists. I'll try to change that. The CIA and LSD story is told in my book, *The CIA Doctors: Human Rights Violations By American Psychiatrists*.

Incest: One Family In A Million In North America

I went to medical school from 1977 to 1981 and I took my psychiatry residency from 1981 to 1985. In eight years of training I received absolutely no instruction on childhood sexual abuse or its consequences. No exam questions, no lectures, no handouts, no case conferences, nothing. Absolutely nothing.

Childhood sexual abuse simply didn't exist. The Bible of Psychiatry I used during my training was the 1980 edition of the *Comprehensive Textbook of Psychiatry*. It was a three-volume textbook with 3,000 pages, two columns per page, that told you everything there was to know about psychiatry.

In this textbook there is one paragraph on the rates of incest in North America. There is one reference to a 1955 study saying that incest occurs in one family out of a million in North America.

In reality, real reality, not psychiatric reality, incest occurs in more than one family out of one hundred in North America. Psychiatry was out by a factor of 10,000.

Nowadays it is no longer possible, politically, for a silver-haired clinician to stand up at a meeting and declare that in forty years of practice, he has never seen a sexually abused child. Nowadays, this doctor would be regarded as an idiot, a dinosaur or both. He always was. Such declarations were applauded at the Old Boys Club twenty years ago

From the perspective of day-in and day-out psychiatry, at the beginning of the third millennium, sexual abuse is not relevant to diagnosis. It is not relevant to treatment. For all practical purposes, it doesn't exist.

"Sure, there's a lot of sexual abuse going on. But we don't deal with that here."

That's the working policy of psychiatry in 99% of inpatient facilities in North America. If you asked a staff member directly, he or she might huff and puff and give you some bureau-speak about comprehensive treatment planning. It's all smoke.

For all practical purposes, in the fine year 2007, incest only affects one family in a million in North America.

In *The Dallas Morning News* on May 19, 1999 (way back in the last millennium), right there on page 9A, was an article on new legislation in Japan. The new laws made childhood prostitution and pornography illegal for the first time. The article pointed out that, "Newsstands and bookstores in Japan stock a selection of magazines featuring glossy photos of little girls in swimsuits or short skirts, with slightly suggestive close-ups of thighs, crotches and buttocks not completely covered by panties."

Full-tilt hard core child pornography is readily available in red light districts in Japan. Interpol has estimated that 70% to 80% of the child pornography available on the Internet comes from Japanese sources.

A Japanese Professor of Psychiatry told me there is very little child sexual abuse in Japan.

"Uh-huh. Very little child sexual abuse in Japan. Thank you, professor."

We've Proven That Schizophrenia Is Genetic

I was taught in my psychiatry residency, from 1981 to 1985, that schizophrenia is a genetic disease. This was not a theory. It was a proven scientific fact. None of my professors questioned the dogma. No one ever raised questions about the data. And no one actually read the original studies. It was accepted folklore. All based on the Danish adoption studies.

The Danish adoption studies were published in the sixties. I was told that they proved the genetic basis of schizophrenia beyond doubt or question. Turns out that was complete bullshit. This is all laid out by Al Pam in our book, *Pseudoscience in Biological Psychiatry*. And by me in my book, *Schizophrenia: Innovations in Diagnosis and Treatment*.

I'm right. Absolutely right beyond a shadow of a doubt. The gene for schizophrenia is a lie. A marketing scam perpetrated by academic psychiatry to get research money and prestige. The public has bought it. The psychiatrists have bought it. The drug companies are applauding. Why? Whatever makes mental illness be biological sells drugs.

Alcoholism: The Disease You Have To Decide Not To Have Anymore

Alcoholism is a disease. This lie has been bought by the public big time. Celebrities talk about battling the disease. AA members talk about the disease. It's more horse.

It took me a while to catch on. My Professors told me that alcoholism is a genetic disease. Like the schizophrenia scam, no one had actually looked at the data. Everyone knew it was true because some big shot researcher from New York or Harvard or UCLA said it was true. This big shot had big grants and published in big journals. His big shot buddies all agreed with him. Who was I, little old Colin

Ross in little old Winnipeg, Canada, to disagree with all these big shots?

I listened to the AA people explain that you have to work your steps.

"Ya got ta work yer steps. Step one comes first. Ya got to surrender ta yer higher power. Ya got ta admit ya can't lick the booze yerself. Till ya works yer first step, ain't nothin' we kin do fer ya. That's how it is. It ain't pretty, but that's how it is."

Wait a minute! Alcoholism is a genetic disease? You've got to make a commitment to sobriety and work your steps? What kind of a biological disease is that? Why don't we have Twelve Step Programs for leukemia, stroke, AIDS, Hodgkin's Disease and kidney failure? Well, duh. The Twelve Steps don't do anything for medical diseases.

OK. I get it. Then alcoholism is not a medical disease. That's why the treatment is group therapy and AA. Makes sense.

"No, ya don't git it. Drinkin's a disease, like the doctor said. Yer daddy drank. Yer grandpappy drank. Yer a lush. It's in yer genes."

Alcoholism is a disease. It's a lie

Dr. Sigmund Fraud

You may have heard of Dr. Sigmund Fraud. He grew up in East Texas, not far from Paris, Texas, I think, if I've got my geography right, in a town called Vienna. Dr. Fraud started a school of therapy called psychoanalysis. Psychoanalysis completely dominated psychiatry for most of the twentieth century. Even today, most psychiatrists who do therapy do psychoanalytic psychotherapy. Psychoanalytic psychotherapy is a watered down version of Fraudian psychoanalysis for lazy people.

In the entire twentieth century, not one single piece of scientific data was generated by psychiatry showing that psychoanalysis works. There is absolutely no scientific evidence of any kind showing that Freudian therapy works. Oops! I mean, Fraudian. Don't get the two confused. This is the biggest of all psychiatric scams.

Throughout the twentieth century psychiatrists knew for a fact with total certainty that 99.9% of the childhood sexual abuse described by their female patients was Oedipal fantasies. This was not a theory or hypothesis. The doctors knew it with the full weight and authority of medical science. They told the women their memories were fantasies. Something doesn't smell right in the history of psychiatry.

You have now completed a brief tour through some top scams in psychiatry. They set the stage for my performance. This book. *The Great Psychiatry Scam*.

"Turn down the lights. Turn up the music. Spot light on Dr. Ross, now. Yeah, yeah. Let's hear some of that sweet shrink music, now. Yeah, yeah. Yeah, yeah. Oh, sweet shrink music."

I. BIRTH TO MED SCHOOL

1

TRUE MEMORIES OF EARLY AMNESIA

"I was born in a class-five hurricane, and I howled, at the night, the rain and the driving mediocrity. But it's all right now, in fact it's a gas. Jumping Jack Flash, it's a gas. Jumping Jack Flash, it's a gas, gas, gas."

Which reminds me of Aunt Jemima, Mexican jumping beans, and flatus. Which reminds me of psychiatry.

Which in turn reminds me of a patient I interviewed as a psychiatrist in Winnipeg in the 1980's. He said that he had been persecuted by Greyhound Bus Line for 2,000,000 years and that the RCMP had decapitated him several days previously. When I asked how he could be talking to me when he had been decapitated, he shrugged, raised his hands as a disclaimer, and said, "I'm just telling you what happened."

If that philosophy is good enough for him, it's good enough for me. I'll make it the foundation of this book.

I was born in Sarnia, Ontario, Canada, on July 14, 1950 at St. Joseph's Hospital. Across the river from Port Huron, Michigan, where we used to go for banana splits. They didn't have banana splits like that in Canada, so we would drive across the Clearwater Bridge to get them. There are a lot of things you can get in America that you can't get in Canada, I've learned over the years. Like expensive malpractice insurance and entry wounds from drive-by shootings.

Before I was born, my mother worked at the Children's Aid in Sarnia, helping unwed mothers, arranging adoptions. During the first year of my life, two unwed mothers lived in our house. I figure they gave me some working class nurturance that helped ground me in practical reality. Also there was the family down the street. Jackie, one of many children in that family, was my friend, the same age as me.

It seemed like he had about fifteen brothers and sisters. They slept in one or two rooms. His dad was an out-of-work alcoholic, and it seems like one of his older sisters wore really tight sweaters and had a kid herself. They had a very chaotic family and the boys broke a lot of rules. Probably half of them are in jail by now and probably a few have died of AIDS. I wouldn't want to be Jackie, but I learned a lot from his family about how other families can be very different, and live by very different rules. It was my first experience in trans-cultural psychiatry.

When I was five, a few people in Sarnia started having TVs. We didn't have one yet, but on Saturday mornings I'd go down to Jackie's and watch *Fury* and some other really cool programs. I loved the TV. Jackie's older brother taught me about picking up pieces of asphalt and chewing them. They lived beside a lumber yard that had great smells, but none as good as the smell of warm tar in the summer.

We had a garden outside in the back yard with tomatoes in it. One time I was walking through the plants and came face to face with a huge spider sitting in the middle of its web. That scared me. There are other early memories.

I remember the tornado of 1955. One man got killed. I remember our next door neighbors coming over to hide in our basement because they didn't have a basement. I remember the pieces of straw imbedded in our back door and the shattered window glass in the bathtub. And our apple tree blown over and my bike across the road under a blown-over tree.

Across the road a man had a tulip farm and down Exmouth Street there was a farm with horses. I remember walking the other way down Exmouth Street with my dad one morning on the way to the store. I was very, very impressed by the huge strides he took and how fast he walked. My mom used to give me a few cents to go buy candy. I liked the black licorice pipes with red sprinkle tobacco the best.

I remember Jerry lived next door, closer than Owen's house. His mom awoke my artistic imagination. She painted. What looked to me like amazing gorgeous paintings of birch trees. It was probably very conventional Sunday-painter art, but it touched me deeply. I thought that one day I could be an artist, a creator of sacred works.

I remember one time it rained a lot. We were wading in a big pond on Melrose Avenue - we lived on the corner of Exmouth and Melrose. Melrose was just a dirt road. I cut my knee on a piece of glass in the pond, still have a scar there. I went to the emergency department and watched as the doctor snipped off a dangling bit of my flesh, then sewed me up. I remember being totally calm and not alarmed at all, and watching the doctor snip off the bit of flesh with clinical detachment. The doctor told me to lie down flat but I stayed propped up on my elbows so I could watch.

I remember we took Jerry on a trip to Detroit with us one time. We walked into a pet store and a Mynah bird croaked, "Hello, Jerry!"

That impressed me and Jerry.

On my fifth or sixth birthday party I ran into the corner of the TV set and had to get stitches. There's a little bump in a straight line there to this day. But I never broke any bones. Another time I was sitting beside a girl I liked in kindergarten and a workman with a very wrinkled old face looked in the window at her. She got scared and cried. The workman got very upset and came in the classroom to try to calm her down, but she only got more scared.

In Ontario we learned to read and do arithmetic starting in kindergarten. I remember the teacher would give us quizzes in which there were four or five objects, all identical except for one. When no one in the class could solve one problem, she called on me to solve it, and I did. I remember being very proud of that. And I remember playing marbles in the school ground, and my collection of gorgeous marbles.

One time on the way home from school I went over to the creek running near the road I walked on. There was a raft I got on and poled along for a ways. It was a semi-rural world. One time the circus came into town right down Exmouth, past our house, elephants walking along and everything.

Another time a teenager got hit by a car in front of our house and died. My dad went out and attended to him. I had to stay in the house. Once there was a power line down in front of the house, I think it was after the tornado. The bare end of the power line shot sparks as the wire flipped around on the road. Sometimes we would drive to London, Ontario to visit my grandfather and grandmother. They had big turkey dinners and great food. Grandpa had been a missionary in Korea, where my dad lived from age six months to thirteen years. My dad told great stories about Korea. And about World War II, in which he saw combat and took shrapnel in the back of his shoulder, in south-eastern Holland.

I didn't know it then, but later my dad said he couldn't look at raw meat for a long time after the war, and had nightmares. One time his pistol jammed and he had to kill a German soldier in hand-to-hand combat. He was the only survivor in his platoon twice. His brother, my uncle Bob, was a pilot. Uncle Bob was shot down, missing in action and presumed dead in the Sahara three times. My grandmother had to wait three times to find out he was alive.

Uncle Bob had two wives die of cancer. His only child, my cousin Robin, was killed when his fighter jet crashed on a training run. He and the pilot he was training bailed out at high speed a couple of hundred feet above the ground when the engines failed, but didn't survive the impact.

My Grandpa Ross was a Gold Medalist at McGill. My Grandma Ross grew up on a ranch in Kansas just north of the Oklahoma border and knew some real Indians. I'm related to the Surgeon-General of the Union Army, William King, through my father, William King Ross.

On my mother's side, I am a tenth-generation Canadian. French Canadian through my Grandpa, A. Sydney Bruneau, who was also a Gold Medalist at McGill. Je suis Canadien. He was a lawyer, was the mayor of Westmount in the early 1950's and lived in a wonderful house on Bellevue Avenue in Montreal, where my mother grew up. It was a beautiful house with many rooms, fine antique furniture, many floors, and a breakfast nook where I ate the best marmalade I ever tasted. Grandpa Bruneau had a study lined with books and a really beautiful collection of canes that he kept in a container. I have a small cane collection too. Grandpa published some literary articles and wrote about Shakespeare. I published a poem about Shakespeare in my collection of poems, *Adenocarcinoma and Other Poems*.

In the summers when she was growing up, my mother lived at Lake Manitou in the Lawrentians north of Montreal, at the summer home. I went there too, and visited my cousins, swam in the lake and watched the grown ups play tennis in amazingly clean, white clothes. I loved the boat house. I went to my Aunt Ida's house near Manitou. She was my favorite aunt because she made us things for Christmas each year, often out of leather. She worked at a TB hospital doing crafts with the Eskimo patients. One year I made her a necklace out of a leather cord and coins I had flattened on the railroad tracks by setting them out for trains to run over.

Aunt Ida died in 1999. I formed a multi-media publishing company in 1995 called Manitou Communications. I chose the name because of Lake Manitou, the fact that I grew up in Manitoba and because Manitou means Great Spirit. The name of my company is Great Spirit Communications. We moved to Manitoba just after I turned seven.

Those are some of the things I remember from my life in Sarnia. I am so glad I grew up in a semi-rural environment in a small town. That beginning helped me stay grounded in the biosphere. As a result, I have never been abducted by aliens.

2

THE WHITESHELL

We moved from Sarnia to Winnipeg, Manitoba in early August, 1957. At that time, there were only two tall buildings in Winnipeg, The Hudson's Bay Company and Eaton's, both six stories tall. The population was about 350,000. We flew on Air Canada in a Lancaster propeller plane, through a thunderstorm. We lived in a rented cabin on West Hawk Lake in the Whiteshell Forest Preserve for a few weeks, about ninety miles east of Winnipeg, until our house was ready. The water in West Hawk is very clear and cold. The lake was created by a meteor and is over five hundred feet deep. There could be sturgeon in it, like the sturgeon in the illustrated *Hiawatha* book that I read when I was a boy. It was from Longfellow's *Hiawatha* that I learned about Gitchi Manitou.

In 1959 we obtained a 99-year lease on a lot on a small lake further north in the Whiteshell. Jessica Lake. My spiritual home. The place where I would like my ashes scattered (it's quite a long ways from the headquarters of the Canadian Psychiatric Association). The Whiteshell is in the pre-Cambrian shield, the oldest rock in the world. There is a lot of exposed granite, with occasional veins of white quartz.

Jessica, like most lakes in the region, is shallow, reed-filled and populated by lily pads, ducks, loons, beaver, many jack fish and a few pickerel. The Whiteshell River flows into Jessica Lake, then back out and onto Rainbow Falls and White Lake. It is part of the old fur trader route, the waterway of the *voyageurs*. Those old hard working ghosts are children compared to the old Indian presences. Across the outlet of the river from our cottage, around the far point, is a marsh I paddle to, with lily pads, irises, bull rushes, and heron droppings. You can dock your boat on the rocks and walk to a few scattered Indian rock formations. I would like my ashes to be scattered there when I die.

In the marsh are beaver houses. On the land are jack pine, birch, aspen, spruce and poplar. Saskatoon berries, blueberries, gooseberries and raspberries can be found. There are stands of wild roses. Very rarely, in the Whiteshell, you can find wild strawberries, especially in the sandy soil over by Big Whiteshell Lake, not far from the Indian Pipe I photographed. There are stands of white pine there, and sometimes you will find red pine. But it is the jack pine that predominate, in the open rocky places.

The spruce and larch predominate in the more marshy areas. Around the point, near the Indian rock formations, you can find crayfish in the shallow water, and many bits of crayfish shell in the heron droppings. Once I found an abandoned loon egg in a nest in the marsh there. Leeches are easily seen, and usually minnows. Often there will be turtles sunning on the rocks, or a beaver swimming out in the water. I have never seen a snapping turtle there, but there is one that sits on a rock just downstream from Pine Point Rapids. It is a prehistoric giant from hundreds of millions of years ago.

I have seen otter, badger, fox, deer, bear, moose, squirrel, chipmunk, rabbit, skunk, mouse, porcupine, and weasel. Prairie chicken, spruce grouse, ruffed grouse, bald eagle, turkey buzzard, great horned owl, blue jay and robin. Meadowlark, killdeer, woodpecker, and warbler. Swallow, great blue heron, merganser and teal, green-winged and blue-winged. Mallard, coot, goose, and many other waterfowl and songbirds. Garter snakes, frogs, toads, dragon flies, devil's darning needles, and once, a luna moth. Many types of butterfly. Caterpillars, lady bugs, water spiders, land spiders, and many unidentified bugs that swim in the water. All these I have known, seen, and studied. Raven and crow too.

I love the wild flowers in the Whiteshell, the mushrooms and fungi, and the lichens. There are many colors of lichen, gray, green, brown, black, orange and yellow. The first flowers in the spring are the prairie crocuses, which grow in a sandy area on the hiking trail to Pine Point Rapids. The trail is still boggy and wet, and there are still patches of snow when the crocuses bloom in April. June brings the lady slippers, white and purple, one of the most profound flowers in the world.

Columbine, lily of the valley, aster, fleabane, tiger lily, white daisy, blue bell, violet, and out on the prairie, as you are driving east to the Whiteshell, William Blake's sunflower. Marsh marigold, the white flower of the buffalo berry, pink corydalis, blossoming bushes of many types in the spring. All these I have seen and known.

The deepest sound in the world is the sound of the wind in the jack pine. The air is clear, cool, and clean. The wind touches your face with its living spirit. The sky is full of clouds, especially in the summer. Huge, towering thunderheads. The high cirrus clouds. In the morning, banks of fog over the lake and the marsh. At night, God is present, in the form of northern lights, green shimmering walls of light in the north. There too is Cygnus the Swan, and the other constellations.

I like to walk up the hill from our cabin. There are two routes, of which I prefer the more southerly. At the top of the hill you can sit and look west to White Lake and the sunset. There are many nooks, crannies, crevices, slopes and surfaces to climb and jump on. There is the thick dark brown lichen that sticks up off the rock, then the flat lichens, the mosses and the grasses. I love the foxtail grass the most, next to the bull-rushes and wild rice in the marshes. There you see the red-winged black bird.

On top of the hill you can look back at the lake, the small islands, the inlet and outlet of the Whiteshell River, the boat landing site across the lake, where the trail to Caddy Lake begins. All sacred things. All the work of God. The rocks are ancient, lasting, and secure. Civilizations come and go, mythologies are born and die, but the rock is always there. The snapping turtle has been feeding in the

Whiteshell River since before there were humans on the continent.

These were a few details about the Whiteshell. Twentieth century psychiatry has come and gone. The Whiteshell remains.

3

MAJOR WORK

We moved to Winnipeg just after my seventh birthday, in August 1957. After Labour Day, I started grade two. I was put in the dumb class but after a few weeks I was transferred to the smart class, where I stayed. In grade three I got my first pair of glasses. The first day I took them to school, my teacher asked me to come up to the front of the class and put them on. I did and everybody burst out laughing. I've always hated wearing glasses, and was very glad when I got contacts for the first time, in my forties. I'm really looking forward to getting laser surgery.

In grade three, everyone was given an I.Q. test in preparation for being put in an experimental program called Major Work. In grades four, five and six there were three classes, the dumb class, the in between class and Major Work, where the suck holes and smart kids were, including me. This was the best education I received until I got to the University of Alberta in 1975. Miss Marshall was our teacher for all three years. We did all kinds of special projects, put on plays, held debates, went on field trips, and best of all, gave speeches in front of the class.

There were about thirty kids in the class. Every week, three kids would give a talk for about ten minutes on any subject they wanted. The first talk I gave was on the Whiteshell. It was so good, Miss Marshall asked me to give it to the grade five Major Work class, which I did. The principal came to listen. Robert H. Smith Elementary School was a magic place. Mr. Peterson, the home room teacher for grade five Major Work, took a soccer ball out onto the playground each recess and kicked it incredibly high up in the air. I loved to watch him do that, and really admired him.

Over the three years, I gave talks on many different subjects. The Whiteshell, bees, rockets, hypnosis, extrasensory perception, Bridey Murphy, famous Canadian doctors, how a radio works. I built a Heath Kit short wave radio with my dad, and listened to it at night before I went to sleep, lying in my bed. I listened to a station from Lincoln, Nebraska, which was a very far away, mysterious place in a big, magic country called the United States. In 2006, I watched one of my sons play hockey in Lincoln - now I am part of that big world.

At Robert H. Smith, I was accepted and nurtured. I was recognized as a gifted child, was put in a special experimental program, and there were no restraints placed on my initiative or creativity. I read many books. Miss Marshall kept a big chart on the wall with everyone's name, and the number of books they had read outside school. Each week I walked over to the mobile library over by Brock Corydon School and took out books. I read about William Osler, Wilder Penfield and other Canadian doctors, about the north and wild animals, detective books, adventure books, all kinds of different topics.

In grade five, Peter and I were assigned as patrols for the kindergarten class, which got out at 11:30, half an hour before everyone else. Then in grade six we were regular patrols. At the end of grade six, I received the Citizenship Award, given each year to one graduating boy and girl for outstanding citizenship, performance, and contribution to the school.

It was in grade four that I decided to become a psychiatrist. My memory, accurate or not, is a single vignette. I was watching TV, black and white. A man was standing by an easel, explaining a diagram. It showed the outline of a human head in profile, with a line running through the middle of the head from back to front. Above the line was printed, Conscious Mind, below it, Unconscious Mind. I decided that I wanted to study the unconscious mind and learn how it worked. I was magnetized by the mystery of the unconscious mind and its strange, magic properties and functions. Little did I know what lay ahead for me, in Junior High School and in the profession of psychiatry.

4

OH, OH, JUNIOR HIGH

The world changed very quickly. Robert H. Smith was right across the alley from our house. I could throw a ball from my front yard over the school fence, into the school yard. I could get to my classroom in a couple of minutes. River Heights was down the end of the block and a couple of streets over. It was outside the cocoon. Instead of being the big kid, I was one of the little people. Some guys in grade nine, some of the flunkies, were even shaving already.

At River Heights Junior High School, we changed classes every period. Some of the teachers were crabby and negative, some were incompetent, and none knew you or cared personally about you the way Miss Marshall did. It was my first training in managed care and private for-profit psychiatry in the United States. Cold, impersonal, big, anonymous. The needs of the factory ground down the needs of the individual. At Robert H. it was different. I counted there. I was a person there. My love of learning was nurtured, my imagination was fed, my intellect was challenged. Not at River Heights.

In grade seven I had an old English teacher named Mrs. Parkinson. She seemed like she was in her seventies to me at the time. Now, of course, I don't consider seventy truly old. Mrs. Parkinson was the first adult who abused and hurt me intellectually, in my spirit and my imagination. I learned important lessons from her about the hostility and destructiveness of the outside world, which I had never experienced or understood before.

Our science teacher was Mr. Sanguin. I wrote in an essay that our science teacher was not very sanguine about our marks. Mrs. Parkinson got mad at me. She told me that Shakespeare said a pun is the lowest form of wit. She told me never to put any more puns in anything I wrote. On top of that, she had Mr. Bell, the Vice Principal, come down to our room, take me outside in the middle of class and talk to me in the hallway. Mr. Bell told me not to put any more puns in my writing again. This is how I almost developed Parkinson's Disease, which consists of a pathological hatred for creativity, wit and intellect, disavowed by the person with the disease. Fortunately, I was genetically resistant.

That was blow number one. The big blow came when I wrote a science fiction story for Mrs. Parkinson. It was about a boy who invented a time lens. When he looked in the lens, he could project himself back into the past, to any time he wanted to arrive at. He sent himself back to the time of Charlemagne. From there he projected himself to ancient Roman times. Then he decided to come back to the present. The problem was, when he came back to the present, he arrived at the moment in which he was projecting himself back to the time of Charlemagne. He instantly went back to the time of Charlemagne.

The boy got stuck in a loop. He could move around from place to place in the past, but every time he came back to the present, he went straight back to the time of Charlemagne. Therefore he could never move forward into the future. End of story.

Not the end of the story for Mrs. Parkinson, however. She read the story out loud to the class, ridiculed it, said it was completely impossible, and had the class laughing at me. That was when I really began to hate and despise the educational system. The educational factory was already brainwashing the future industrial drones and psychiatrists. I was already on the outside looking in, where I have been ever since. Thank you, Mrs. Parkinson, for ejecting me from the twentieth century's industrial complex so early. That did my soul good. Mrs. Parkinson did wonders for my integrity.

I had learned a related lesson two years earlier with Miss Marshall. Miss Marshall was never hostile, attacking, or belittling the way Mrs. Parkinson was, but she was wrong once, and I knew it. This was the first time I realized that grown ups could be wrong, not know the answer, and then try to bullshit their way out of the jam.

Miss Marshall was explaining about the rotation of the earth. I asked her, if the earth is rotating at such a high speed, why, when you jump up in the air, don't you come down several miles away? The earth should rotate a considerable distance underneath you while you are up in the air. At first, she didn't understand the question. Then she did, and provided her answer. She said that the air pushes you along, so you stay above the same spot.

I said, yeah, but if the wind is pushing you along when you are up in the air, then when you are standing on the ground, it should blow you over. There should be a huge wind all the time. Miss Marshall said that the air pushed you along, and that's just the way it was. That's how it worked. I stopped pushing for a better answer, and realized that she was faking it, didn't know the answer, and didn't have the guts to admit it. This was an important lesson in hypocrisy, lying and general phony behavior by grown ups, of which I have seen a great deal in psychiatry. But I still liked Miss Marshall, I just knew she had limitations. For that, I could easily forgive her.

Later, I learned that the answer to the problem was first provided by Galileo, who discovered the laws of angular momentum. Galileo's book, *Two New Sciences*, made a great impression on me when I read it less than ten years later. Besides his stupendous genius, I was most interested in the fact that Galileo was kept under house arrest by the Catholic Church for years for saying that the earth orbits the sun. The Catholic Church did not offer an official apology for this crime against humanity until 1992. Mrs. Parkinson's heirs will never apologize to me, but I don't need their apology, because I transformed her intellectual persecution of me into a valuable lesson, and used it to build a deeper and more spiritual discipline for myself. One that helped me survive the ugliness, pettiness, hypocrisy, superficiality and persecution of twentieth century psychiatry.

Things went down hill from there. Instead of loving the education I received at school, I grew to hate it. Mindless information crunching for the lobotomized. Standardized testing. Report cards. I still maintained an average over 90% even into grade nine. But things were never again the same. I have never gotten back to Robert H. Smith, have never had a benefactor, have never found an institution that valued and wanted my gifts. I've always been on the outside looking in, never accepted by the living dead. A mixed curse and blessing.

In grade eight we had a substitute I really despised. I forget her name. She was about two hundred and forty years old and decided she was going to teach us about rhythm in poetry. Within five years I was studying Gerard Manley Hopkins on my own. In my book of poetry, *Adenocarcinoma And Other Poems*, you can find several examples of sprung rhythm, the rhythm refined and developed by Hopkins. Likewise, in my 1000-line poem, *Songs For Two Children: On Dissociation and Human Energy Fields*. In my poetry, you can find examples of a property of language taught to me by the English literary critic, F.R. Leavis. In certain passages in Hopkins, Blake, Eliot, Donne and Shakespeare, the rhythm of the line actually enacts the meaning of the words, as in Hopkins' poem, *The Windhover*. This is not something you find in the scribblings of the hackademics or current literary giants.

Our substitute was going to teach us about iambic pentameter. She wrote a couple of lines, from Houseman I think, on the board, then pounded the chalk on the board as she read out the lines, pounding with each accented syllable. She made poetic meter dead, ugly, arbitrary and stupid. This is the attitude of the denizens of the industrial complex in North America early in the twenty-first century. They have been taught to hate poetry. To see it as irrelevant neo-Romantic fluff. The natural human love for meter and rhyme is attacked, suppressed and banished by the educational system, at least it was at River Heights in the 1960's.

The educational system began to do some amazing things in Junior High. Less than 10% of the students enjoyed music class, for instance. Everybody else hated it and found it completely boring, including me. Despite the fact that I took clarinet lessons for a year. Despite the fact that my parents met in the choir at McGill University. My brother earns his living as a clarinetist, my sister sings in local operas. We played recorder duets and trios in our home. We had a piano and an organ in our home. And I loved rock music as much as any kid, and listened to it all the time.

Go to any living culture in the world. Australian aborigine, Bushman of the Kalahari, English private school, or Tibetan monastery. You will find a spontaneous, spiritual love of music that is fostered, valued and nurtured. At River Heights, the educational system taught hatred of music. Everyone hated music class, except for a few geeks. What kind of a civilization is that? A society that tries to destroy the natural human love of music, rhyme and rhythm? Substitutes dead, mechanical noise for music, when the children were listening to the marvelous sounds of rock and roll on the radio. My hatred of music class came in handy when I read D.H. Lawrence's description of a recorder choir in an English public school – I got what he meant.

Thank you, River Heights Junior High School.

I remember when a substitute came to teach math for us one day, in grade eight. He was absolutely the coolest teacher I ever had in Junior High. Instead of mechanical training in the machinery of arithmetic, he opened my mind to the wonder of numbers. I don't remember the details, but he showed us patterns in numbers. Sort of like 18, 27, 36, 45, 54, 63, 72, 81. The two digits always add up to nine. I'm good at arithmetic but have absolutely no mind for higher mathematics. I just can't get there. At university, I had to work incredibly hard in an introductory calculus class, just to get a mark that wouldn't bar me out of medical school.

The educational system fostered a hatred of learning in the students at River Heights. It created a population suitable for industrial training after high school, but unsuitable for a real liberal arts education. That is one of the major problems in psychiatry today, the complete failure of liberal arts education in North America in the late twentieth century. The standards of thought, scholarship, evidence and argument in psychiatry are below those I would expect in a good high school debating club. I'm not exaggerating. I am completely serious and literal. The intellectual standards controlling psychiatry today are inferior to those I would expect in a good high school debating team, or a gifted A Level student in England.

But I did make the basketball team and was the highest scorer all three years of junior high. If I had a little more height, was born in the United States, and had proper coaching, I probably could have played for a small college on a scholarship. Oh well. Never would have made the NBA.

5

EXPELLED FROM SCHOOL - MY SECOND ACHIEVEMENT AWARD

My first award from the educational system was the Robert H. Smith Elementary School Citizenship Award, which I got in 1962. The next badge of honor was being expelled from River Heights Junior High School in 1965. By this time, I had played a trick on the unwitting behavioral managers of the inmates of River Heights Junior High. They gave detentions as punishment, believing that detentions would discourage undesirable behavior. Bad news, Neanderthal Man. Cro-Magnon Man is a little more complicated than that.

By grade eight, I viewed detentions as a badge of honor. I was proud to be one of the people with the most detentions in the school. The other guys who were regulars in detention are probably all on skid row or in jail now. What was I doing there? I became a rebel. I inverted the value system being foisted on me by the school. I was very interested in the bad boys in the school. Not sexually. No. My eyeballs were firmly locked onto the female breasts in the school. The bad boys had a quality that attracted, inspired and interested me profoundly. Marlon Brando and James Dean had it in the fifties, Elvis had it. Mrs. Parkinson didn't have it. Neither did the music teacher.

There was a whole other quality of being that was repressed, feared, discouraged and eventually expelled from River Heights. River Heights Junior High School was a goody-goody factory for conformists. Nine to five men. Depressed housewives of the future. But there was another group, already marginalized and alienated. In our school, they were the Blue Boys. They wore blue lumber jackets, pointed shoes, long hair and tight jeans. The sluts hung out with them, not the good girls. They smoked and drank. Soon they would have motorcycles.

This was Winnipeg, Canada in 1964 and 1965. There were no street drugs, no one had guns, except for hunting, no one ever got stabbed or robbed or assaulted in my neighborhood. No one's house was broken into. I didn't know anyone whose parents were divorced. Being bad didn't mean being antisocial or criminal on any serious level. I wasn't interested in the Blue Boys because they were future criminals or failures. They were alive. They were real men, just not matured yet. They stood with their shoulders hunched forward, their hands in their front pockets, in a bunch, off to the side, exuding sexuality, danger, breaking of rules, and a dark presence and energy. It wasn't evil. It was like the energy of a tree. Dark, pagan, pre-conscious, sensual. It was another way of being, that I would meet later in English farmers and Canadian Indians and Eskimo above the Arctic Circle. That I would touch in the books of D.H. Lawrence.

The Blue Boys could have been the gypsy in D.H. Lawrence's novella, *The Virgin and the Gypsy*. They embodied and exuded the energy of the horse in *St. Mawr*. Not a cerebral version of sensuality, a bodily one. The real thing. Real life. Ancient life, that goes back to the pre-Socratic philosophers and earlier, back before the ancient Greeks, to the rocks, trees, wind and sky of the Whiteshell.

At age fourteen, I didn't have a conscious intellectual map of where I was, or what I was experiencing. I rebelled instinctively. I became such a disruptive influence in my grade nine class that I was sent home for the last week of school before Easter. The only reason I wasn't expelled permanently was that my family was moving to Sicily at Easter. How did the educational system deal with me? In Major Work, they provided a nurturing, sheltered workshop for my growth and learning. At River Heights, the system simply couldn't tolerate me. I was expelled. And I'm proud of it to this day.

My scorn for River Heights Junior High School and its expulsion of me, is exactly the feeling and attitude I have for academic psychiatry today. Academic psychiatry is just one big River Heights Junior High School.

"Yo, Goliath, check out my sling shot!"

6

SUMMER IN SICILIY

Easter, 1965. Air Canada to Rome. Then a Fokker aircraft to Catania, Sicily. I forget the name of the airline, maybe Alitalia. Having read books about Billy Bishop, the Canadian World War I ace pilot, and the Baron von Richthofen, I was most impressed to actually be aboard a real Fokker aircraft. We stayed at the Jolly Hotel in downtown Catania. Suddenly, the world had gotten infinitely bigger. Prior to moving to Sicily, I had been to Montreal, and had heard French spoken. I had been to the Seattle World's Fair, Yellowstone Park, the Dakota badlands, and the Black Hills. But never this far, in geographical or cultural space.

On the ride in from the airport, I saw a graffiti message on a wall in black paint, *U.S. Assassins*. This was incomprehensible to me. It was obvious to me that the Americans were not assassins. They followed the rules of the Boy Scouts of America, just like the Canadian government and army. Why would some Sicilian think the Americans were assassins? It was almost thirty years later that I read about CIA assassinations around the world, and realized that the Italian rebels, whether they were leftists, rightists, or anarchists, were probably just unhappy about historical facts.

Looking out my hotel room window into the alley several floors below, one night, I saw an old woman come up to the garbage bin behind the hotel, forage through it for food, and take food away with her. This was a new experience. I actually got it that there are starving and homeless people in the world, real people. Such things were pieces of theoretical information back in River Heights. Not real facts, abstract facts. At River Heights Junior High there were no black students, no Asians, no Muslims, it was pure WASP middle class mid-west monotheisim. Actually, monotonotheism.

We ate real Italian food every day. Real Sicilian pizza, like *quattro stagione*, my favorite. We went to Taormina, saw old ruins, and walked on small cobble-stone streets. Then there were the clothes. Ordinary real guys actually wore sports jackets when they didn't have to, and not boring ones like in Canada. Incredibly beautiful sports jackets, well tailored, made out of all kinds of interesting materials. I got myself a green corduroy sports jacket with a double slit in the back. I loved that style with the double slit, it was so cool. The Italian guys looked great in those sports jackets on the backs of their motorcycles.

The Italian girls were gorgeous. They had a beauty never seen in Winnipeg. Not as incredible as the women in Florence, but gorgeous. Olive skin, dark raven hair, dark eyes, sensual lips, full bodies, and an ease and naturalness I had never encountered. One girl, Alba, lived not far away from our apartment, and I talked to her a bit at parties I went to, or when she came to visit friends at our apartment complex. She had a classical beauty of skin, hair, facial feature, bearing and manner I didn't know existed in the world.

Everything was so intense, alive and real. The architecture, the statues, the sun and beach, the snorkeling in the Mediterranean, the pasta, bread, clothes, language, the ice cream even was delicious in a way never approached by North American ice cream. The Sicilian peasants standing guard in the lemon orchards with shotguns amazed me. They were tough, and didn't play life by the Boy Scout Rules of North America. Big lizards ran through the orchards with their bellies several inches off the ground. Somehow, even the lizards would be against the rules in Canada.

Early in our stay, an Italian man, some kind of PR or marketing guy for the oil company, had dinner with my family. He was unbelievably cool, completely unlike any man I ever met in Canada, except my grade nine gym teacher, who was from England and wore English leather boots. This Italian man drove a sports car, I think, and talked about snorkeling. He said that he dove to 45 feet himself, and talked about men who dove to 120 feet. He said he would take me snorkeling. I was awe struck. He never did, but I dove to 45 feet on my own anyway.

One time I was sitting in our Alfa Romeo while my father was in a building doing something. The keys were in the ignition. We were blocking another car's way, so this Italian man hopped in our car, started it, threw the clutch in reverse, backed out quickly, and re-parked the car. I was bowled over by his ease, confidence and athletic driving, the way he changed gears with speed and authority, and backed the car up so quickly. It was so unlike the button-down attitudes, body motion and minds of Winnipeg, Canada. A whole different feel for life.

I missed my friends in Canada a lot, especially my girl friend. I wanted to be back home, much as I enjoyed the summer in Sicily. I didn't fit in on the American naval base where I was to go to school for the next year. We had a few weeks of school after I moved there, then got out for the long summer.

I remember one statement delivered in a southern drawl by one of the military brats, "God, Colin, you're a hurtin' sucker."

One time when I was on the base to go to a movie, the military guy on duty wouldn't let me into the movie theater because I had long hair and was wearing sandals. A hardened Beatle-maniac by this point, my hair was less than an inch over the top of my ears. Another time I was standing at the magazine rack in the PX looking at an issue of Life magazine. It had a photo spread of California surfers with Beach Boys style surfer hair.

This really hot girl came up and said to me, "You'd like to look like them, wouldn't you?"

To which I replied, "Yes."

It was a tiny exchange, but it gave me one of the few hints that it might be possible for me to be accepted, somehow, sometime, in this bizarre, alien culture. I remember the sailors driving though the narrow streets of Catania in huge American cars that almost filled the entire street. They were as out of place, as incongruous, as alien, as actual visitors from another planet would be. I saw how ethnocentric Americans are, although I didn't know that word at the time. No one else in the world can be so glaringly themselves at a glance, and stick out so far, as Americans in Europe.

This was the first time I was directly subjected to American propaganda. At school we were told how the Americans single-handedly won World War II. The rest of the Allies were a minor supporting cast. These people were full of themselves. I couldn't stand them. That's why I ran away. These were the people who lynched blacks in the fifties. I had never met them before. Everyone in my family was very clear that no one should rock the boat on the American view of history at school. Just keep quiet, my parents instructed us at the dinner table.

The people I liked the best, of all the kids who went to school on the base, were a half-Italian boy, John, and a Sicilian-American family. The family had moved from America to Sicily to run a business that seemed to be Mafia-related. I found out in my reading in the 1990's that the father had worked for the OSS during World War II. God knows who he was really working for in the 1960's, or on what.

John spoke pretty good Italian. I went with him to stay with his Italian relatives up north in Viareggio for a week, where I had a really nice time. I got to live in an Italian household, eat with an Italian family, and speak Italian, the little bit I could. These people accepted me in a warm, open, genuine fashion, even though I was a strange foreigner. I liked them a lot. John got me a good deal on a switch blade and a stiletto at the local market.

In the evenings we would go walk up and down on the wide sidewalk at the coast, and watch all the other people walking up and down. I had never experienced this kind of people watching before. It was great. So many beautiful, well dressed people, so interesting and cultured and alive. I bought some really great clothes at the stores there, sweaters and shirts mostly. The quality of the clothing was levels and levels above anything you could get in Canada, in material, style and workmanship.

Later, back in Winnipeg, I took my Sicilian sports jacket to a tailor for altering. He was Italian. He was astonished, and said to his young assistant, "This is a real Italian jacket."

Then to me, "Where did you get this?"

I explained to him, and he said, "Catania. E una bella cita."

To which I replied, "Si, e una bella cita."

This nearly exhausted my Italian vocabulary. My nickname with my friends in Winnipeg, from 1965 on, was Carlo Rossi. I coined this when looking at restaurant table umbrellas with "Rossi" on them in Sicily.

I ran away from home. In early September, 1965, having just turned fifteen, I planned and executed The Great Escape. I packed my packsack before going to sleep, including my passport and the little money I had, and put it under my bed. I lay on my bed until after midnight, till I was sure my family was asleep. Then I got up, took about forty dollars in Italian Lire from my mother's purse, and left.

The apartment guard asked me where I was going, to which I replied, "Vacazione."

I took a bus to the train station and took a 4:30 A.M. train to Pisa. From there I hitch hiked to Paris, then took the train and ferry to Dover. Going through customs in Dover, I was behind an east Indian man whose suitcase was opened by the customs officer. It contained dozens of bags of spices, any one of which could have been drugs. I still remember the pained look on the face of the customs officer. Fortunately, this allowed me to be waved through without any questions. I then hitch hiked to London and got a bus to Heathrow Airport, where I slept for three nights. I had to sleep in a different terminal each night because the airport police threatened to arrest me if they saw me there the next night.

I had the BOAC desk wire my grandfather in Montreal asking for a ticket to Winnipeg. I explained that my family was on vacation in Yellowstone Park and not reachable, and that I had cashed in my return ticket to Winnipeg. I checked with him every hour on the hour that the BOAC desk was open. Finally, on the third day, he said that a ticket had been approved and that I could catch a flight later that day. But he was very puzzled because the telegram had come from my parents in Sicily.

My comment was, "Yeah."

By the time I boarded the plane at Heathrow I had about three dollars left. I had been living predominantly on jelly doughnuts and water from the water fountain for three days. I was met by four friends and one of their mothers at the Winnipeg airport, stayed at my friend's house for a while, and went to boarding school that year in Winnipeg.

The journey from Pisa to London was very interesting. While hitch hiking through Viareggio, I met one of John's family members and explained to him that I was on my way to Genoa.

"Vacazione," I said.

He wished me well, and left on his bicycle, while I continued with my hitch hiking. Three weeks later this man wrote to John's mother to say that he had met me while I was on vacation.

I got rides from a number of interesting people. In northern Italy I got a ride from an Italian man in a sports car who took me across the French border. He stopped to do some clothes shopping, and I translated from French into Italian for him.

North of Nice, I was hitch hiking at 8:00 P.M. outside an apartment complex when the concierge asked me where I was going to sleep, to which I answered, "Je ne sais pas."

The family took me in, and provided me a bed and a delicious French dinner. They talked a lot with me, showed great interest in my vacation, now a *vacation*, and took my address in Sicily. They corresponded with my parents for several years afterwards. The concierge drove me ten or fifteen miles up the road in the morning, to a better hitch hiking location.

On the way north I was provided a gourmet lunch at a restaurant by a French family that had picked me up, for free. The kindness of these strangers touched me, and I was very grateful for it. Most of the way from central France to Paris was a single ride with a Frenchman in a red sports car. He wore driving gloves and drove at great speed through the *Massif Central*. There were many near collisions. For a while he raced an Englishman in an English sports car. Until he pranged his right headlight on the Englishman's left rear, ducking back into the lane after an attempted pass was thwarted by oncoming traffic. I remember watching the chrome rim of the headlight roll down the road ahead of us.

The two cars pulled over to the side of the road. The two men got out, exchanged information, and I chatted briefly with the Englishman. Then I got back in the French car and we carried on. What struck me was the manner of the two men. They were both totally calm and cool. They were like brothers in a racing fraternity. The little fender bender was like a testament to their mutual risk-taking and driving audacity, rather than a regretted event. They had complete mutual respect. Both were cultured, suave, good-looking, and apparently wealthy, at least by my standards. It was a glimpse into another culture, another world. When the Frenchman dropped me off on the outskirts of Paris, he gave me instructions as to the best street for picking up prostitutes.

Nearly broke, I instead slept on the ground behind an apartment building near the *Gare du Nord*. In the morning I got the train to Calais, then the ferry to Dover. An English crewman said that in fourteen years of working on the Channel ferry, it was the roughest crossing he had ever seen. Entire families were vomiting on the deck at once, and vomit was sloshing back and forth across the deck as the ferry rolled from side to side. I felt better standing out in the air on the open deck, rather than inside with the sliding puke.

Walking through Dover, I was thrilled to see real mods and real rockers in the streets. It was 1965. The Beatles, Rolling Stones, Dave Clark Five, Ferry Across the Mersey, the House of the Rising Sun. I was there. Fifteen years old. Me, Colin Ross from Winnipeg, Manitoba, all by myself. Unthinkable. Really neat.

I got a ride from some mods on their way to a party. They had Beatle haircuts, one wore a turtle neck and a sports jacket. Absolutely nobody dressed like this in Winnipeg. In London, I changed buses in Trafalgar Square and thought about asking some hippie types to take me in, but I feared they might turn me over to the police, so I took the bus to Heathrow Airport. I have to mention one of my most cherished achievement awards. While on the run in Europe, I was on the Interpol wanted list. Not bad for a kid from Winnipeg, Canada, eh?

7

GROUNDED AT BOARDING SCHOOL

St. John's Ravenscourt School, Winnipeg, Canada. The absolute ultimate in suck hole schools. One of my friends in River Heights sang a ditty about the football team: "Peaches and cream, peaches and cream. We're the boys from the Ravenscourt team. We're not rough, and we're not tough, but boy are we determined."

I had a foolproof plan for how not to get accepted at Ravenscourt. When I went for the interview with the Head Master, I'd tell him I didn't want to be there, I wanted to be with my friends in River Heights. The day came quickly. My friend's mother drove me out there, and I went into the Head Master's office. It was old England to the hilt. Lots of wood, leather, antiques, and other accoutrements of the traditional English boarding school.

He asked me a few questions and I explained that I didn't want to go to Ravenscourt at all. I wanted to live at a friend's house in River Heights and go to Kelvin High School. Imagine my dismay when the Head Master told me I was accepted. My plan had back-fired. He said he knew perfectly well that I didn't want to go to Ravenscourt, but he expected me to lie and pretend I did. He had already decided to reject me when I pretended I wanted to go to his school. When I told the truth, he changed his mind and decided to take a chance on me.

Foiled, I thanked him. I classified this experience as a major lesson in tactics; I now understood the negative consequences of *the reverse don't throw me in the briar patch strategy*. Brer Rabbit asked not to be thrown in the briar patch, when that is what he actually wanted. He got the opposite of what he asked for, and so won the logic game. I asked not to be admitted to Ravenscourt, when that was what I wanted. I got the opposite of what I asked for, which is what I didn't want, and so lost the logic game.

Boarding school was very tedious. I had run away from Sicily to Canada, but was no closer to my friends during the week than if I was in Europe. I spent a lot of time brooding in my room. My English teacher, who lived in residence, said he had never met anyone who brooded so much. I only got out for a few hours on Saturday, my only release into the real world.

I was the best basketball player in the school. There were very few good athletes, and very few good scholars. All this changed dramatically after I left. The school started admitting girls, and students excelled in many areas. When I was there, it was mostly mediocrity, among the students.

I didn't appreciate it at the time, but there were gifted teachers there. If I wasn't so turned off by the educational system, and so cooped up and restless, I probably could have learned a lot there.

The best friend I made at Ravenscourt was Jim. His family was the wealthiest, most patrician family in Winnipeg. His father was later a Federal Cabinet Minister. The first true skyscraper in Winnipeg, named after the family, was built on the corner of Portage and Main, the most important intersection in Winnipeg. Everyone in Winnipeg has heard of the Richardsons. I stayed at their house on weekends from Christmas to Easter, and Jim toured Europe with me and my family in the summer of 1966. The Richardsons were major Ravenscourt benefactors.

Here's how I scored negative points with the staff at Ravenscourt. At Easter, a bunch of boys from Ravenscourt and one friend from River Heights went to Banff skiing, in the Rocky Mountains. We took a lot of hard liquor with us and did a lot of drinking. Mr. Richardson and the RCMP found out, so when we got back to Winnipeg, we were restricted to the grounds of Ravenscourt for the rest of the school year. The only time we got to go off the grounds was to go to church on Sunday at a local church. Easter to the end of June. Murder. The next year, Jim Richardson switched to the University of Winnipeg, and completed high school there.

Imagine the threat to the revenue, reputation, recruiting power, and traditions of Ravenscourt our drinking spree in Banff generated! Because of me, Richardson money might pull out.

Twenty years later, a friend of mine never associated with the school was at a Ravenscourt party. He mentioned to a teacher who had been there in my time that he knew me. The teacher almost went ballistic on the spot, looked very angry, and refused to comment.

I am glad to know I have had some impact on the educational system in Winnipeg.

8

LIVING NEXT DOOR TO MICK JAGGER

My family returned to Winnipeg in the summer of 1966, and my dad was told that in November he would be transferred to Esso Europe, based in London. We left Winnipeg on November 6, 1966. I got to go to a regular North American high school for two months, Kelvin High School. Since I knew I was leaving the country before the first report card, I never did a single piece of homework in two months.

When I shampooed my hair in the morning for picture day at Kelvin, I put on some of my Italian clothes and headed off for school. My hair was more fluffed up than usual because of the shampoo that morning, and particularly curly. The Vice Principal stopped me in the halls and told me I was expelled from school until I got my hair cut. Hooray! Another achievement award! Presented to me by Vice Principal Small Mind of Kelvin High School, Winnipeg, Manitoba, Canada.

I was able to negotiate having my picture taken before going home. I got a miniscule amount of hair cut off, and kept it more slicked down while at school for the remaining weeks.

My next school was Haverstock School, Chalk Farm, London. It's a working class, industrial English public school, that is, a municipal government-run school. Its students are working class English children and immigrant children from many different countries. To meet the principal, we walked up a tiny, winding staircase to a small, modest office. My mother, my sister and I chatted with her, and she asked me what I wanted to be when I grew up.

I replied, "A psychiatrist."

The principal was flabbergasted. She had never had a pupil at her school who wanted to be a psychiatrist. The usual answer was a trade of some kind. She made me start at the first year of O Levels instead of the second year, saying that I wasn't advanced enough for second year, due to my Canadian educational background.

The next year I went to what's called a Crammer College in Notting Hill and completed my O Levels in the fall, and one A Level in the spring. O Levels and A Levels are supposed to take two years each. By the end of Crammer School I was just about ready to begin my new career as a high school drop out. My parents moved back to Canada in 1968, to Edmonton, and I attended the East London Polytechnic for a year, failing both my courses before I officially dropped out of school in 1969.

When we moved to London in 1966, we lived for a while at the White House Hotel on the southeast corner of Regent's Park. I try to stay there every time I go to London. Then we moved into a large apartment in Harley House on Marylebone Road, where I lived until the summer of 1968. We were on the second floor on the right side of the entrance. The next entrance to the east was where Mick Jagger lived, on the top floor, left side.

I met him a few times and chatted briefly. Once I got him to read some of my poems to see if he could set them to music. He said he couldn't. One time I talked to him, to tell him that I had seen Scotland Yard detectives descending the staircase behind our apartment, which also served his apartment. The garbage was collected from garbage cans set out on the landings at the different levels on the staircase. Scotland Yard was looking for drugs in his garbage. He thanked me for this tip. I may have contributed to Mick Jagger evading arrest on drug charges in the 1960's. This was the period when Scotland Yard was targeting rock stars for surveillance and drug busts.

We used to watch girls sitting outside the apartments for hours, hoping to catch a glimpse of Mick Jagger. Two girls were particularly rabid fans. One time they sat for hours, then left for about ten minutes to take a break. Mick Jagger came rushing out of his entrance, jumped in a taxi, and was taken away during this break period. The two girls came back and sat for a couple of more hours. Other times I saw Brian Jones, Keith Richards and Marianne Faithful getting in and out of taxis.

One time I was walking along the sidewalk, coming home, when Mick Jagger had just gone in and Keith Richards was getting out of a taxi. As I walked up I said, "Hi."

I was amazed to see a look of terror and panic in his eyes. I was being totally un-fan-like, didn't stop, didn't change my gait, and didn't ask him for anything. I formulated the theory that he might be experiencing psychological problems.

Another time I was walking along Edgeware Road at night when John Lennon, Paul McCartney and Ringo Starr went by in an open jeep. Ringo looked right at me. These were incredible experiences for a sixteen-year old kid from Winnipeg. I went to a concert of the Pink Floyd at the Round House before they recorded their first record, and I saw Procul Harum at a club with 400 people in it, where they sang *Whiter Shade of Pale*. Allen Ginsberg read one of my poems a friend gave to him on the street, but Ginsberg never contacted me to say what he thought. Another time I met Manfred Mann at a party.

These are people whose faces I gazed at for hours on record covers, counting off the hours in my dorm at Ravenscourt, dreaming about a bigger world outside the school grounds. I always wanted to be part of that bigger world. When I watched the Academy Awards on our basement TV in Winnipeg, in grades four, five and six, I thought I would like to be there some day, on stage, receiving an award.

Already, at sixteen, I was aware that the Manfred Mann who stood before me was a smaller being than the figure who had filled my imagination when I stared at his record cover at Ravenscourt. Already, the magic of the rock star had begun to fade. A few nights ago I watched a documentary about Eric Burdon, and was saddened by the waste of talent and potential, the destruction of human creativity caused by years of substance abuse. But there is more magic in rock than in psychiatry.

Yes, I believe in magic.

At Haverstock School, for the last couple of months of the year, I had a substitute teacher who had just graduated from Downing College, Cambridge, where he studied English under F.R. Leavis. Peter introduced me to Pound, Eliot, Yeats, Hopkins, Lawrence, Blake and Leavis. He showed me *The Windhover*.

I read it, and exclaimed, "That's amazing! The words are actually doing what they're saying!"

Peter read my poetry. I deepened my reading back to Donne, Surrey and Wyatt, then out to philosophy, anthropology and history. When I returned to Winnipeg in the summer of 1967, I was forever disconnected from my friends in Canada. My English friends were intellectuals from Downing College, including Morris Shapira, who edited Henry James. My trip to Winnipeg was an interesting ethnographic expedition, but I was no longer of that world.

At the World's Fair in Montreal that summer, I was gawked at by American tourist families because of my long hair. I felt relief when I ducked inside the English pavilion, and was greeted by an English woman working there, who looked at me as a perfectly normal person, instead of a hippie freak. It was at age sixteen that I came into full adult consciousness, in England. I was on stage with Yoko Ono before she met John Lennon, at a performance art piece in which she invited audience members to come up on stage.

I dropped out of high school and studied D.H. Lawrence, F. R. Leavis and William Blake. I learned the logic of Blake's poem, *The Little Fly*, from reading Leavis, and became a student of logic. Not just abstract logic, formal logic, or philosophy department logic, but the logic of living things, and living relationships. Double binds, and more intricate logical structures that I learned from patients in the 1980's and 1990's. The borderline entrapment loop and the borderline paralytic loop, that I write about in my book, *The Osiris Complex*. I created more complex logical structures in aphorisms, published in my collection of poems as *100 Aphorisms: On The Nature of the Spirit*. English literature took me deeper into nature and the mind than rock music could. Rock music takes me deeper than Houseman, deeper than all but the top tier geniuses in English literature.

Yes, I believe in magic.

9

GO NORTH, YOUNG MAN

Early in 1970, I was almost out of money and living in a trailer (a *caravan*, in English lingo), outside Bath in western England. The trailer sat out in the open on Charmy Down, Upper Swainswick, beside an old World War II airfield. There was a pillbox half a mile away that had a bat living in it. In the fall I could eat handfuls of delicious brambles off the bushes, and in the winter I could walk under the stars, looking up at Orion, Vega, Capella, Lyra the Lyre, Sirius, Draco the Dragon, Cygnus, Polaris and the Little Dipper, the Big Dipper, and other stars and constellations I knew by name.

I studied the moon, the presences in the landscape, and the gravestones in the twelfth century churchyard, down the hill. I walked for hours through the woods, alone. Sometimes I would go two days without talking to another human being. I read, and thought, and studied the living cosmos. I studied my own states of consciousness, and learned to be with the rocks, the wind, the streams, and the earth. I learned a technique of empathy with natural things. How to experience rockness, treeness, or earthness. But that's for other books, *Spirit Power Drawings*, *Songs For Two Children* and *Human Energy Fields*.

At my request, my father got me a job at the Esso refinery in Norman Wells, Northwest Territories, Canada. He advanced me my airfare back to Canada, and I left England. I could carry all my possessions at the same time, including all my books and clothing. In many ways, I was richer then than I am now. I went in for the job interview in Edmonton, was hired, and passed the company physical. It was time to go north, young man.

At the Industrial Airport in Edmonton, I watched another company employee seeing his son off, and listened to the father's warning to watch out for the native girls, and be careful. A combination of freight and passengers was loaded on the propeller aircraft, and we took off. It was April 19, 1970. I ended up living in the Northwest Territories most of the next five years until I started courses at the University of Alberta in September, 1975.

Norman Wells was a town of about 250 people, which expanded to about 350 people in the summer, on the banks of the MacKenzie River just south of the Arctic Circle. It was the site of the world's northernmost oil refinery. My job was to work at the Portco Plant, reconditioning oil barrels, but the Portco hadn't opened for the summer season yet. A couple of white guys, an Indian from Fort Franklin on Great Bear Lake, and I spent the first few days moving used oil barrels from a chaotic pile in one location to a neatly stacked pile in another. This was to get them ready for reconditioning in a few weeks.

A 45-gallon oil drum is fairly heavy just by itself. When it is partly full of ice, and has more ice and snow encrusted on the outside, it can be *really* heavy. At this time of year it is still full winter in Norman Wells - the spring thaw hadn't started yet. My first day of work was a Wednesday. On the Thursday I tried to write a letter home to my parents, but couldn't. My wrists hurt too much to use a pen.

By the end of the summer I was in the best physical condition of my life, with great upper body strength. For most of the summer we worked twelve-hour days six days a week, with overtime after forty hours. I could really relate to the passages in *Anna Karenina* about peasants cutting wheat. A lot of time was spent stacking drums. We did this by laying them on their sides in a row. Two drums would be set upright at the end of each row to hold the horizontal drums in place. Then a second layer of drums would be stacked horizontally on the first, then a third on the second. If I stood beside a stack of drums and extended my arm straight up in the air, my outstretched hand reached the middle of the fourth row.

No one had ever stacked drums five high. This was thought to be unattainable. I was the first to do so. The technique is as follows; you lift the drum up so that it is sitting at a 45-degree angle, one edge of the bottom surface touching the ground. Then you put your right hand on the top edge and your left hand on the bottom edge. You then lift the drum up in the air in a snatching motion, pushing it upwards with your right thigh as it comes up to thigh level. The drum is then lifted up above your head, like a weight lifter would a bar. You stand with arms stretched out like a weight lifter's, one hand at each end of the drum, the drum horizontal in the air over your head.

Next, you shift the drum so that your left hand is at the middle of the drum and your right hand on the edge. The drum is now pointed directly at the stack, with your right hand at the back end. What you do is run at the stack two or three steps, and as you are getting close, throw the drum up on top of the fourth row with your right hand. It goes up in the air and comes down on the stack, forming the fifth row of drums. If you are unsuccessful, the drum tries to fall back on top of you, and you have to get out of the way.

I thought this was petty impressive, throwing a 45-gallon oil barrel up higher than I could reach with my fully extended hand. We also stacked the drums on flatbed trucks for transport. By the end of the summer, I was able to stack a full truck as fast as four guys could feed me drums from the ground, which was pretty fast. I was in great physical shape.

The Portco Unit was an old assembly line manufactured in Cleveland in the 1930's. The first stop was the Steamer. Five drums were set upside down on steam pipes, one per pipe, and steamed out. Then they went to me on the Rumbler. I had to stick several chains inside them, set them on the Rumbler, and the Rumbler rocked them back and forth and rotated them at the same time. This was to knock rust and debris off the inside. I then took them off the Rumbler, fished the often-knotted chains out using a hook, flipped them onto a rinser one at a time, rinsed them out, and passed them onto the Caustic guy.

The Steamer and Rumbler were outdoors, looking out over the four-mile width of the MacKenzie River, over twenty miles of uninhabited forest, at the MacKenzie Mountains in the west.

The Caustic guy put the drums in cabinets where they were cleansed with caustic soda, then they went to the Painter, who spray painted them, then to the Stenciler, who stenciled the appropriate information on the top. Different colors of barrel were for different grades of fuel. The drums were then strapped together on pallets, five at a time, filled with fuel from a hose, and stacked by forklift in preparation for shipment up and down the MacKenzie River. Our crew would recondition and fill 320 oil barrels in a twelve-hour day.

The work was so monotonous and repetitious that I had to turn it into a sporting event, in order to survive. I learned to load and unload the Rumbler without turning it off, to maximize efficiency. And I learned to roll the barrels on their edge to the Caustic guy, a friend who was an excellent basketball player. I would roll the drums as far as ten feet from me to him, without either of us touching them, and he would receive them on the roll without error. All the while, the drums were rotating on their lower edge while the drum remained at about a 55-degree angle. Without the sporting event aspect, I might have gone psychotic from monotony.

I spent about ten dollars a week and saved all the rest of my money. I worked at Portco till September, returned to England, then returned to the Northwest Territories again in the spring of 1971, and stayed there until I injured my hand in 1974.

In spring, 1971, I was not rehired by Esso to work in Norman Wells because they had a new affirmative action program of hiring northern residents, which meant natives. In the spring, I hitch hiked up to Hay River, on the south shore of Great Slave Lake. I got a job helping repair barges for a week, and earned enough money to fly into Norman Wells, where I was now hired by Esso on the grounds that I was a local hire. I worked there till being laid off in August. The reason I was laid off was that I was a local hire, whereas the summer students, sons of Esso employees in Edmonton, had been hired down south. They were not laid off.

I returned to southern Canada, spent three weeks in the Whiteshell, and then moved to Inuvik, Northwest Territories, in late October. I spent the winter in a shack without running water, in the native part of town, then moved back to Norman Wells at the end of June. I spent two more full winters in Norman Wells in a shack without running water, and most of a third. The first winter in Norman Wells, I also had no electricity. It was a ten foot by twenty foot construction shack built by the U.S. Army during the Second World War. I rebuilt the interior and the roof after moving in, and the next year added on an eight by sixteen foot kitchen, which I built myself.

During World War II, the U.S. Army built a pipeline from the oilfield at Norman Wells, across the MacKenzie Mountains into the Yukon. Their base camp, across the river from Norman Wells, was called Canol. They did this to establish a secure supply of oil into Alaska, due to concern about disruption of oil tanker traffic on the Pacific Coast by the Japanese. At the end of the war, they simply abandoned the place. Over the years, it was raided by northerners for lumber, buildings, caterpillar tractors, wire, and all kinds of materials. One winter someone had hauled my shack over from Canol.

I didn't own it. I was a squatter. The shack sat not fifty yards from the MacKenzie River. It was my first real home outside my parents' home. It was the first home of my two beautiful, intelligent, creative children, both born in Inuvik. Or, wait a minute! Creative? Intelligent? I must be thinking of someone else's kids. My kids were the two scrubby brats living with their mother and their dead-end loser father from down south. In 1976 and 1977, I spent the summers in Norman Wells.

While I was a high school dropout, driving trucks, pounding nails, and being unemployed quite a lot, in Norman Wells from 1971 to 1974, I couldn't get no respect. All of a sudden, in the summer of 1977, when I got word that I had been accepted into medical school at the University of Alberta, things changed. People almost started calling me "Sir" or "Doctor" on the spot. All of a sudden I was respectable and respected. Instead of being at the bottom of the social ladder, I was at the top.

I spent many, many hours walking in the bush around Norman Wells. In the fall and winter, I hunted ptarmigan, a northern grouse that turns white in the winter. I must have shot three hundred total over the years I lived there. I saw wolf, moose, caribou and bear, beaver and muskrat. I ate grayling that I caught with a net myself, and picked blueberries. Outside Inuvik, I picked salmon berries, which are like a pale pink raspberry. I pretty much went native.

During this period I read widely in anthropology, focusing on circumpolar shamanism and the Athabaskan linguistic group of North American Indians. My in-laws were native, and I ate dry meat, dry fish, moose meat and caribou. Nothing tasted better than Dall sheep from the Rocky Mountains. Except perhaps the lake trout from Great Bear Lake. I flew in helicopters, Cessnas, and DC-3s. It was one of the richest, deepest periods of my life.

I continued to study my own states of consciousness, and subtle modulations in my awareness with changes in the external environment of the bush. One of my favorite spots was on the shore of the MacKenzie River, which is littered with driftwood in all sizes. You can make a fire on the shore very easily with driftwood, and sit and watch the water flow by. In the spring there will be literally thousands of ducks and geese overhead at the same time, during the peak migration.

Immediately behind Norman Wells is a range of mountains about 3200 feet in height. From the top, in late June, you can watch the sun dip down close to the horizon, then move back upwards without setting. The midnight sun. In Inuvik, in the winter, it gets light about 11:45 AM and is pitch dark again shortly after 3:00

PM.

One of the most profound things about the Canadian Arctic is the light. In Inuvik, in the middle of winter, walking outside town in search of ptarmigan, the snow is many different colors, the most intense combinations of white, blue, purple, pink and yellow as the sun rises. I have never seen an intensity or quality of light anywhere else in Australia, New Zealand, China, North America or Europe that comes anywhere near the dawn light in Eskimo country.

Then there are the MacKenzie Mountains, twenty miles west of Norman Wells in the spring. It is solid dark green spruce from the far side of the river to the mountains. Then the snow-covered, pure white mountains rise up out of the plain. Countless surfaces, cliffs, canyons and plateaus are visible. All white. Until they are lit up by the afternoon light. Then the mountains become ethereal and lift up off the face of the earth, hovering in the air. Planes of white, pink, yellow, pastel red, purple and blue such as I have never seen. It is the most ethereal thing I have ever seen, next to shafts of sunlight coming through the summer thunderheads in Manitoba. I have never seen anything more spiritual or immaterial in the natural world.

The closest settlement was Fort Norman, a native community fifty miles south on the MacKenzie River. Once I saw a bush pilot floating down the river in his float plane. He had run out of gas on his way in from Fort Norman. Several years earlier he had gone down in a blizzard in the central Arctic. Before he was rescued, he ate part of one of his dead passengers. I remember one spring, walking along the road out to D.O.T. Lake, which is south of town. It had rained and then frozen during the night. A grouse was sitting in a spruce tree, its feet frozen to the branch.

Another time, a tourist from down south got flown over to the MacKenzie Mountains to hike by himself. A grizzly got him. All they found was his bones. You can die very easily in the bush. It is not a place to fool around with. In the winter I would go out in the bush alone, but not far, and would “make fire” in the snow. I wasn’t trying to be macho. I was studying the states of consciousness of so-called primitive, pagan peoples. By creating analogs in my own mind.

There is another way of knowing and being. It isn’t cerebral or cognitive. It is a more sensual, dark, physical way of communicating, knowing and being together, with other people, and with the natural world. The Indians still have this other way of knowing, though they don’t talk about it, take it for granted, and have no intellectual language for it. White people who talk about “communing with nature” are completely missing the point. The white way of being with nature is cerebral, technically, solipsistic. It is a way of being with one’s own cerebration, not with the other. I explain this more clearly, at greater length, elsewhere.

The point is, I was studying. As hard, as intensely, as when I went to medical school, or wrote my academic textbooks about multiple personality disorder and schizophrenia. It was just a different field of study, and a different way of knowing. Norman Wells is still alive in my subconscious mind. In my dreams, I may yet again transform into a raven and fly in the canyons of the MacKenzie Mountains. Or speak to Ptarmigan Spirit. Or make fire on the shore of the MacKenzie River.

It is a different mode of consciousness. Please, don't translate it into urban sentimentality about nature. I was there. I *lived* it. My problem, which I am glad to have, is how to bring this mode of knowing into the English language. Hopkins talked about *inscape*. That's as close as anyone but D.H. Lawrence has come in the last 150 years. Call it my retirement project. Or call psychiatry my retirement from my deeper work. Your choice, dealer.

10

WHAT IS THAT CRUNCHING SOUND?

Early in the 1970's, the native people of the Northwest Territories began to politicize. Several political organizations were formed, one of them being the Metis Association. The Metis Association had a government grant to supply lumber to Metis people in the MacKenzie Region to upgrade or repair their homes. I worked for the Metis Association, organizing the transport of lumber into Norman Wells under this program. On March 27, 1974 the lumber arrived at the airport in a Bristol Freighter, a cargo airplane that sits on the tarmac at an angle like a DC-3. Its nose section opens up for unloading of the cargo.

I had spent nine months of the previous year working for a company that unloaded airplanes at the airport, until quitting. I loaded and unloaded 727s, DC-3s, Hercules freighters, helicopters, barges, trucks, whatever. I drove a forklift and also used my hands and muscles to move freight. I was very familiar with the forklift and aircraft.

In order to unload the lumber off the Bristol freighter, I stood on the forks of the forklift, then the driver raised the forks so that I was lifted up to the level of the freight deck. I was looking at the plane, with my left hand behind me, resting on the fork frame for balance and support. All of a sudden, my hand got caught.

I yelled, "Stop. Stop. Lower the forks. My hand. My hand."

I was driven to the nursing station, where the nurse removed the thick leather mitt and wool mitt liner that saved me from amputation. My skin was torn open for about three inches on the back of my hand. A tendon was visible. I felt no pain. I told her to take my wedding ring off and put it on my right hand, before the swelling set in. The nurse put a dressing on, and phoned the closest doctor, who was in Fort Franklin doing a clinic, and got an order to give me a demerol injection.

I flew out to Edmonton on Pacific Western Airlines that evening, and was admitted to Charles Camsell Hospital. A Sikh orthopedic surgeon, Dr. Singh, operated on my hand the next morning. Two days later, the first dressing change. My hand was unbelievable. It was huge and swollen. There was a row of big black stitches. The skin was an incredible mixture of colors, purple, black, red, blue, even some green tint. I trembled and sweated just looking at it. Dr. Singh looked very concerned and told me not to breath directly on it.

I took painkillers for two days only, and never really experienced any pain after that. When I held my hand up and looked at it, the fingers were spread apart the distance they would be in a normal open palm posture. But they were all touching. There was no space between them. Serious swelling. In May, I had a second surgery. Altogether I had five surgeries; the initial work, a second procedure, the first skin graft, a procedure to loosen up adhesions in my crushed knuckle, and the second skin graft. I needed a second graft because I formed a thick layer of keloid scar tissue on the first graft.

The second time, a plastic surgeon regrafted me, injected steroids into the hand, and made me wear a tensor bandage for a year to suppress the keloid. When I first started physiotherapy in 1974, the only finger I could touch to my thumb was my index finger. The others wouldn't move that far. I didn't have enough strength to hold a dime between my thumb and index finger. The swelling was still going down measurably, when an occupational therapist measured it weekly, several months later. I did physiotherapy until August. When I first got my cast off, and started doing rehab exercises for my wrist, to regain my strength, I did wrist curls - with just the bar. I couldn't lift the bar if there was any weight on it other than the weight of the bar itself.

I made friends with my physiotherapist and later we published a paper together on doctors' attitudes towards physiotherapy. We surveyed a group of physiotherapists concerning their experiences with doctors. They reported a great deal of rude, condescending, unprofessional behavior by doctors, nebulous orders, failure to return pages, and lack of understanding of physiotherapy. I submitted my paper to the *Canadian Medical Association Journal*, naively thinking that the medical profession would like this problem brought to its attention, so that corrective action could be taken. I had seen the tremendous value of physiotherapy from my own experience with rehab.

Surprise, surprise. The paper was sent out to several M.D. reviewers, and I was sent copies of their written comments. The paper was rejected by the official journal of the Canadian Medical Association, but later published in the *Canadian Journal of Physiotherapy*. The M.D. reviewers were angry and irrational. Mild versions of foaming at the mouth. Their reasons for not publishing the paper were ridiculous rationalizations. The doctors were in a huff and didn't want to hear the legitimate, politely expressed comments of the physiotherapists.

I had been under the illusion that things were going to be different in medicine. Unlike the baloney I dealt with trying to get my literary work published, in medicine, I thought, scientific standards would prevail. Evidence and data would count. Not so, I learned. Politics, personal pathology, stupidity, acting out and prejudice have lots of room in medicine. At first, I was in denial. I thought maybe it was just a couple of bad reviewers, or the subject matter. In other areas there would be reason and science, I told myself.

It turned out this is true. Much in medicine is based on science and data. But there is a whole lot of folklore, superstition and prejudice too. I mean in general medicine. When we get to psychiatry, oh my God! Little did I know what the future held.

Later, in medical school, I got to go in the OR with the plastic surgeon who operated on my hand. And I sat in the doctor's lounge off the OR at Charles Camsell, eating my lunch while Dr. Singh poured incredible amounts of Tabasco sauce on his food. I wouldn't want to be the mosquito that bit him.

For a couple of months, immediately after the injury, Dr. Singh had a metal rod in my hand to stabilize the fractured metacarpal bone. About 3/8 of an inch stuck out through the skin. It came time to pull it out. Dr. Singh worked on it with some pliers, rotating it and loosening it up. Then he tugged on it, but it wouldn't come. So I braced myself and grasped my left wrist with my right hand. As he and I were setting up to perform this little procedure, the nurse looked horrified and left. Dr. Singh stood up, set himself, and suddenly gave a big, quick yank. Out came the rod. I really admired his ability to take control and get the job done, even such a tiny job.

Months after the initial surgery, a nurse told me that after the first surgery, Dr. Singh thought I was going to lose the hand. Now I can play the recorder, tie shoelaces, shoot a hockey puck and perform all the other functions I need to in life. But I don't have the dexterity to be a surgeon. And the hand still tolerates cold more poorly than it did before the injury. I have experienced the marvels of modern medicine first hand. Or, more exactly, left hand.

I also learned something about nurses because of my hand injury. When I was back in for my first skin graft, I was unable to wash my own hair. My personal nurse was assigned to five or six patients, her entire workload for the day. I saw her for less than five minutes a day. I had to negotiate for three days to get her to shampoo my hair for me. She did so only with much cajoling, and only after I told her I would get everything set up, and it would take her literally one minute. She finally agreed, but reluctantly, and washed my hair with sighs and expressions of annoyance. This was my first experience in the incredible laziness of nurses. Not all nurses, but too many.

Another amusing experience occurred when a group of about twenty health care professionals in white lab coats came marching in with Dr. Singh on his rounds. He put my X-ray up and started talking about my case. They all acted as if I didn't exist and wasn't there. I got up out of bed, walked around so I could see my X-ray, and listened to the short lecture. This made them very uncomfortable. They couldn't accommodate two facts at the same time: 1) I was a patient, and 2) I was a human being.

I learned as a patient that the physiotherapists and occupational therapists were much more normal, healthy, genuine, caring and humane than the nurses. Also more intelligent and better educated. They did a lot more for me and had a lot more technical knowledge. They treated patients well and were really interested in working directly with patients. The main goal of the nurses seemed to be to avoid direct patient contact, and to spend as much time as possible smoking, charting, or sitting in meetings.

My experience with nurses did not go uphill from there. Overall. Individually, I met and worked with many excellent, dedicated nurses. But as a profession they're a pretty forlorn group. Almost as bad as doctors.

11

ESCALATING EDUCATIONAL PLANS

Before my hand injury I had been thinking about taking a government-subsidized six-month carpentry course in Fort Smith. After my hand injury I changed my mind. It was time to get out of physical work. When I was in Edmonton from March to August, 1974, I talked the Worker's Compensation Board into paying for me to take my grade twelve math. I planned to go to the Northern Alberta Institute of Technology (NAIT) to take a two-year course in business administration, then return to the Northwest Territories to work for the company set to build a gas pipeline down the MacKenzie Valley. I figured I would need math for this. All I had was grade ten math.

I took the math course through the Adult Education Department, while living in an apartment in Edmonton. Then I decided that if I was going to do two ten-month study years at NAIT to get a diploma in business administration, I might as well do four eight-month years at the University of Alberta, and get a B. Comm. degree.

Then I decided that if I was going to go to university to take Commerce, I might as well take pre-med courses in the first two years, and see if I got into medical school. If I was going to take pre-med, then I would need to do my high school science courses. So I took grade ten, eleven and twelve chemistry, physics and biology by correspondence in the spring of 1975, while living back in Norman Wells.

I finished high school in June, 1975, just before my twenty-fifth birthday. My year at East London Polytechnic, 1968-69, I rarely attended classes and wasn't the least bit serious about my studies. So I count my real period as a high school drop out as seven years. Six if you want to be conservative.

I am so glad that I spent this period out of the educational mill. I really lived, for an extended time, in two distinct cultures, both very different from urban southern Canada. An intellect in England. An unemployed bum in Norman Wells. In both settings, I studied, thought and read as hard as I did at medical school. I obtained two Ph.D.s at the Colin Ross Autodidact University, one in English and one in Anthropology.

Next came that most bizarre and exotic of all ethnographic expeditions. Pre-med and medical school.

12

PRE-MED

In my first year of university I was twenty-five years old, married, with two children. I had lived on two continents and in three distinct cultures. My classmates were children. I took two years of English in pre-med, with one of the most brilliant people I have met, Professor Christopher Drummond. For my troubles, I received the Priscilla Hammond Memorial Award in English 200. This is an award given to one out of all students taking introductory English at the University of Alberta.

I was back in Miss Marshall's class. For English. The other courses were different. I took inorganic chemistry, physics, English, economics and mathematics. They were the typical anonymous classes in huge lecture halls with 17,000 students per class. Except for physics. My teacher there was Dr. Overton, a biomedical engineer in the Faculty of Medicine. I became a normal subject in his research on gamma spectroscopy (unpaid), and acted as a normal subject in a radioactive lung scanning study.

I read about twenty or thirty books in the philosophy of science that year. A whole other branch of my education. Riddle me this. There is a problem in popular expositions of relativity theory that I have never gotten resolved. Maybe a psychiatrist can help me, if any read this far in *The Great Psychiatry Scam*.

According to relativity theory, as expounded at the popular level, all motion is relative. Observations change as a function of the location of the observer, but the location of the observer is arbitrary. Take a train moving through a desert landscape, for instance. This is a common example used in explaining relativity theory.

An observer is standing in the desert watching a passenger train go by from his right to his left at 60 mph. Directly in front of him, on the far side of the tracks, a large cactus sticks up above the top of the train. This is the observer's reference point.

On the train, a pitcher is throwing a baseball to a catcher, at 60 mph. The pitcher is to the observer's left, the catcher to his right. The pitcher sees the ball travel away from him at 60 mph, while he and the catcher remain stationary with respect to the train. The catcher sees the ball travel towards him at 60 mph while he and the pitcher remain stationery with respect to the train. Both the pitcher and the catcher see the cactus moving by them, in the same direction, at 60 mph.

The observer in the desert sees the ball remain stationery in the air, not moving with respect to him or the cactus. He sees the train move at 60 mph from his right to left, until the catcher's glove hits the ball. This shows that all motion is relative.

It shows that we make arbitrary assumptions about the absolute nature of motion based on our arbitrary position as observers.

Clear. Good. I get it.

Now turn to the Twin Paradox, another illustration used in explaining relativity theory. It's the basis of many science fiction movies. If a rocket ship accelerates towards the speed of light, it undergoes a Lorentz contraction. Time slows down. Here's what happens to the twins in the Twin Paradox.

One twin gets on the space ship, accelerates to the speed of light, and travels for fifty light years. Correcting for the amount of time required to accelerate up to the speed of light, time has stood still for the space voyager. He experiences being away from earth for only fifteen minutes. When he gets back, his twin has aged fifty years and is living in a retirement home in Florida. The earthbound twin is on Viagra. The space voyager has aged only fifteen minutes, and has experienced only fifteen minutes of elapsed time. He's ready to party, without Viagra.

Wait a minute. I thought all motion was purely relative. Sure, during the brief period of acceleration up to the speed of light, the twin in the spaceship experienced accelerations that were not undergone by the earthbound twin. This occupied the 7.5 minutes required to reach the speed of light, plus the 7.5 minutes required to decelerate and land. The rest of the time, the twin in the spaceship was traveling at a constant speed, 186,000 miles per second, and experiencing no acceleration.

It should be purely arbitrary which twin is traveling away at the speed of light, and which is standing still. Observers looking through telescopes on other planets, or in other spaceships traveling various directions at various velocities, would make different observations. It's all relative. Einstein said. And we get it. Right? This is what the red shift in astronomy is all about. Right?

But wait a minute. The Twin Paradox tells us that motion is not relative. Absolutely not relative. There is a very meaningful and real differential aging. The twin who went away is fifty years younger than the one who stayed on earth. If it was all relative, and the position of the observer was arbitrary, why wouldn't the earthbound twin be the one who didn't age?

There is an unresolved problem in the popular exposition. The inner contradiction is not recognized, discussed or solved in any of the twenty or thirty books I read. This problem in the philosophy of science was analyzed by the same mind, mine, that has noticed things about patients, things like multiple personality disorder, that go right by most psychiatrists. Consider the theory that my observations in psychiatry are accurate.

If the twin who leaves the earth ages less than the one who stays behind, and time stands still for him while he travels at the speed of light, then he has become immortal. For a while. Until he decelerates. It turns out that the problem of immortality is actually a problem in physics.

Stated another way, the unresolved problem in the Twin Paradox leads to one of two conclusions: 1) the problem has already been solved by theoretical physicists, therefore it is only a problem in the popular exposition, or 2) it is a real unsolved problem in theoretical physics. From (2) one goes unavoidably to the conclusion that modern physics cannot explain how clocks work, except under Newtonian conditions.

I made one observation in my physics class that illustrates the same property of my mind. In our lab, in our introductory physics course, we did an experiment on elastic collisions on frictionless planes. We didn't actually have a frictionless plane or purely elastic collisions, but we had a crude experimental apparatus that made a good enough approximation for introductory teaching purposes.

We rolled ball bearings down a ramp. They then hit a target ball bearing on the smooth, flat horizontal surface we had set up. The angle of incidence of the moving ball on the target ball could be varied by adjusting the ramp. What we did was measure the angle that the target ball went off in, depending on the incoming angle of the ball coming down the ramp. Don't worry about the details or the logic.

The point is this. I noticed that there was a constant symmetry between the angle of travel of the target ball and the angle of travel of the moving ball after the impact. The relationship of the angles was such that a right angle was always preserved, if certain lines were drawn on the surface. We had been asked to measure angles and write down numbers. I noticed that there was a constant geometrical symmetry in the phenomenon. This was no big deal to the physicist. But it was to me. I actually saw, as an original, independent observation, the aesthetically beautiful conservation of symmetry in physics, in nature.

The physics teacher responsible for the lab part of the course said that he had watched thousands of undergraduates perform this experiment. None had ever noticed the geometrical conservation of symmetry in the experiment. He said that the conservation of symmetry is a fundamental principle in quantum mechanics, and in all branches of physics. Again, consider the theory that I might observe real things in patients other psychiatrists miss. It is the same habit of mind. Observe carefully. Consider novel possibilities. Think synthetically. Look for the constant in the pattern. Do not close your mind prematurely. Do not accept dogma. The dogma could always be wrong. Inside the certainty of the dogma, there could be a more interesting unanswered question, a deeper problem for observation and analysis.

I might be right about the Great Psychiatry Scam. Keep this in mind for later chapters.

I asked the physicist in charge of the lab another question. He said he couldn't answer it.

Consider a thermometer set in a track that is completely frictionless. The coefficient of friction is zero. This is a thought experiment, so don't quibble about practicalities. The molecules in the thermometer are moving around at random, in so-called Brownian motion. It might help to think of it as an extremely small, microscopic thermometer. Eventually, if we wait long enough, by pure chance, all molecules in the thermometer will be moving in the same direction for a short period of time. Make the period of time, the size of thermometer and the distance of movement as small as you need. It won't change the theoretical problem.

During that short period of time, what will happen? The temperature of the thermometer will drop to absolute zero. The thermometer will move down the track. When the short period of time, the instant, is over, by pure chance the motion of the molecules will again become dis-aligned. The motion of the molecules is random throughout, but for that instant, by chance, all molecules move in the same direction. After the instant, the thermometer will return to room temperature.

This is interesting because the thermometer has moved through space without expenditure of energy. According to the physics taught to me, this is impossible. But it's just a matter of time. Not much time, if you consider small enough objects and distances. In fact, if you consider a microscopic enough level of observation, this is a general phenomenon going on in the universe all the time.

Well, that nails down the physics of levitation. Recently, I read about an experiment in which physicists were able to transfer information from one beam of light to another beam of light without any transfer of energy. The information was manifest as energy configurations in the light beams, using lay language, which is all I have available to my mind. That's it. Mental telepathy just became a physical possibility. From there it's only two steps to right angle turns at high velocity in alien aircraft containing biological occupants.

The purpose of this introductory section, Birth to Med School, of *The Great Psychiatry Scam* has been several fold. The subtitle of the book is *One Shrink's Personal Journey*. It couldn't very well be personal if it wasn't personal. I wanted to give you a palpable sense of my character, experience, and sense of humor. If you can't tell whether I'm joking or serious sometimes, that's funny.

Who is this man, Colin Ross, making such a critique of psychiatry? Where is he coming from? Is he merely negative and crabby? Is he delusional? Or is he right? The man, the subject of our study, has been shaped by his experience, and guided by his temperament. Also by discarnate entities and overseers too arcane to mention.

II. MED SCHOOL, SHRINK TRAINING

13

CLASSMATE PUKING STORIES

When I started medical school in September, 1977, my daughter was two years old and my son was four. They both followed in my footsteps to become uneducated dropouts in their early twenties. I'm very proud of them for that. I supported my family throughout pre-med and medical school. Entirely. Through grants, work, loans and my mother paying my rent, but nothing else. From the time I started pre-med in September, 1975 till I got my M.D. in May, 1981, my wife worked a total of three months. She did so in 1981 while I stayed home and ran the household, and trained for a marathon while my son and daughter were at school.

In June, 1981 I completed the Winnipeg Marathon in 3 hours and 17 minutes.

The first day of medical school we had a talk by the Dean of Medicine. He told us that from that day on half of us would be in the bottom half of the class. This nearly created a mass psychiatric crisis on the spot. A room full of Type A over-achievers can't take such news. Thank God for denial. You could feel the demons of denial rushing up from Hell, to tell each student he or she would kick everyone else's butts on final exams. One hundred per cent of my classmates believed they would be in the top half of the class. Fifty per cent were delusional. The rest were obsessed, compulsive and correct.

I soon found out one thing about medical students. They are bloody difficult to out-perform on memorization contests. They are fanatics at it.

We were assigned lockers on the first day. This was a big step up in the undergraduate universe, to have your own locker. There was wealth and equipment everywhere. The financial power of medicine was writ very large, in microscopes, lab equipment, fancy lecture theaters, and the manner of our professors.

During those first weeks I got to know some of my classmates a little. On Monday morning, before gross anatomy class (which is gross, let me assure you), the guys would pile into the boy's locker room. It was the boy's locker room, not the men's. They would tell each other stories about what they had done on the weekend. I remember one of the guys telling about how he had puked at a party on Saturday night.

This story was responded to with the same macho guffaws and approval that I remembered from high school. River Heights Junior High School, even. I realized that my classmates, who would be doctors in four years, were developmentally arrested in early adolescence. I was more developmentally advanced at sixteen than they would ever be. This experience is the basis of my theory that 95% of North American males are developmentally arrested in early adolescence.

The jackass adolescent males set the tone of the class. One became Class President. Another drank beer during lectures in first year. Later, after completion of his anesthesia training, he committed suicide with a mixture of street drugs and anesthesia drugs. During medical school this student's adolescent buffoonery and substance abuse were regarded as hilarious. By his classmates. He was a great guy, real funny, such a clown! He was on a fast track to suicide. He was probably impaired in the OR numerous times.

The developmental level of the humor in my medical school class was the same as I heard in my twelve-year old son's locker room, before and after hockey games. I once drove him and two other members of his team to an in-line roller tournament in Midland, Texas, the sole adult in the vehicle. I was back in medical school. These boys were wonderful, normal twelve-year olds. And funny too. But it isn't funny when you're 27 years old, married with two kids, and your classmates at medical school are early adolescent jackasses. I felt so sorry for the patients.

The stupid, inane, narcissistic, entitled, relentless humor of my classmates was a major stress to me. I thought it might be unbearable, and for the first six weeks of medical school I thought I might actually have to drop out. Then I adjusted.

"Shields up, Commander. Activate cloaking device." That became coping strategy number one.

I was very careful not to tell anyone I was going into psychiatry. If you told anyone you were going into psychiatry, you would be ex-communicated immediately, and never taken seriously again by your classmates. The attitudes towards psychiatry were crystal clear. Psychiatry is Mickey Mouse. Psychiatry isn't scientific. Psychiatry isn't real medicine. The only people who go into psychiatry are people who need psychiatrists themselves. That's what the real medical students thought, the ones who were going to become real doctors.

14

MEETING YOUR CADAVER

We didn't have to do gross anatomy the first day of medical school. Thank God. Everyone in the class was most relieved. All we got was a brief lecture from the Professor. But a few days later it was D-Day, or C-Day, or X-Day, or some kind of bad day. It was time to "meet your cadaver."

The most amazing thing about meeting your cadaver was there was no preparation for it. We medical students were not treated like human beings. We had no feelings, no personal reactions, no psychological needs. We were there for purely instrumental reasons. The carbon-based life forms on the dissecting tables were dead. The carbon-based life forms called medical students were just lumps of bio-functioning coal. There was no gap between the living and the dead, in terms of their feelings being catered to by the Anatomy Professor.

It is pretty scary to start dissecting a cadaver. We were all terrified that we would have to unwrap its face, and start cutting on a dead person's face. A wave of great relief went through the crowd when we were told that dissection of the head and neck wasn't till after Christmas. As best we could guess, the head would stay wrapped till then.

C-Day arrived. From the safe lecture room, we took the long, long, long walk into the gross anatomy lab. It was immediately next door. We divided into groups of five students per cadaver. The dissection for the day had been demonstrated at the front of the lecture theater by the Professor. I was glad I was sitting a fair ways back.

There it was. Or he. Or him. Or something.

The cadavers were wrapped in cloth soaked in formaldehyde. Medical students delight their families by coming home with the smell of formaldehyde on their hands, which proves to family members they have been touching the guts of dead bodies all day. This is not a good aphrodisiac for some women, others don't mind.

The cadaver turned out not to be human. Sure, it had once been a living man. But not now. Now, it wasn't even a dead man. It was some kind of ingeniously constructed plastic model of a human being soaked in formaldehyde. Or not exactly plastic. Some unusual substance I hadn't seen before. When we cut open the major blood vessels, they looked like they were full of blood sausage like I used to buy in England. Except it was a gross, inedible blood sausage. Well, not that gross, really. Just interesting.

Once we got over the *idea* of dissection, the reality was profoundly interesting. Not counting the face. We dreaded that up until we actually unwrapped it. Then it too was interesting. I published a poem entitled, "Dissection" in *The Lancet*, while in medical school, that captures the experience with more precision than is possible in prose.

In the whole year, there was not a single sentence from any Professor about our emotional reactions, the meaning of the cadaver, or how we felt. The same turned out to be true all the way through medical school. You are just thrown into things. There is major social pressure not to wimp out.

The first time you see major trauma in the ER? Just suck it up. Blood flowing freely in the OR? Suck it up. Nobody even tells you to suck it up. Actually, you don't have to, because you are a cadaver too. A being without history, heart or soul.

There is a mythology in our culture that doctors are really intelligent and highly educated. They aren't dumb. But really, you don't get any education in medical school at all. Medical school really isn't a university education. It is purely a technical training. Doctors really aren't educated beyond the early undergraduate level. By serious standards, my standards, they have never received a liberal arts education beyond the high school level. I'm not talking about gifted high school. I mean average high school.

I take it back. Actually, many doctors are very dumb. Dumber than average people. They are uneducated barbarians in many ways. Louts. Starting with meeting your cadaver, doctors are systematically trained to ignore their feelings, treat themselves as machines, and act the same towards everybody else.

On the first day of medical school, most of my classmates were decent, humane, sensitive people. But they got socialized out of that. Over the four years, they got transformed into insensitive, shut down, know-it-alls with little respect for patients. It started with meeting your cadaver. It was not done by conscious plan. There was no organization to it, no conscious planning.

Meeting your cadaver was an initiation ritual into a strange culture. A petri dish of chauvinism, reductionism and hatred of the human spirit. Med school. It is a fraternity. The first hazing was in the gross anatomy lab. Many others would follow. Watch out if you have two X chromosomes, no Y chromosome, and a desire to be a surgeon in this culture! No Y makes you a double X, a pornographic film star maybe, but not a real surgeon.

"Chrone chrone chromosome, can't be in the surgeon zone. Surgeon zone, surgeon zone. Our zone, our zone. Red rover, red rover, you can't come over. Unless you want to spread your legs, then we'll fertilize your eggs. Ha, ha, ha, ha, we all fall down. Or go down. Or something."

15

MEMORIZATION CONTESTS

Now, I have a pretty good memory. But I never won any memorization contests in medical school. Didn't have the extra twenty hours a week to waste. Not like my adolescent, single classmates who lived at home with their parents, had no life, and racked up another twenty hours a week of studying above what I logged. We wasted an incredible amount of time in medical school memorizing useless trivia.

One person in my class turned nineteen in first year medical school. The life experience of most of the class consisted of living at home in a conventional, white suburban middle class family, going to school, taking two years of pre-med, and walking in the door of the medical school. My classmates were children. Their development ground to a halt in first year medical school, buried under an avalanche of memorization and deviant socialization. It was already more than half a decade delayed, fixated by our culture, in many cases. A few students were older, more mature, had some life experience, or came from a different background, but they were a minority, and anomalies.

It was a WASP, high-powered technical school. Acquisition of information. Not knowledge. Not education. Not the ability to create, reason, analyze or read. The logic system taught in medical school is one simple, rigid decision tree for differential diagnosis. That is it. The rules are straight-forward. Your job is to acquire facts. Godzillions of them. More facts than one hundred people could memorize in a lifetime. It was difficult to adjust to the realization that you could never learn it all.

I remember being in the bookstore the first couple of days of medical school. The first year students were considering buying extra texts, beyond the required ones. They wanted to learn as much as possible, to be the best doctors possible.

We reacted with incredulity when the second year students told us, “Don't get that. It's not on the exam.”

We couldn't understand how anyone could take such a mercenary approach to medical education. Wasn't it a sacred thing to be accepted into medical school? Weren't human lives going to be in our hands? If there was something you didn't know, a patient might die. Within a few weeks, we had abandoned such idealism completely.

“Get real,” became our working motto. “Real” meant jumping through every hoop put in front of you by the circus masters.

There was such a huge quantity of information to memorize each week, there was no time or energy left over for *curiosity*. Once I spent some extra time in the gross anatomy lab on a Friday afternoon, dissecting our cadaver's armpit. By myself. I wanted to see the brachial plexus. A classmate came into the lab, asked what I was doing, and was incredulous that I was studying something that wasn't going to be on the next exam. He genuinely couldn't grasp my motive. This was a few months into first year.

In our neuro-anatomy class, we had to memorize structures at different levels of the brain and spinal cord. We had a manual with pictures of dissected brains and spinal cords for study. There were numbered dots at the locations of the different structures. On another page, a list told us the name of the structure that corresponded with each number.

We spent so much time memorizing this material, and quizzing each other on it, that eventually we quizzed each other on the numbers.

My study partner would ask, "Thirty-six?"

I would reply with the name of the structure. Without looking at the picture. We had both the numbers and the names memorized. Then on the exam, we got the same pictures and numbers. I could have gotten the same mark on the exam if there were no pictures, just a list of the numbers.

By the end of medical school, no one could remember even 10% of this material. It is completely irrelevant to the practice of medicine except for neurologists, neurosurgeons, neuro-pathologists and neuro-radiologists. But this is how the entire medical education ("education") went. Everything was taught by specialists who taught us as if we were going to enter their specialty, or, often, sub-specialty.

It was acknowledged that 50% of the class would go into general practice or family medicine. But the Professors communicated nothing but scorn for family practice. If a bright student (= a top memorizer) said he was going into family practice, this was lamented as a great loss and waste of talent by the Professor, whether he be surgeon, pathologist or internist. The hierarchy was very clear. Neurosurgeons at the top. Next cardiac and plastic surgeons. Then orthopedics. Then general surgery. Drop down many levels to internists. Obstetricians a little lower. Then pediatricians. Then family doctors. Then way down, off the ladder in the swamp, psychiatrists.

The best students were the ones who memorized the most. Most of which was irrelevant trivia. We spent hours memorizing different types of blood cells and all their precursor cells, and learning how to recognize them under the microscope. Nobody but hematologists, pathologists and some oncologists would ever use 95% of this information. But we memorized it.

On and on it went. Micro, micro detail in all subject areas. No attention to gestalt.

No attention whatsoever to the humanity of medicine, except for a few token hours in a couple of courses. A classmate of mine transferred to a different style of medical training in place at the University of Calgary, three hours drive south of the University of Alberta, which is in Edmonton. Calgary had a three-year program, ten months per year, with a different approach and format. Much more oriented to clinical reality and integrated learning. Based on the assumption that the first step is to train future family physicians, half of whom will actually enter other specialty training programs after graduation.

At the University of Alberta, the Calgary program was regarded as soft, shaky and suspicious. Ten years later, I'm sure, graduates of the two programs would be indistinguishable on multiple choice exams. But they were soft down south because they didn't grind it out the way we did. This attitude wasn't based on reality, scientific reality. It was all superstition, folklore and tribal custom.

In the middle of this, I did learn an incredible amount of interesting information. There is no way you can be a doctor without knowing a mountain of facts. But there was such overkill. Cramming in so much stuff that no mind could possibly retain it. Then there was the examination system. Multiple choice questions. Nothing but. Except for a couple of exams in a couple of courses in first year. The assessment of my skill as a physician was solely through multiple choice questions, on exams.

It took me a while to figure out that memorizing facts and multiple choice questions (MCQ) go together. You couldn't test the ability of a student to read English literature critically with multiple choice questions. Or the ability of a biochemist to design original and creative experiments. Or an architect to design buildings people would travel on airplanes to see. Real creativity, in arts, sciences, or technical fields, can't be tested by MCQ. Nor can real analytic or synthetic thinking.

No problem. None of that is relevant in medical school. Nor in psychiatry training. In my four years of psychiatry training, I never wrote an essay or wrote a short answer to a question. All my written exams were MCQ. This is why psychiatrists can't think or create. If they ever had it, it was ground out of them. Since psychiatrists are at the average high school level in their liberal arts education, they wouldn't want anything but MCQ anyway. Might look bad. Couldn't perform on essay questions. This is a problem, because life is an essay question, not an MCQ.

If you meet a psychiatrist with any brains or creativity, this isn't because of his medical and psychiatric training. It is *despite* his years in the meat grinder. Or hers. I was in the 25th percentile in my class on MCQ exams. What does that tell you? I have over one hundred and twenty-five publications in the peer-reviewed medical literature. Been invited to speak on four continents. No doctor with such a profile got there because he was good on multiple choice exams, or had a lot of facts memorized. Such doctors, myself included, do have a lot of facts memorized, but that is such a small fragment of the story.

MCQ IQ is such a puny variable, in the equation for predicting who will be a superior doctor, researcher, or teacher. Medical schools act as if that's how you get into heaven. St. Michael looks at your MCQ results.

"Praise the Lord. Say, Mike, is Jesus going to be on the exam?"

16

LECTURES ON NUTRITION

As well all know, nutrition is important to health. In medical school I had a couple of lectures on nutrition out of thousands of hours of training. The Professor who gave our nutrition lectures drank chocolate milk out of a carton and ate potato chips while talking to us. He was overweight, poorly groomed, and badly dressed.

There's your message and your meta-message. The message at my medical school was delivered in words.

The real message, the meta-message, delivered in tone of voice, body language and posture, was, "Nutrition is bullshit, boys and girls. Yer gonna be doctors. Leave that nutrition shit fer the nutritionists. They're cute girls, and they ain't got nothin' better ta do. 'Xcept maybe in the kitchen, er in the bedroom."

The only time nutrition was taken seriously in medical school was when it was delivered I.V. inside the hospital. Parenteral nutrition through a line into a vein was the real thing. Real medicine. But diet? No way. That was Mickey Mouse stuff way below the level of expertise of the M.D.

No one told us that straight up. The message was deniable. But that was the meta-teaching. It was delivered by looks, tone of voice, side comments, condescension towards nutritionists, and negligible time for nutrition on the curriculum.

Then there was the nutritionist who came to give my class a talk. She was amazing. Very, very nervous. She had bought into the male chauvinist medical mind game. She was just a little old weensy nutritionist talking to the scary, really smart medical students.

While she talked, a rash began to appear on her chest. Below the upper border of the rash, her skin was bright red. Above, it was a normal white. The line separating red from white was pencil thin. This line steadily moved up her chest, then up her throat, stopping at her chin line. It took about fifteen minutes to move from her upper chest to her chin. My classmates were mesmerized, but uncomfortable. Then, as she got near the end of her lecture, the line started to move back down her throat.

I doubt that the students retained any information at all from the lecture. But I learned something about the immune system. We don't understand it.

How the heck does the body do that? How can you have a rash separated sharply from normal skin that travels across the body? How is that regulated? What are the immunological signals involved? I never did get my Nobel Prize for figuring that out. But there is a Nobel in the solution to the problem. It's clearly a problem in psychoneuroimmunology. Possibly even psychoneuroimmunoendocrinology. I assure you, those are complicated areas of medicine, too complicated for most people to pronounce.

I saw a patient while doing clinical interviews on the medical ward, to learn interviewing skills. He drank three to four liters of caffeinated coke per day, plus a lot of caffeinated coffee. He was highly allergic to bee stings, and had to carry a bee sting kit with him everywhere. His feet sweated all the time, no matter what the temperature. And he had irritable bowel syndrome.

I'll bet that all these problems were symptoms of one syndrome. He was probably treating his allergy problem with caffeine, which has the same effect as the injectable adrenalin in his bee sting kit. He probably had a chronic allergic problem that resulted in irritable bowel syndrome. He said his feet sweated less the more coke he drank. I'd call that a nutrition problem. A problem that could be entered and analyzed through the door of nutrition. If you could understand why this man consumed so much caffeine, I think, you could solve his irritable bowel syndrome.

I was one of the first two graduates in the new M. D. With Honors in Research Program. It didn't involve any formal certificate, but I did nine months of original research in immunology during medical school. This occupied my summer between second and third year, and all my elective time. I published two papers in immunology journals based on my research, one of which I wrote myself and was first author on. It has the catchy title, "Suppressor T Cells Derived from Early Postnatal Murine Spleen Inhibit Cytotoxic T-Cell Responses."

The other paper, on which I was third author, was, "Expression of Ly-5.1 Antigen on the Effector and Regulatory Cells Involved in Cytotoxic T-Cell Response to Transplantation Antigens."

Because they weren't clinicians or M.D.'s, and didn't have stupid attitudes towards psychiatry, I told a number of the Professors and researchers in the Department of Immunology that I was going into psychiatry. One of them asked why I was doing research in immunology if I wanted to go into psychiatry. Why wasn't I doing psychiatry research?

My answer was, "Because I want to understand the logic of biological systems."

The immune system is an amazing thing. I learned a lot from studying it. A lot about how biological systems are controlled, and how they can go wrong, and be manipulated from the outside. The immune system is very incredible because it has *memory*. It has more memory than any other part of the body besides the brain. And it can tell the difference between self and other.

When the immune system gets tricked or mixed up, it mistakenly thinks that the body's tissues are foreign bacteria or viruses, and attacks them. This is called *autoimmune disease*. I was intrigued by the analogies between autoimmune diseases and psychiatric patients who attack and self-mutilate themselves, as if their own bodies are outside enemies.

I published a paper in the *Journal of the Royal Society of Medicine* while in medical school entitled, "Basic Research by Medical Students."

In this paper I talked about different classes of scientific argument I had learned by studying the thought of one of the immunologists in the Department, Peter Bretscher. I also included a poem entitled, "Peter Bretscher and the Theory of Immune Class Regulation" in my *Adenocarcinoma And Other Poems*. Peter Bretscher was the most creative intellect I met in medical school, by a long shot.

While in the Immunology Department, I attended Visiting Professor Lectures in both the Departments of Immunology and Biochemistry. I remember one lecture that really impressed me. I forget the exact content, but I remember that the researcher wanted to solve a certain problem in viral biology. Even to realize that the problem existed was brilliant. But before this scientist could start to study the problem, he had to solve a series of incredibly difficult technical problems. The methods he created to detect and isolate viruses were incredibly clever. Astonishing in their ingenuity and originality. Breathtaking.

But that was just the start. Then, using these brilliant techniques, he went on to pose and solve a complicated problem in a really clever, original way. I said to myself, "Wow. That's really clever."

I had the same reaction at a variety of different lectures. Also to experiments I studied in my molecular biology class in pre-med. Really, really brilliant people thinking in a way never seen in psychiatry. Ever. Really creative science. New logic forms. Ways of thinking no one had invented before. Entirely new approaches to problems no one had ever dreamed of before.

I went to talk to a biochemist about nothing in particular a couple of times. This was in 1979. He told me that in the future, computers would be made out of DNA. Friends of his had shown that if you shine light on DNA, it changes its shape. You can then manipulate the DNA to change back to its original shape, at which time it gives off the energy it absorbed as light.

I thought to myself, "OK. How do we get from there to a computer?"

While I was thinking this, he explained that basically what you had there was an on-off switch. Shape A is on, shape B is off. Once you have an on-off switch you have a binary logic system. Once you have a binary logic system, you have a computer.

This is what I really admire in science, the ability to think *outside the box*. To invent new logic, new ways of looking at problems. To ask new questions no one else has asked before. I have never found that kind of science anywhere in psychiatry. There was no real science in my nutrition lectures. No food for thought. From a nutritional point of view, my med school lectures were a very bad diet.

17

PLENTY OF KIDNEYS, NO ETHICAL PROBLEMS

In four years of medical school and four years of psychiatry training, I had a couple of hours of lectures on ethics. That was it. The Professor who gave us our ethics lectures in medical school was a big shot in Canadian medicine. His name showed up in the *Canadian Medical Association Journal.* He had a national reputation and was in charge of a major section of the Department of Internal Medicine. He was no nobody.

The Professor told us that in the kidney transplant field, there would be no ethical problems if there were enough kidneys. The only reason ethical problems arose was because there were fewer available kidneys than people who needed transplants. Therefore doctors had to choose who got to be on the top of the list, and who on the bottom. That was it. End of discussion.

In many ways, doctors are brain dead. Literally, without exaggeration, the top 5% of any graduating high school class has more brains than the Professors of Medicine, when it comes to ethics. And many other things.

This is what is so hard to grasp. The doctor. The brilliant, high-powered surgeon who operates on brain tumors. The heart transplant surgeon. The internist who runs the kidney dialysis and transplant program. Complete imbeciles on many topics. It is very hard to grasp that this is the truth. It's not bad attitude on my part, paranoia, conspiracy theory, or the result of one too many alien abductions. It is simply a fact. My Professor was an idiot concerning ethics. He couldn't keep up with a high school debating team in a debate about ethics.

Is this surprising? Yes and no. It is surprising because our culture has bought into a myth of the medical doctor as educated and intelligent. Doctors in fact are not educated. They are *trained*. There is a big difference. It showed up in my ethics lectures.

At my medical school, all ethical problems would vanish if there was enough technology available.

"Ethical problems only exist because we don't have enough equipment, enough supplies, enough money, or a complete understanding and cure for every disease. In the brave new world of the future, there will be no need for medical ethics, because everyone will be cured."

In the meantime, at my medical school, we fooled around with token lectures on ethics because of some kind of outside pressure from who knows who, some bureaucrats or lobbyists or something. Inside medicine, we knew, ethics was Mickey Mouse shit.

"Get the Hospital Chaplain in if there is an ethical problem," we were taught.

We were taught to have scorn for the Hospital Chaplain while pretending to have respect for him. Not that the doctors fooled anyone.

It was obvious to everyone that the doctors did not take the Hospital Chaplain seriously. He was way down the ladder, lower than psychiatrists, lower even than social workers. At least social workers could help get someone discharged, or get the patient's family off your back.

I never read the Hippocratic Oath in eight years of medical training. Not as part of my training. I never read any physician Code of Ethics. No such Codes were handed out, discussed, asked about, or made the subject of MCQs. I did read the Hippocratic Oath on my own. But it was not part of my training.

Ethics, inside medicine, was "academic" or "philosophical." Both those words are used to designate Mickey Mouse hobbies for Professors in the Faculty of Arts. Eggheads who do no real work in the world. People who never deal with real problems. People who pretend to be Doctors. Everybody knows they aren't real doctors. Only the M.D.s are real doctors. The Faculty of Arts bozos have just stolen the title, Doctor, to get some prestige. They aren't fooling anyone. That becomes obvious on the first day of medical school.

Entering medical school is like emigrating from rural Bangladesh to a luxury apartment in Manhattan. Now you're in the big money. The part of the University people really take seriously. Where the real doctors are.

One question. How did the psychiatrists sneak into the Medical School? Everyone knows they aren't real doctors. Somehow they managed to worm their way in. But they aren't fooling anyone. Except themselves. That's the number one feature of The Great Psychiatry Scam.

Shrinks are real doctors? Give me a break. That lie is a violation of medical ethics.

18

PSYCH ROTATION

The first clinical rotation I did was in psychiatry. In med school, you spend the first two years sitting in lectures and going to labs. You get a tiny amount of exposure to real patients. Then in third and fourth years, you do clinical rotations. I did the mandatory ones. Twelve weeks of surgery, twelve weeks of internal medicine, eight weeks of pediatrics, eight weeks of obstetrics and gynecology, and eight weeks of psychiatry. Then there were elective slots, which I devoted to my immunology research.

The entire class began its clinical rotations at the same time. Everyone wanted to talk to everyone about their experiences in the first few days.

"What was it like? What did you see?"

One of the students had psychiatry for his first rotation. He was most impressed by a manic woman who bought three grand pianos in one day. But no one wanted to hear much about psych. Psych didn't count. The students really, really wanted to hear what it was like in the OR. That was the citadel, the inner sanctum, the holy of holies. We all knew it. We all sweated about it.

I finally got there. But not till the next chapter.

I did my psych rotation at a peripheral hospital. That means a smaller hospital that is not one of the two major university teaching hospitals. The really high-powered stuff goes on at the main medical school teaching hospital, which is where the Dean has his office, the medical students take lectures, etc.

At the peripheral hospitals there may be a little bit of neurosurgery done, but that's only because the OR is booked at the Big Place. No heart transplants or anything like that. If psychiatrists did brain transplants, it wouldn't happen at the peripheral hospital.

I finally made it. I decided to be a psychiatrist at age nine. Now, at age twenty-nine, I was doing it. Kind of. I had already been disillusioned by the psych lectures in second year. Boring, boring, boring. The lectures made me even more certain not to tell anyone I was going into psychiatry. What an embarrassment to be associated with such boring lectures! How could you take *psychiatry*, and make it boring? Psychiatry?

You can't be interested in life and not be interested in psychiatry. Psychiatry has got it all. Anthropology, madness, incest, rape, murder, mania and melancholy. Brain chemistry, Sigmund Fraud, Carl Jung and his archetypes. Psychiatry intersects with everything. Sociology, religion, witch doctors, poetry, lust and apathy. There isn't an element of life that doesn't border on psychiatry somehow. There are hundreds and hundreds of documentaries in the lives I have touched as a psychiatrist. Powerful and moving stories of tragedy, comedy, perversion and self-defeat. Awe-inspiring stories of survival and triumph.

How could you take the Bible, Shakespeare, Blake, Lawrence and Eliot, and make them boring? Easy, in an English Department. Or life, and make it boring? Easy, in a Psychiatry Department. I was already disappointed in psychiatry before I started it.

I soon learned the purpose of psychiatric assessments inside hospitals. Take a complex, textured, marvelous human life, and reduce it to a simple formula. Then give the right drug. Or no, drugs, plural. Well, no, not the right drugs. The wrong drugs. Some absurd combination of drugs. Psych patients may have had the right stuff, but they didn't get the right stuff. Not from their psychiatrists.

In medicine, giving numerous different drugs in an unscientific fashion that doesn't make sense is called *polypharmacy*. Except in psychiatry, where it's called *standard practice*. As a medical student, then as a psychiatry resident, then as a psychiatrist, I saw hundreds and hundreds and hundreds of cases of wild, crazy unscientific polypharmacy.

I would estimate that of the cases treated by the other psychiatrists on my 23-bed inpatient ward in Winnipeg, where I was a staff psychiatrist from 1985 to 1991, no less than 25% of cases were locked-down, water-tight clear malpractice cases, based on ridiculous polypharmacy. But in ten years of being a resident then a psychiatrist in Winnipeg, I heard of only one law suit against an inpatient psychiatrist, a suicide case that didn't have anything to do with medications.

I quickly surveyed the lie of the land as a medical student. Right off the bat I saw a typical profile I would see again over and over and over. Psychiatric malpractice polypharmacy won't stop till the fat lady dies from drug toxicity. The current farce of biological psychiatry is that fat lady. Pill pushing witch doctors hiding behind the disguise of biological scientist.

"Sorry, no, I retract the above statement. It is an insult to fat ladies. Sorry, ladies. I will never again compare you to psychiatrists. What was I thinking?"

My psych rotation was back in the days before Prozac and the other new antidepressants, which are much safer and have far fewer side effects than the old tricyclic antidepressants. How many patients did I see who were on a tricyclic antidepressant, an antipsychotic medication, an anticholinergic medication for the side effects of the antipsychotic medication, a sleeping pill, an anti-anxiety pill, a narcotic pain killer, and another antipsychotic for anxiety on a prn basis? Prn means "take as needed" as opposed to a fixed regimen like twice a day or three times a day.

"I would need one hundred pairs of hands to count the ways I love thee, colleagues. Or to count the number of sickening polypharmacy prescriptions I have seen. Year 2007 and still counting."

The only real question was whether the polypharmacy victim was also on lithium or not. It was not unusual to see people on two or three drugs of the same type, such as two or three antipsychotics, two different antidepressants, or two or three different anti-anxiety drugs. This was common. Routine. Every ward on every day.

I learned something else about psychiatric prescriptions. And something else. And something else. Commonly, routinely, a whole series of prescribing errors were made. These were:

1. Too many different drugs at one time.
2. Drugs not matched to diagnosis.
3. Diagnosis not matched to symptoms.
4. Symptoms not described adequately to support the diagnosis.
5. Symptoms not tracked to follow drug response over time.
6. Multiple drugs increased, decreased, started and stopped in a short time period, making the effect of any change in the patient impossible to attribute to any one drug or dosage.
7. Too low a level of a drug to work.
8. Too high a level of a drug given without good reason and with serious side effects.
9. A drug not given for long enough to assess its effect.
10. Patients discharged with prescriptions for a month's supply of numerous drugs, way beyond the amount required for a guaranteed successful suicide attempt.
11. Diagnoses changed to justify drug changes, when the change was not supported by clinical observation or documentation.
12. Trying drugs just to see if they will work.
13. Failure to recognize or treat serious side effects.

This mess went on all the time, in many, many patients. I remember a teenage girl I spent hours talking to during my psych rotation. She was obviously seriously disturbed. Looking back, the only diagnosis I would give her is histrionic personality disorder. During a period of a few weeks, she rotated through a bunch of psychiatric diagnoses, each one followed by a change of meds. I figured out how the process works.

When the diagnosis is schizophrenia, antipsychotic meds are given. But they aren't working. The psychiatrist only spends five minutes every second day talking to the patient, but he knows the meds aren't helping because the nurses tell him. All of a sudden, the patient's symptoms begin to change. Not in reality.

In the psychiatrist's mind. Symptoms of schizophrenia start to fade out, and symptoms of manic-depression start to fade in. This takes a few days.

All of a sudden, the teenage girl didn't have a psychosis anymore. She had an affective disorder, now called a mood disorder. Manic depression.

"OK, nurses. Pull out the lithium containers. Our girl's getting lithium. They should put it in the tap water. Hell, why not? Does no harm. We could treat all the manic-depressives in the country. Just like we put fluoride in the water."

The psychiatrist was only half joking. Probably would have done it if the civil rights nuts weren't in the way.

The problem was not the patient. Or the field of psychiatry. It was, and is, the psychiatrists. Sure, psychiatry is a pretty Mickey Mouse branch of medicine. But it's not *that* bad. Not as bad as psychiatrists make it.

Another thing I noticed is that psychiatrists just make things up. I saw this a bit in the rest of medicine, but nowhere near as much as in psychiatry. Psychiatrists "know" all kinds of things about patients, not because they know them, but just because they know them. This knowledge doesn't come from observation, data, or science. It appears to be caused by seizure activity in the brains of psychiatrists.

The psychiatrist "knew" the teenage girl was manic-depressive, not because he had observed that to be the case, but because he wanted to give her lithium. He had nothing to offer except pills in different combinations. So he rotated her through different combinations. This went on for a month until she got bored with being in the hospital and went home. In a month no one did anything that helped her the slightest bit.

Then there was the two-year old boy with an extremely severe case of attention deficit disorder with hyperactivity. He was up all night, totally out of control behaviorally, spitting at his parents, climbing all over the filing cabinets in the family doctor's office, and just generally raising hell and driving everyone crazy. He was admitted to the hospital for observation and diagnostic assessment.

Absolutely amazing! In the hospital, his behavior was completely normal. The whole thing was a parenting problem. This little rascal escaped salvation by Ritalin only because the psychiatrist did a good job. He actually watched, listened and thought about the situation.

"Great," I thought. "This is what I went into psychiatry for."

The boy stayed in the hospital, was discharged without any therapy plan and without any psychiatric follow-up.

"Wait a minute," I thought to myself.

I didn't realize this was the standard pattern. People come into psychiatric wards, get a diagnosis and some pills, but have no real follow-up. Everyone is too busy doing psychiatry to do any psychiatry.

It took me a while to figure out that none of my Professors were seeing seriously mentally ill people themselves on a long term, ongoing basis. With a tiny number of exceptions. No schizophrenics. No manic-depressives. No anything. My Professors of Psychiatry were not doing much psychiatry. They were teaching, and going to meetings, and talking to nurses, and reading charts, and going to the Doctor's Lounge, that I noticed.

But none of the Professors seemed to be spending much time with patients. Neither were the nurses. I soon realized that nobody was actually spending much time doing psychiatry. Whatever psychiatry was supposed to be. I was trying to figure that out too.

The patients spent most of the day sitting around, smoking, talking to each other, watching TV, waiting for their meds, and sleeping. Every once in a while they would complain to the nurses or cause a little trouble. We always had a needle for that.

They would go to a few groups. But the groups were weird. They seemed to involve some kind of common sense counseling and pep talks. Nothing happened in the groups that seemed to require any expertise or post-graduate education. For sure, you would never see a psychiatrist doing a group. In four years of medical school and four years of psychiatry training, I watched one psychiatrist run one therapy group. And it was major weird.

Happened in medical school. I went over to a clinic that was part of the main teaching hospital. They had a group there run by a psychiatrist. I sat in. For the entire hour the psychiatrist did not say one single word. He made not one single facial expression. We assumed he was alive, but thinking back, how did we know for sure?

The patients spent most of the group complaining about how the shrink never said a word, and trying to get him to answer their questions. He wouldn't even explain why he wouldn't explain anything. Part of the time they talked about how the message must be that they have to solve their own problems. One person said he thought it was stupid that the psychiatrist was sitting there analyzing what they projected on him, when anyone would be pissed off at a doctor who never said anything.

I agreed with the patient.

The sick thing is, this was high-powered psychiatry. Group therapy based on psychoanalytical principles. This shrink wasn't regarded as a joke by the other shrinks, kicked out, or told to do real therapy. No. He was tolerated. And paid.

Not only tolerated, but respected. Other shrinks thought he was doing deep therapy. We could have brought a wino in off the street at 10% of the price, and gotten more accomplished.

That was it for group therapy training by psychiatrists. I was done.

I didn't figure it out in my psych rotation, because it only lasted eight weeks. The doctors were all busy, and there were summer vacations going on. It didn't even sink in until a while into my residency.

You never get to watch psychiatrists doing psychiatry. In four years of training to be a psychiatrist, I never watched a psychiatrist do a complete diagnostic interview. I never watched a psychiatrist conduct a complete, formal mental status exam. I never watched a session of psychotherapy. I never watched a psychiatrist give ECT. I watched a couple of hours of a shrink doing family therapy. Two one-hour assessments by a shrink for the short-term psychotherapy clinic. That was it.

In four years of training to be a psychiatrist, I watched psychiatrists doing their work for less than one full day total. In my surgery rotation, I was in the OR for 6.5 hours for one procedure. I got to watch as many hours of a surgeon working in one day as I did psychiatrists working in four years of specialty training to be a shrink.

Why is this? There are all kinds of hocus-pocus Fraudian rules about how private psychotherapy is, but I know the real reason. Shrinks are embarrassed that they don't actually have any skills. They don't want anyone watching them because they don't want the Scam busted.

Based on my own direct observation, I have absolutely no idea what shrinks do in their offices with their patients. I literally, without exaggeration, based on direct experience, know the same amount about the procedures of Nepalese Yak herders as I do about North American shrinks.

"Does this sound like *medical* training?"

In my psych rotation, I diagnosed my first case of multiple personality disorder, in 1979. Published it in a special issue of *The International Journal of Clinical and Experimental Hypnosis* in 1984. A funny thing about that paper - I submitted it after I obtained my M.D. I think the editor assumed I diagnosed the case while I was a psychiatry resident. I never told him I was a medical student at the time. I wonder if he would have published it, if he had known?

Good old Martin Orne, the editor. Little did I know at the time that he was a TOP SECRET hypnosis contractor for the CIA. Buddies with the shrinks who built Manchurian Candidates for the CIA. At the time I had no idea about such things. Now I do. And I have proof.

"Think the shrinks will be stirred up about that? About my book, *The CIA Doctors:*

Human Rights Violations By American Psychiatrists? Where I tell the whole story, and document it. Hmm. I wonder."

I thought I would get some reaction to diagnosing a case of multiple personality. But no. They just let me loose on her. No training. No supervision. I wrote in the chart that I was talking directly with an alter personality. No call from the Chairman of the Department. No axes thrown at me. I just did my thing, me, a third year medical student. I even presented the case as part of my performance evaluation for my psych rotation. No reaction.

"Uh, huh. Uh, huh. And what other diagnoses did you consider?"

I got a good mark, not fabulous, but good.

Now what was the deal here? I diagnose the first case of multiple personality disorder seen in western Canada, ever. I treat it therapeutically. And I get an OK mark? That's it? I read more of the existing literature on multiple personality disorder than all the shrinks in the Department combined had read. I publish the case myself. And I get an OK mark? It doesn't add up.

Either the shrinks believed my diagnosis was accurate, in which case it was an astounding performance by a medical student. Or they didn't, in which case they should have pulled me off the case, and maybe put me in a case. Just in case I was a case. They did case me out. But they didn't do either. Didn't react one way or the other. Gave me my mark and went back to the Doctor's Lounge.

I didn't get it then. I don't get it now.

I remember another young woman with serious anorexia nervosa. She was way under weight, exercised like a fiend, and ate one tenth of an ounce of food a day.

I was sitting talking to her when I made what I thought was a pretty good suggestion, "You know, avocados have a lot of calories in them. You could eat a very small amount of food, half an avocado, and take in three or four hundred calories. That way, you could gain weight without having to eat too much."

She looked at me like I was from outer space, but thanked me politely. I was an utter novice at understanding anorexia nervosa. But I could diagnose, treat and publish a case of multiple personality without any real supervision. My supervisor had never seen a case, didn't know any shrinks who had seen a case, and couldn't recommend a single thing for me to read.

At this point, I had barely, vaguely heard of *dual personality*. I hadn't read the books or seen the movies, *Sybil* and *The Three Faces of Eve*. No one had mentioned multiple personality in the shrink lectures. I had never seen it on TV, hadn't really thought about it. But I was already, without knowing it, off and running on my career as a multiple personality nut. More on that later.

My psych rotation came to an end. I saw some psychotic people. An amazing, full-tilt post-partum psychosis in a previously normal woman. Her husband stared at her in alarm while she writhed on the floor and wrestled with the staff, screaming gibberish. Or jibberish. Or ju ju jibbish. Or something. Whatever it was, it was scary.

A young schizophrenic woman had *erotomania*. She knew a stranger was in love with her. He sent her secret messages from his house across the street - a certain movement of the curtains, the way he walked down his driveway. I was amazed when my supervisor told me there was a word for this. The symptom had been seen before, and catalogued. There is a pattern to madness, I realized. That was interesting.

I knew this already, but now it really sank in. There are patterns and regularities in insanity. Order in chaos. Perhaps meaning too. None of my classmates asked me about my psych rotation. I didn't tell them.

19

SURG ROTATION

Surgery was my most mostest rotation. I was assigned to a very gifted Scotsman as my supervisor. I wrote a poem about him in my collection of poems. He was by far the most artistically evolved, aesthetically disciplined, rigorous, passionate clinician I met in medical school. And by far the best technician.

One day in the OR, I passed his supreme test, the only medical student to have done so in ten years. Like all Professors, he liked to quiz the students on ultra-obscure trivia. This was amusing for him, but a pressure cooker for the students. His ultimate question?

"Where are the dimples of Venus located?"

The intern, other med students, nurses and anesthetist in the OR looked blank.

I piped up, "Over the posterior sacro-iliac junction."

"Where did you learn that?" he asked in utter astonishment.

"I'm not sure, Catullus maybe," I replied nonchalantly.

He had an incredible collection of utterances. Och. Ech. And many variations on those. He used to talk about how medical students had gone downhill recently. The evidence? They never wore ties anymore.

Nurse too were in the dumpster. The evidence for that? The current fad for holistic nursing. He also talked about "filthy smokers" a lot. As a thoracic surgeon, he had seen many, many examples of the effects of smoking on the human body. He knew two people named Colin Andrew Ross. Me, and Colin Andrew Ross, the thoracic surgeon who died while out jogging while I was at medical school. No relation. Never met him myself.

Too bad. I was looking forward to saying, "Hello, are you Colin Andrew Ross? Nice to meet you. I'm Colin Andrew Ross."

My supervisor had the most exquisitely precise operating technique. He was like a watchmaker in his precision. The procedure that lasted 6.5 hours involved a huge incision that exposed the woman's entire abdomen and chest cavity. In one glance I could see her spleen, liver, stomach, heart and lungs.

The procedure was to remove the cancerous bottom half of her esophagus, free up the top half, and splice in a piece of bowel to form the bottom half of her esophagus, if I remember right. I remember that the blood loss for the entire procedure was 50 cc.

His dissection was meticulous and perfect. All bleeding perfectly controlled and minimized. All movements of the scalpel sure, economical, and accurate. The tissues and structures revealed as cleanly and clearly as pictures in an anatomy text. You always knew exactly where you were and where you were going. Complete order, control and precision. I admired him tremendously.

He operated on another woman to make a biopsy for lymphoma, based on part of her pericardium he removed, which is the lining of the heart. This involved another huge incision going from the front of her chest to way around her back. During the procedure, he invited me to hold her beating heart in my hand, which I did. He just wanted me to have the experience.

Later, on follow-up rounds the next day, he examined her incision. I looked at it with awe. Each stitch, of which there were dozens, was at exactly the same angle. Exactly the same length. Exactly the same space apart. Exactly the same tension. And the incision was perfectly closed. It was a work of art.

This man was a real doctor. He was the most literate M.D. I met in medical school. He had by far the highest, most refined artistic temperament of all the clinicians I met. In ten years of thoracic surgery, he had never lost a patient in the OR. He cared more about doing the absolute best for his patients than any doctor I ever met, before or after.

One thing I did really pissed him off. A woman came into the outpatient clinic for injection of varicose veins. He injected a compound into the right spot that made the vein scar down at that spot, closing off the varicosity. He showed me how to mark the spot and do the injection. Then he finished that leg while I did the other. Injecting the right spot is kind of tricky, and it doesn't always work. I hit a higher percentage on my injections than he did.

I tried to console him by saying it was probably beginner's luck, but that didn't work. He gave me the highest mark any student ever got under him. That is the single achievement of which I am most proud in medical school. He let me do three procedures myself, with very close, hands-on help and supervision by him. An appendectomy. A breast lump biopsy. And a pilo-nidal sinus. That experience alone made the slog through medical school worthwhile.

One day we were in the OR operating on a man's lung. Dr. Fraser pointed out that he was a smoker. You could see little round dots all over the surface of his lung. This was the surface next to his chest wall, which is called the *pleural surface*. The lung is divided into partly separate lobes that have fissures in between them. You have to separate the lobes by hand to see the hidden *fissural surface*.

I exclaimed, "The smoke doesn't go to the fissural surface."

Dr. Fraser replied, "What do you mean?"

I pointed out that the fissural surfaces were healthy and pink, with no little black dots at all. He said that in ten years of thoracic surgery, he had never noticed this. I commented that there is probably some principle of lung physiology that isn't understood, hidden in the newly observed fact.

Don't forget my previously mentioned theory. Maybe the multiple personality I see in psych patients is really there, just missed by other shrinks. Almost all other shrinks.

Then there was the dark side of the force. My Dante-esque decent into the nether regions of incompetent surgery.

"Beatrice. Beatrice. Where were you then?"

I watched Dr. Fraser remove a gall bladder with complete precision, and 10 cc of blood loss. A perfect dissection and a suturing job as good as a plastic surgeon. Then I watched a gall bladder removed by Dr. Butcher, who I believe grew up in Lyons, France.

In this other procedure, there was at least half a liter of blood lost. There was fuming, pressure and tension by the surgeon. The stitching up of the incision was a mess. During the procedure, blood was welling up from a cut artery, and the intern had to do heavy duty suction to clear things up enough to cauterize the bleeder. It was Hamburger Hill. You couldn't tell where you were, or what the structures were. If I did five gall bladders under Dr. Fraser's supervision, I would have been able to do a lot better job than this Professor of Surgery.

I had no idea about the range of competence among surgeons, before I did my surg rotation. It is big. Very big. Believe me, infections, complication rates, and death rates go up as skill goes down. I could tell as a med student that it makes a huge difference. How was this problem policed by the Head of the Department of Surgery?

One day the Head and the Chief Resident were standing in the hallway when I came walking up.

The resident said to the Head, "We could get Colin to do the procedure."

I thought he was joking. But he wasn't. The Chief Resident absolutely refused to go into the OR with the aged family doctor who was doing a hernia repair shortly. He said he couldn't stand it. The upshot of the conversation was that the Head and Chief Resident agreed that the patient would be better off with me in the OR, than with the doctor in there alone.

It was wild, gross, criminal malpractice. This was the third or fourth time the doctor had repaired the same hernia. It kept breaking down because of his incompetent surgical technique. The patient was a healthy man in his thirties. The Hippocratic Principle, "First Do No Harm," had long since gone out the window.

The man's groin was hamburger by the time the doctor had stabbed around in it for a while. I had absolutely no idea what was what, where he was, or where he was going. Neither did he. At one point he was holding the suture up in the air with one tool, a surgeon's version of a pair of pliers, and was trying to pass the needle end of the suture around behind the vertical portion of the suture. He was holding that end with another pair of pliers called a *needle driver*.

It took him three or four tries. His depth perception was so bad, he kept passing the needle driver in front of the suture instead of behind it. This was a few feet from his eyes in a brightly lit OR.

The doctor insisted that the anesthetist keep the patient in a very light state of anesthesia. He didn't like his patients over-anesthetized. At one point in the middle of the procedure, the patient sat up and started talking to the doctor. The doctor told him the operation was still going on, and said he should lie down. He wouldn't, so the anesthetist had to push on his chest to get him back down. Later, he sat up again.

At one point, the surgeon held up a mushed bit of flesh, and asked me, "Do you think that's the vas deferens?"

He was planning to tie it off, which would render the patient sterile on that side if it was the vas. The vas is supposed to be carefully avoided during a hernia repair.

I answered, "The quality of the dissection is so poor, I can't tell."

To which the doctor responded, "Oh well, if it is the vas, he's still patent on the other side."

Patent means open.

I was sent in to help another family doctor do an appendectomy. He dropped tools on the floor a bunch of times. He was very nervous throughout. When he was closing up, he had to ask the OR nurse what kind of suture to use at different levels, because he didn't know himself.

There are too many Dr. Butchers in psychiatry. Dr. Fraser was deeply disappointed when he found out from an intern, near the end of my rotation, that I was going into psychiatry. He considered it a complete waste of my talents. I know one thing for sure. Doing my surgery rotation wasn't.

20

MED ROTATION

Internal medicine encompasses many things. Cardiology, neurology, gastroenterology, hematology, infectious diseases, rheumatology, oncology. The list goes on. An internist takes four years of specialty training, at least that was the situation in Edmonton in 1980. Two to four years of pre-med. Four years of medical school. One year of internship. Four years of internal medicine.

You can be a general internist, or a sub-specialist, such as a neurologist. An internist is a fancy family doctor who doesn't see kids. A pediatrician is an internist for kids. Or an internist is a pediatrician for grown ups. Or something.

The rotations in surgery and medicine were the two biggies. My twelve weeks were divided into three blocks. Eight weeks at the main University Teaching Hospital, four weeks at a peripheral hospital (the same one where I had my hand surgery), and four weeks at the W.W. Cross Cancer Institute. They were very different places.

At The Cross, as everyone called it, there was a lot of tragedy. I saw a mother of several young children, a woman in her twenties, who was not responding to treatment for leukemia. She would die soon.

A man in his late forties had a spinal cord tumor. He had a bald head, and was a tough, funny man who spoke real straight and got right to the point. He was in a wheelchair. The tumor was progressing and not responding to treatment. He had just lost control of his bladder for the first time.

This man looked up at me and asked, worried and tearful, "I'm going to get it back, aren't I? Tell me I'm not going to be like this forever."

To which I replied, "I don't know. I'm just a third year medical student. I honestly don't know."

I think he thought I really did know, and was holding back on him.

A gorgeous young, nineteen year old girl was admitted for some chemotherapy. Her leg had been amputated for a sarcoma. The tumor had spread to other parts of her body. She was dying. She wore a baseball cap, her complexion was great, and she was full of spunk. It got to me. This was someone almost old enough for me to date. I wanted to hold her, or make it OK somehow. Part paternal, part boyfriend. It really upset me that she was so gorgeous, brave, and alive.

She saw this on my face, and said, "Can we just get this over with?"

I had to do a routine admission history on her. We talked a bit. She said she was tired of it. Every time she came for chemo, the medical student doing her history was choked up, because she was young, about the student's age.

Another woman in her early twenties had cancer of the ovaries, metastatic. I had to do a history and physical on her. That bothered me. She would be dead in a year or two. They let her bring in her own marijuana and smoke it in the hospital. I admired The Cross for that. The doctors and nurses were willing to break the rules for the best interests of the patient. They didn't get all hung up on attitudes and propaganda about marijuana. They were actually rational about it.

From most doctors, all you hear is irrational, unscientific negativity about marijuana. The negativity about marijuana is irrational because it's so far out of proportion to the attitudes about alcohol. Alcohol is an incredibly dangerous, destructive drug that fills hospitals and morgues. None of my Professors had ever seen a medical complication of marijuana in an inpatient, or a victim of a car accident involving marijuana. The complications of alcohol were everywhere on the medical and surgical wards. Yet marijuana got slammed, and alcohol got off easy. Why?

Only one reason. Alcohol was the Professors' drug of choice. Plus, they bought their own propaganda. I heard ridiculous stern warnings about the harm that marijuana smoke can do to your airways. The warnings were factually correct. It wasn't the facts that were in question, or the problem. It was the unscientific attitudes. The emotions. The high level of social tolerance for alcohol.

My Professors told me about marijuana being an entry drug for heroin and speed. True, in a tiny percentage of users. It wasn't the data I disputed. It was the attitudes. The moral intensity about marijuana was way higher than it was about alcohol. Reality was staring everyone in the face. What is true about alcohol?

Alcohol is an entry drug for alcohol. That's why it's so dangerous.

The Cross was the best place I worked. The building was clean and full of light. The staff was really dedicated, and treated the patients with respect. All the bad attitudes I saw towards patients elsewhere, simply didn't exist at The Cross. Cancer is too serious.

I remember seeing plastic bottles marked, "Levodromoran." They gave out narcotics in such quantities, that they kept them in jugs. Not because they were giving out too much, or were lackadaisical. There was just a lot of pain at The Cross. Physical and spiritual.

A man in his sixties talked to me about his wife, and how much he was going to miss her. Her breast cancer had spread to her lungs, and she had trouble breathing, even on home oxygen. She was brave and optimistic, but he told me, privately, that he didn't think she was coming home this time. I was so touched by his love, commitment, and grief.

I had one little triumph. I had to do a routine admission history and physical on a woman in her late fifties or early sixties with breast cancer. Medical students do long, thorough histories and physical exams as part of their learning. By the time you hit internship, the written history you do has shrunk by 75%. I was still thorough.

I examined her cranial nerves. Eye movements, sensation on her face, tongue movements.

“Oh, oh. She can move her tongue to the left normally, but can’t move it to the right. This means a metastasis in the foramen magnum on the left,” I thought to myself.

I told the internist. He didn’t really believe it, but went to check for himself.

“An actual cranial nerve palsy,” he said later.

He was very impressed that I picked it up, and said he didn’t often see a clear, specific involvement of a cranial nerve like that. The next day, the woman got radiation to that specific area in her brain. If I hadn’t picked up on her inability to move her tongue to the right, the metastasis would have grown and grown. I probably prolonged her life. Me. That felt good. I did that. That was me being heads up, thorough, and knowing my anatomy. I actually did something as a doctor.

I also met Bonnie again, a nurse I had done the admission history and physical on the previous month, at the smaller peripheral hospital. She had been admitted there for diagnosis of leukemia. I got to look in the microscope with the hematologist at her blood, and see the tell-tale characteristic abnormality, that proved her diagnosis. Her white blood cell count was extremely high, when her family doctor drew her blood. She had gone to him for a really bad fever and sore throat. Boom! Within a few days, the hematologist was telling her she had leukemia.

Now she was at The Cross for really heavy duty chemotherapy. She was in isolation, with incredible nausea, vomiting, diarrhea and sores in her mouth. She looked deathly. But she went into remission. Bonnie went into remission and later won the Alberta Nurse of the Year Award. She and I published a paper together in *The Canadian Nurse*, talking about what the experience was like, from our two different perspectives. For me it was moving and instructive. I learned a lesson about the depth of the human spirit, in the face of tragedy.

I was walking down the hall in The Cross one day, in 1980, when I bumped into a man I knew in Norman Wells in 1970 and 1971. At that time I was a high school drop out, an unskilled laborer. Now I was a medical student, with a white lab coat and stethoscope. His attitude changed but did not change. We stood outside his wife's bedroom and talked about her metastatic breast cancer. She was in her mid thirties. He knew she would make it. I knew she probably wouldn't.

I was able to connect with him on the Norman Wells level. One of the guys. But I was no longer one of the guys. I was the doctor. Even though I wasn't a doctor yet. Whatever criticisms I have of doctors, whatever my degree of alienation from my colleagues, now, then I had crossed the threshold. There is no going back. You either are a doctor or you aren't. I am. A real one. To this day. That is why I am so angry at my shrink colleagues. They are faking it and ruining it. For power, prestige and financial gain. It's a scam. A heresy.

Medicine is sacred. Solemn, serious, and profound. The healer. Whether it be western medical doctor, Chinese foot doctor, or circumpolar shaman. It is the calling that counts. Not the technology. Being a doctor is an attitude, a discipline. You have to set your personal history aside. Your own needs, and gains, and wants. Your own ideology. You have to focus on the patient. What is true about the patient now? What is wrong? What can I do to help? It is the patient who counts. It is the patient who gives meaning to the doctor. Not the other way around.

If the doctor was born into an Inuit culture in the 1700's, it wasn't his fault that his culture lacked modern technology. He could still be a doctor. He could still do these essential things. Be there. Be focused on the patient. Make as accurate a diagnosis as possible. Bring the best available technology to bear on the problem.

Set all the politics aside. The financial self-interest. The personal psychopathology. What is medicine's fundamental beef about managed care? The interference with this sacred trust. This mission. This focus. On the patient. Doing the best for the individual patient in your office, on your ward, or in your OR. Even, after death, in your morgue. The autopsy is part of living medicine. Even though the patient is dead, the medical duty persists. Managed care shits on that every day.

More on managed care in the third last chapter.

I had nothing to offer my old friend from Norman Wells. Chemotherapy, from this point on, probably had nothing to offer his wife. But our talk was valuable to him. It helped. He got to talk to the doctor. The doctor was really there, and listened, and heard. Didn't bill him, or write in a chart about him, or change his wife's biology. Didn't write a prescription, or a letter. Didn't check his pulse or his lungs. Just listened. Just spent time, being there, being the doctor. Genuinely focused and present.

I was glad to help. I never saw him again.

At the smaller peripheral hospital, things were different. At the main University Teaching Hospital, there are about 75 interns and residents per square foot. As a medical student, everything you do is checked, monitored and reviewed to death. You don't get to do much yourself. This is very comforting and reassuring, at first. Then it just gets to be a pain.

At The Camsell, Charles Camsell Hospital, Edmonton, Alberta, Canada, I was back on familiar ground. I had been a patient in the OR there myself a bunch of times. There were lots of native and Inuit patients. It was great.

There were no medicine residents at The Camsell. "Medicine" has two meanings, which can be confusing. In one meaning, medicine is the entire field, encompassing surgery, obstetrics, internal medicine, everything. In its other meaning, medicine means specifically internal medicine. So I was doing my medicine rotation. This is different from a flying camel, which is a rotation you do in figure skating.

There was only one intern, who was on call only one night in three. And there were four medical students, if I remember the count right. This meant that each time you were on call as a medical student, you had a 2/3 chance of having no intern around. The staff internists were all at home. So it came down to you. You were on the front lines all by yourself. Normally this was undramatic and no big deal. But not one Sunday morning.

I arrived at Camsell Hospital Sunday morning to take over call. A nurse asked me to come look at a patient I knew already. He was a native man in his early thirties with an amazingly distorted, misshapen rib cage, who was dying from alcoholism. His liver was so shot that he was yellow from jaundice. An intense, bright yellow you could spot at a glance from fifty feet away. That morning, something else was wrong.

He was blue around his mouth. This meant he was dying from not being able to get enough oxygen. Could or might die shortly.

"What to do?"

He was already getting oxygen by nasal cannula. I had learned about the hypoxic drive to respiration. Usually respiration is driven by the need to blow off carbon dioxide. The body senses the too-high levels of carbon dioxide in the venous blood, and this is the signal that drives respiration. If you have chronic lung disease, though, and can't blow off enough carbon dioxide, your body gets used to the high carbon dioxide levels. You lose your hypercarbic drive to respiration.

In this scenario, the body shifts over to a hypoxic drive to respiration. Your breathing is driven by the low oxygen levels instead of the high carbon dioxide levels. This means that if you give the patient too high an amount of oxygen through his nose, artificially, he may stop breathing. Pressure number one.

I increased his oxygen flow a little bit and told the nurse I wanted to get a blood gas. She told me the technician was at home and would have to come in. I could draw the blood but couldn't operate the machine that did the reading. After a wait, the technician told me the results.

His pH was 6.9. This was mind boggling. I had never heard of a patient with a pH that low. I didn't even know you could be alive at 6.9. Not that he looked very alive. He was halfway into a coma, blue around the mouth, and otherwise bright yellow.

We paged the staff internist on call, but he was out jogging, we learned later. All I knew was, he wasn't answering his pages. So I ordered an amp of bicarbonate. This brings your pH up. We repeated the blood gas, and the pH had gone up a tad. I gave him another amp. It went up a tad more.

Now the nurse from ICU started to get on my case. We had moved him from the regular ward to the ICU. At least it was called an ICU. There were no doctors there, just more nurses than usual. The nurse was a real bitch. She started bad mouthing me and telling me I wasn't doing anything for this patient except giving him bicarb.

She regarded that as a pathetic, useless intervention. I had never even been in a real ICU at this point. Finally, after a couple of hours, the internist on call showed up. We talked about our marathon training. I was preparing for my 3:17 marathon the next year. His time in an Edmonton marathon was faster. And we also talked about the patient.

The internist and I walked into the ICU, he assessed the situation, turned to the bitchy ICU nurse, and said, "Give him another amp of bicarb."

She almost blew a gasket. After giving me shit for being the stupid medical novice, it turned out I was doing exactly the right thing, at the right dose, at the right pace. This really pissed her off, and she lost face in front of the other nurses. Later the internist started a fancy medicine by I.V. drip that helped stabilize the patient a bit more. He died three days later. There was nothing anyone could do for him.

One time I was looking for a nurse in the evening, when I was on call. There were two wings on one floor. The elevators came up in the middle of the floor, beside one outer wall. Then you walked into a central area where there were two nursing stations, facing each other. Each nursing station served half of the floor. From one nursing station, you would walk down a hallway to the far end, make a right turn, walk along a bit, make another right turn, then walk up the hallway on the far side of the building back to the nursing station. There were patient rooms all along the hallways.

There was no nurse at either nursing station. I walked around all the halls on the floor twice and couldn't find a nurse. Checked in every patient room. Not one nurse anywhere. I searched the floor for seven or eight minutes.

Finally I found the nurses. They were in an obscure conference room that you reached through a back hall I didn't know existed. They were in there smoking and doing report.

It was in medicine that I learned about "doing report." This is what the nurses call it when the shift going off tells the shift coming on about all the patients. It is a necessary activity. But it is also a dragged out free coffee break. Often it's literally dragged out, since so many nurses suck enthusiastically on ciggie butts, while doing report.

I figured out that nurses spend very little time with patients. Most of an eight hour shift is devoted to charting, doing report, talking on the phone, talking to doctors, taking a break, and standing around behind the nursing station. Although I wasn't there to study wild life biology, I also learned a lot about mammalian territorial behavior. Behind the nursing station is a fortress. There are no stone walls. But it is a highly demarcated space.

Patients are absolutely not allowed to come behind the nursing desk. That is frowned on big time. And the nurses don't like to come out from behind the nursing desk. They spend absolutely as much time in the nursing station as they can. Occasionally, to keep up appearances, they make a brief foray down to a patient's room to actually do some nursing. But that is minimized by the use of nursing assistants.

There are inferior sub-nurses, who have various titles, who go out and take the vital signs. Orderlies handle most of the poop and wheel chair driving. The nurses give out the meds. Just about everything else they've downloaded onto other personnel. And they hold onto the meds real tight. Giving out meds is their domain, their turf. Which is handy, because that means more time behind the nursing station counting out meds, arranging them, doing inventory, and generally fiddling around at the med cabinet.

Actually giving the meds to patients takes hardly any time at all. It is done fast and impersonally, with a condescending sing-song tone of voice.

"Here are your meds, Mr. Smith."

The attitudes of nurses towards doctors is mixed up. They are angry because the doctors don't give them no respect. They're angry because the doctors get paid so much more. They want to be respected as equal colleagues. They've got their panties in a knot because they don't have enough political power in the system. But when the going gets tough, all the liability and responsibility is dumped on the doctor pronto. The nurse is all of a sudden just following the doctor's orders.

"What do you want to do, doctor?" is a favorite question nurses ask medical students all the time. Pressure. Sweat. Anxiety.

Simultaneously, of course, the nurses are trying to snare an intern or resident as a marital entrapment trophy. Makes for a fun work place.

I learned about phone calls for Tylenol at 3:00 A.M. The nurses love to phone the sleeping medical student on call for a Tylenol order in the middle of the night. It's one of the highest ranking sadistic power trips nurses pull. The students try to have prn orders for everything under the sun on every patient's chart, to prevent these phone calls. But there's always some new admission or something, so you can never stay ahead of the game and win.

I think the nurses carve notches under the nursing station desk, every time they make one of those phone calls. Probably, the nurse who makes the most middle-of-the-night calls to medical students and interns in a year gets a free admission to a male strip joint or something.

I remember at the main teaching hospital, we had a yeller on the ward. A yeller is an old person who has had a stroke, who yells all day for no reason. This woman was non-stop, high volume and incredibly aggravating. She didn't even say words. It was just a high pitched, demanding, whining sound. You could hear it on most of the ward. The usual dope had no effect on her. Finally, the medicine resident decided to get a psych consult. He said he knew this really bright young psychiatrist who had just finished his residency.

This guy was really up on his psychopharmacology. He would know just the right drug to give her, to shut her up without over-sedating her. The drugs we had been using either had no effect or put her to sleep all day.

I was there when the hotshot psychiatrist came striding up. I diagnosed extreme pathological narcissism after three seconds. He was like a movie star with an entourage, except he was by himself. His entourage was only in his head. The patient couldn't speak or understand, so he just ducked his head in her room, then came back to the nursing station.

With a great flare, he said he knew exactly the right drug for her. It would control her yelling without sedating her. He had had good experience with it. He expressed condescending amusement at our primitive attempts to control her with haloperidol. This other antipsychotic would do the job.

It was complete bullshit. The new drug didn't work any better than the haloperidol. And that was it. We never saw him again. That was all the help he had to offer. Probably too busy making high-powered medication decisions for hundreds of other patients to spare time for us.

I remember the look of resigned scorn on the nurse's face when I talked to her about the fact the new wonder drug wasn't working. She didn't expect anything better from psychiatry. I made very sure not to give her hints I was a future psychiatrist. Too embarrassing.

I saw all kinds of complicated, interesting cases in medicine. Learned lots about numerous exotic and rare diseases. But what filled the wards? Nothing fancy or high powered. It was all diseases of living. The wards were full of people who had run out of time. Their bodies had taken all they could. Obesity, no exercise, alcoholism, smoking, and not taking your insulin properly. Unhealthy people with unhealthy lifestyles who had finally broken down. The machine was worn out.

I learned about real medicine. The trenches. Not trench mouth. Trench disease. That's different. Most of medicine boils down to pus, puke, pain, blood and diarrhea. That's what you basically deal with all day. Add swelling, redness and shortness of breath, and you've about got it. Real medicine isn't about rare genetic diseases, obscure infections, or unpronounceable forms of cancer. It's about common, everyday degeneration of the human body.

There aren't very many young patients on the medical wards. Or there weren't then. This was before AIDS. Take cardiology, for example. Sure, I saw a few cases of specific arrhythmias, valve defects, and familial lipidoses. These were specific medical problems affecting young and old. But that wasn't the day-to-day bulk of the caseload.

Most of the strokes, heart attacks, circulation problems, and related cases followed the same pattern. Overweight, no exercise, high blood pressure, high cholesterol, smoking, didn't take your insulin properly. These are non-technical factors that have to do with psychology and sociology, not the biology of medical diseases. The problem wasn't so much the biology of blood pressure and cholesterol. It was the fact the people didn't take care of themselves. These were diseases of sloth and self-neglect.

In this mix of risk factors for cardiovascular disease, family history was only one factor out of six. It was swamped out by the other five: obesity, smoking, lack of exercise, high cholesterol, high blood pressure. The people who had the family history, but took care of themselves, were not filling the wards.

It was not very glamorous in internal medicine. And it was not very happy. The morale was not good. Morale was much better in pediatrics, obstetrics and surgery. In fact, obstetrics didn't even seem to be part of medicine. I spent an afternoon in an obstetrician's office, during my obs rotation. Obs rotation means obstetrics rotation.

An afternoon in an obstetrician's office can be very pleasant. I saw a parade of young, healthy, glowing, happy mothers-to-be, all with normal pregnancies. They all loved their silver-haired obstetrician. They all looked forward to the future.

In medicine, it was mostly death, dying and decay. People nearing the end of their lives, who would never be the same. People with no glow. Grey, unhealthy, depressed people with no future. It's a tough field to work in.

In surgery there's a lot of the same, but you can save a young healthy person's life, and give them a future. You can actually do something. Internal medicine is so impalpable. You write orders in charts, look at lab values, do the odd physical exam. But you don't actually help anyone directly. It's all indirect and cerebral, except for a few procedures like colonoscopy with excision of polyps, which are minor surgery.

Surgery, on the other hand, is like carpentry. A carpenter and I built a deck at my house in Winnipeg, before I moved to Texas. That was really fun. And satisfying. And real. There was an actual deck you could stand on, feel and look at. Same with surgery. You actually directly do something in surgery. It would be great to be a surgeon. I'm not idealizing surgery. It's just that it has this wonderful, concrete reality to it. The patient would have died. Now she can live another sixty years, healthy normal good years.

In medicine you're just fighting inevitable decay, with minimal and declining quality of life ahead. I'm exaggerating. But that's how it feels. At least on a University Hospital inpatient ward. Hospitals are negative energy vortices. No other building in our culture houses so much suffering and bad news.

21

BRAIN ROTATION

"Back to surgery. Not back surgery. Brain surgery. Back to brain surgery. Not the back to the brain, just the brain. Nothing to do with the back at all. Brain surgery. Get it? It ain't brain surgery. Get it now? Brain surgery."

Because I did my surgery at a smaller hospital, I got to be first assist on three neurosurgical procedures. Usually, as a med student, you are way down the pecking order. There is the Chief Resident, the Junior Resident, the Intern, and then the Student. There may be more than one resident and intern. You, the student, get to stand at the back of a big crowd in the OR and get a good view of nothing.

The basic job of the student is holding the retractor. This is a little tool with a curved end that is used to pull back the end of the incision, to give the surgeon a better view. It's great fun holding it for an hour or two while your arm cramps up and you can't see what's going on.

Not so in these three operations. An arteriovenous malformation, an aneurysm and a meningioma. The meningioma was a young Chinese girl. That's how we talked.

Not, "Sue Lin has a meningioma."

No, we'd say, "The meningioma in Six." Meaning Operating Room number six.

So the brain had a meningioma, or maybe the meningioma had a brain, I'm not sure which. Our job was to take out the meningioma and leave the brain. Which we did. I say "we." I watched and the neurosurgeon did the work.

It was a most impressive experience. Getting through the scalp was a surprisingly bloody experience. The scalp bleeds like stink. Then he drilled three holes in her skull using a shiny, sterile bit brace drill. Then the electric saw to saw a line connecting the three holes to each other. Then off comes the piece of skull, revealing the meninges.

The meninges are like a thin layer of leather covering the brain. You get through them with scissors. Then the meninges are folded back to reveal the living brain. This is one of the most stirring experiences I have ever had, to see the living brain moving up and down with the pulse of the blood. It looks like it is breathing, alive. Of course, I knew it was alive, but it was amazing to see what an alive thing it was, this brain.

A network of blood vessels covered the surface, and you could actually see the sulci. Clearly. Not eighteen inches away. Incredible.

The procedure went without incident. The most remarkable event occurred when the surgeon was stitching up her scalp, during what is called “closing.” The curved needle at the end of the suture broke in half, pinged off the lens of my glasses, bounced off the wall, and disappeared.

His immediate question was, “When was the last time you cleaned your glasses?”

He didn’t say, “Oops.” Or, “Sorry.”

I replied, with composure, “I clean my glasses several times every day.”

To which he responded, “That’s good.”

He got a new needle driver and continued suturing up the scalp. He was the surgeon. I was the student who might have carelessly contaminated his OR by not having clean glasses for his broken needle to ricochet off. It broke because he put too much leverage on it. Never mind that I might have been blinded if I wasn’t wearing glasses.

The AV malformation was a woman in her thirties. She had been experiencing severe headaches for a while, which she had never had before. The neurosurgeon operated because there was a risk the AV malformation might rupture like an aneurysm. An AV malformation is a tangled mess of abnormally interconnected veins and arteries in which blood pools. Everything went fine.

The aneurysm was a middle-aged woman. Prior to opening up her head, the surgeon showed me the X-ray study in which the aneurysm was shown by dye injected into her carotid artery. There it was, clear as day.

Inside her brain, the surgeon exposed the aneurysm in order to clip it off and prevent it from rupturing. He pointed it out to me.

I remember thinking that you really have to know what you’re doing to be a neurosurgeon. I couldn’t tell the difference between the aneurysm and the middle cerebral artery. But he clipped it off, closed up, and we were back in the doctor’s lounge.

The anesthetist came in and told us the woman was waking up, but was paralyzed on the right hand side. She was taken back into the OR, opened back up, and the clip was removed. He had clipped off her middle cerebral artery, not the aneurysm. All he could do was stick in a little gauze packing to help things scar down, and get back out.

I talked to her over the next few days. She was totally paralyzed on the right hand side of her body, slurred her speech a little bit, and had trouble finding words. Already, within a few days, she had taught herself some association tricks to find words. I forget the specifics, but if she was trying to remember the word "community" she might say to herself, "bridge."

This would make her think of community, for some reason.

I thought back to the general surgery resident who helped us with dissection in gross anatomy in first year. He said that neurosurgery was a "gloomy" profession. I couldn't grasp what he meant. He said that during his neurosurgery rotation, he spent morning after morning going to check up on people who had had six, nine and twelve hour procedures the day before. Some never came out of coma, some were paralyzed, some couldn't speak.

There was so much work, and so little health. He said it would be too depressing for him. Now I knew what he meant.

But I agreed with my Professors. Neurosurgery is indeed at the top of the heap in medical specialties. No doubt. There is nothing like operating on the brain. Even heart transplants don't come close.

22

MEDICAL INTERN

In your internship you learn what health care economics is all about. Plus you get initiated into a sadistic, primitive cult called medicine.

On July 1, 1981 I started a two-month rotation in internal medicine as Dr. Colin Ross, or, alternatively, Colin A. Ross, M.D. I had a hospital I.D. badge with "Dr." on it. Now, when people called me, "Doctor," it wasn't nurses being sarcastic, Professors being kind, or patients being mistaken. Now, finally, I really was a doctor. Sort of.

My starting salary was $15,600.00, on which I supported two adults and two children and carried a debt load. I was physically inside the hospital about ninety hours a week. I was paid a gross of $300.00 a week for these 90 hours. Given the insane Canadian tax rates but my high number of dependents, and low salary, let's say I took home $225.00 a week.

Normally, in construction, I would get time-and-a-half after forty hours. For 90 hours worked, I would actually get paid for 115 hours. This means my take home pay as an intern was based on a rate of $1.95 an hour. This was less than I made as an unskilled laborer in Norman Wells eleven years previously. The Norman Wells job included free room and board.

For $1.95 an hour, I performed duties that had the potential to kill people. Things got better, of course. By the time I was near the end of my psychiatry residency, in late 1984, my take home pay had risen to almost $8.00 an hour. This was after subtracting taxes, legal fees, spousal and child support payments. Finally, in the fall of 1985, when I was a full-fledged psychiatrist and Assistant Professor, I got to purchase the second car of my lifetime, at age 35. The car my mother had sold me for $1.00 in second year medical school, I turned over for a profit to a Japanese college student. She paid me $300.00 for it, fair market value.

At age 35, I couldn't actually afford to purchase a car. But I did lease a Toyota Corolla, with no air conditioning, electric windows or tape deck. After a year, I exercised the purchase option.

Without being told, I was told as an intern not to whine about my 90 hours a week. The Professors had to do it when they were interns. I was going to do it. My Professors spoke with anger and scorn about women who took soft rotations in residency because they were having kids. They weren't real doctors, weren't dedicated, and were only good for family medicine and pediatrics at best. Not anything serious.

"Dedicated," meant being a self-destructive workaholic. It meant being emotionally shut down, angry, and condescending towards patients, lower professionals on the totem pole, and the world in general. Us and them. Doctors and lay people. We went through the ritual, they didn't. We're in the club. They aren't.

There are rules at the Club. It is forbidden to write, *The Great Psychiatry Scam*. Simply not cricket. Gentlemen don't speak that way of each other. Certainly not at the Club.

"Dash it all. What's the world coming to, when a chap writes a book with a title like that? Medical chap, too. Canadian. Might expect that from an American. Not a Canadian. Has he forgotten the Queen?"

"Quite, quite, Cedric. Couldn't agree more. Sherry?"

"Yes. Harrumph. Someone should write that Ross chap a letter."

"No need, Cedric, no need. The False Memory Police will take care of him."

"Yes, quite. Jolly good bunch they are too. What?"

23

DON'T HAVE SEXUAL INTERCOURSE WITH PEOPLE'S HEADS

Dr. Gordon Lambert, Head of the Outpatient Department, Department of Psychiatry, Faculty of Medicine, University of Manitoba, Winnipeg, Manitoba, Canada, said to me, in late August, 1981, "Don't have sexual intercourse with people's heads."

He used the vulgar vernacular term. Four letters, first letter is neither "e" nor "g." I don't want to cause any hysterical faints in sensitive readers, so I have edited his remark to make it more polite. He was very angry when he said it.

What was going on? Why did Dr. Gordon Lambert think I wanted to fuck with people's heads?

I was just completing two months of internal medicine, and was about to start four months of outpatient psychiatry as a first year psychiatry resident. I brought three cases to the Outpatient Department Intake Meeting, because I wanted to follow them in psychiatry. Two were later included in a poem entitled, "On Leaving the Outpatient Department," which I published in the *Canadian Journal of Psychiatry*.

One was a woman whose father was admitted for investigation of severe abdominal pain. A needle biopsy of his pancreas showed that he had cancer of the pancreas. He died about a month later. He was an alcoholic, as was his son-in-law. The woman, my patient's daughter, wanted to work on why she married an alcoholic, when her father was also alcoholic. There were a lot of things wrong with the marriage.

When I presented the case to the room crammed full of nurses, residents, psychiatrists and social workers, everyone though that was fine. Dr. Lambert OK'd my seeing her. I had my white lab coat on, and my stethoscope, and felt a little out of place. But it was cool to really be in psychiatry.

The next case was the wife of a man who had just died of multiple myeloma. She had borderline personality disorder and proved to be completely untreatable. My supervisor ended up speaking to her to explain why she wasn't benefiting from therapy and wouldn't be able to see me anymore. She was a major handful. But she was approved no problem.

The third woman was the wife of a man who had just died of bowel cancer at age thirty-three. He had several young kids. I had prescribed him amazingly high doses of I.V. morphine in the last two weeks of his life, and he died alert and pain free. The purpose of her seeing me in the Outpatient Department, I said, was to work short-term on her unresolved grief and adjustment to being a young widow. Seemed as reasonable to me as the other two cases.

Dr. Lambert forbade me to see the woman in the Outpatient Department, and gave me a piece of advice to start my psychiatric training.

He said, to the astonishment of everyone present, in an angry voice, loudly, and with agitation of his musculo-skeletal system, “Don’t fuck with people’s heads.”

Later, when I was ensconced in the Outpatient Department, several psychiatric nurses apologized on behalf of Dr. Lambert. They said they had never seen him like that.

Dr. Lambert was dying of liver cancer. He lived less than another year.

I learned, in my first fifteen minutes of contact with the Department of Psychiatry, Faculty of Medicine, University of Manitoba, Winnipeg, Manitoba, Canada, that I was going to be abused by shrinks.

I would be abused verbally, politically and legally. Injected with personal venom disguised as professional opinion. Be a mirror for the disavowed shadow selves of my colleagues. Function as a punching bag for mentally ill shrinks. Get hung as a whistle blower. Be excluded and back stabbed. Eventually write *The Great Psychiatry Scam*.

Later, in the 1990’s, I learned that Dr. Lambert had referred his patient, Val Orlikow to Dr. Ewen Cameron in Montreal. Dr. Cameron wrecked her brain with drugs and electric shock. He did this on purpose under contract to the Canadian Government. Cameron had to get money from the Canadian Government because his TOP SECRET contract with the CIA had run out. He taught the CIA how to erase people’s memories. His guinea pigs were patients like Val Orlikow.

Cameron erased people’s memories with huge doses of electric shock. He gave his patients LSD and mescaline and hung out with the top CIA mind control doctors in North America. All this is totally documented. Dr. Lambert had no problem referring Val Orlikow to Dr. Ewen Cameron. It was OK for Dr. Ewen Cameron to have sexual intercourse with people’s heads.

24

SIGMUND FRAUD: THE PSYCHOANALYSIS SCAM

Sigmund was the biggest Fraud in twentieth century psychiatry. All the other Frauds were Small Frauds compared to him, Small Fry. Sigmund was Dr. Big. Now, at the beginning of the twenty-first century, biological psychiatry is the number one scam, but biological psychiatry only took over in the late 1970's and early 1980's. Dr. Fraud ruled the roost before that. He was the main cock. The shrink chickens gobbled around in his shadow. Tried to swallow his shadow. Become pregnant with his genius. It was an oral fixation.

"Cock a doodle do. Cock will do will do. Everywhere you look, cranny, crevice, nook. Sigmund Cock is there. It really isn't fair. He gets all the chicks, the licks, and kicks and tricks. I'll have to doodle do, and tell them what is true."

"Chicky, chicky, chicks, the Cock has played a trick. His name is Sigmund Fraud. The Cock is now outlawed. You've got a brand new God, a brand new barnyard boss. I'll help you grieve the loss."

"He's big, he's strong, he's tough. Say, have you heard enough? Ready now to play? The game has certain rules, it sure is not for fools. Scholarship and science. Thought and reason, both in season, are now your brand new boss. Chicky chicky chicks. Can you play or not? Is Fraud Cock all you've got? Or want or need or know?"

"Oh, oh, I forgot you're only chicks. Your brains don't work too quicks. In fact they works real slow. You always gobble rocks, when looking for big Cocks. It's a barnyard hazard thing. Ya'll join me now and sing."

"Sigmund Cock is dead. Reason rules instead. Sigmund Cock is dead. Reason rules instead."

In the fall of 1981, as a first year resident in psychiatry, I started going to monthly psychotherapy meetings. They were held in the homes of local shrinks, on Wednesday evenings. This was really it. Not only did I get to hear the Professors talking about their own private psychotherapy cases, but I got to see their big homes and expensive furniture. This was a big deal for a poverty struck resident.

It took me two or three meetings to catch on. It was all phony. There was no real therapy going on. The psychotherapy meetings were an elaborate social ritual with rigid rules. They had nothing to do with medicine. I had just come from real medicine, so the contrast was apparent. After twenty years in psychiatry, you forget, and it's harder to notice. It wasn't hard in the fall of 1981.

We would listen to the Professor present the case, then people would pipe up with wise comments and deep questions. The residents who attended usually just listened, because they weren't deep enough yet to say anything.

The pecking order was clear. In the entire Province of Manitoba, there was only one fully trained, certified, card carrying psychoanalyst. All the other shrinks practiced psychoanalytic psychotherapy, which is a watered-down version of psychoanalysis for amateurs who never took the full training. The psychoanalytic psychotherapists all deferred to Dr. Big.

They didn't defer just in an intellectual way. They communicated feelings of inadequacy and inferiority through tone of voice, facial expression, body language and the content of what they said. They all agreed that Dr. Big was the really big supervisor you needed to consult on really difficult cases. They were all amazed at how fast he could go deep into the subject matter. Penetrate to the core of the conflict.

Later, a resident had a miscarriage while doing a rotation in adolescent psychiatry under Dr. Big. He told her that the reason she miscarried was that she was conflicted about being a mother. This was an unsolicited comment, made in public shortly after her miscarriage.

There was no lynching. This was just another deep interpretation by Dr. Big. No Faculty Member was incensed by his behavior. No one stood up and said that Dr. Big was an intellectual fascist. A male chauvinist power tripping abuser. A dick. No. He was Top Cock on the totem pole.

I listened to the shrinks present their cases. After half an hour of verbiage, the audience would not know whether the patient was married. Would not know basic facts such as marital status, current job or financial situation. None of this was mentioned. Not relevant. Here, at this high-powered summit of Manitoba psychiatry, this peak of performance, we were concerned with the analysis of defenses. Analysis of transference. The Reality Principle didn't get in the way, ever.

At the end of the hour, numerous incomprehensible remarks had been made about the patient's unconscious ego defenses. What was the conclusion? Always the same.

"Good case. A very resistant patient. Keep up the good work."

No one commented on the fact that there was zero change in the patient's life, symptoms, function, preoccupations, conflicts, or anything, after four or five years of deep analysis of transference.

I realized that no patients were getting better. The therapy wasn't doing anything. There was no therapy, really. This was not medicine. There was no analysis of data. No objective findings. No lab tests. No physical exam. No science.

The psychotherapy meetings didn't take place in the Faculty of Medicine, intellectually or geographically. They weren't medical. They were part of the Faculty of Arts. Except there were no real standards of scholarship, thought, debate or argument. No one ever disagreed with anything.

The psychotherapy meetings weren't part of the Faculty of Arts either, really. They took place in limbo. The shrinks got paid very well by the government, lots more than Professors of Arts or Science get. You could make lots of money in The Great Psychiatry Scam. That was clear. There were rules.

No one raised any real objections. Everyone respected the pecking order. Complete absence of change in the patient was never evidence against the theory or the therapy. It was resistance. The problem was in the patient, not in the shrink. You just had to do more therapy in the same way for longer. In the end, if the shrink was at risk of dying of boredom, he could *terminate* therapy.

There was a whole lot of bizarre jargon.

"Why do the Fraudians talk about *terminating* therapy? Isn't there a big Fraudian slip going on here? Why do they want to murder their patients to get rid of them? Do they despise them that much? "

I remember at one of the meetings, there was a particularly incomprehensible, meaningless conversation going on about a case, when a deep shrink spoke up. He said this was an example of *phallic narcissism*, reminiscent, even, of conflict over *the phallic breast*.

The reaction in the room was deep. Everyone got nervous. Insecure. A little frightened.

"Ooh. Phallic narcissism. What the hell is that? I'd better look like I know what he's talking about. Don't want to be caught with my pants down here."

Another Big Professor asked this Littler Dr. Big to explain what he meant. He couldn't. No one had the faintest idea what he was talking about. But no one stood up and objected. No one peeped a critical peep. Too chicken.

There was no way you could afford to blow the whistle on this charade as a resident. Goodbye graduation from the Department of Psychiatry. So you kept quiet. And bought in. It wasn't even psychoanalysis, really. It was a very provincial effort at psychoanalytical thought. But you couldn't blow the whistle on that either. You too were from Winnipeg. These would be your colleagues in four years. You would depend on them for referrals and self-esteem. The in-group. The peers. It was no more scientific than a cargo cult.

I stopped going to the meetings after a while. I was very interested in psychotherapy, but I wasn't learning anything. Training in psychotherapy consisted of the imposition of arbitrary rules on the therapy sessions, and not much more.

In four years of psychiatry training, I wasn't actually taught any specific techniques by the Fraudians. It was all vague, nebulous ideas and general principles. For instance, I was taught that I should end sessions on time. This was important because patients might resist doing real work by staying too long.

What, specifically, I was supposed to do to keep sessions on schedule, other than watch the clock, was never explained. Then there was *processing* and *working through*. This is what you did in therapy. Nobody had the vaguest idea how to do working through, or what it consisted of, except a lot of time. Residents were told, through facial expression, tone of voice, and body language, that they couldn't grasp the depth and subtlety of working through because they were green. Later, when they too were Professors, they might get it.

Especially if they took psychoanalytic training. One resident was in psychoanalysis. He was paying his Professor over $20,000.00 a year for therapy out of his pocket, and working a ton outside his residency to pay for it. When the Professor moved to another city, the resident moved with him.

This wasn't therapy. It was sadistic financial exploitation of a resident and creation of pathological dependency in the resident. In my book it was unethical malpractice. Ding a resident for twenty grand a year?

"It's outrageous. What a rip off! Scandal! Scandal!"

Not in the Department of Psychiatry. No, this was good psychiatry. Deep training psychoanalysis. Fraudian Professors ripped off their residents for millions of bucks in the twentieth century, via bogus strung-out training analyses. If there was any integrity in psychiatry, all this money would be refunded. Where else in the University do graduate students pay their Professors tens of thousands of dollars out of their own pockets, directly into the Professors' pockets?

If chemists or engineers did this, they would be kicked out of the University. Of course, chemists aren't as deep as shrinks. Maybe that's the difference.

I did challenge the rules of the Club once in my third year. We had weekly group psychotherapy supervision with a Little Dr. Big. Dr. Chicken Little. We presented our cases and got high-powered supervision. I commented on one case that there was no change in the patient after three years. The other resident got upset and asked why I was attacking him.

This was the problem. Everyone was so insecure, and so bought into the Scam, that no criticism was allowed. There couldn't be any real analysis because the

Scam couldn't survive it. I wasn't in medicine. I wasn't really a doctor anymore. I had been to medical school, sure. But I stopped practicing real medicine in September, 1981.

A few times I brought up the idea of doing some psychotherapy outcome research. My supervisors shot that down fast.

"How do you measure the effect of psychotherapy?" was the standard question.

This was not posed as a scientific question. It was said in an amused, dismissive, condescending fashion. The point of the question was to stop the conversation. The belief was that psychotherapy is so rarified, intrapsychic and subtle that attempts at objective measurement are meaningless. Everything always got turned upside down.

The rules and methods of Fraudian therapy are untestable. Fraudian therapy isn't *unscientific*. It is *ascientific*. Dr. Fraud's theories and methods of therapy cannot be tested scientifically. They don't have anything to do with science.

It took me a while to figure out that there isn't a single piece of scientific evidence supporting Fraudian theory. In the entire twentieth century, not one Fraudian analyst has conducted one scientific study to show that Fraudian therapy works. Not one. Zero. They just don't do it.

Not only don't they do it, they actively discouraged me from even considering doing a scientific study of therapy. It would be a waste of time.

"What would you measure? Symptoms?"

The word *symptoms* was said with scorn. A focus on mere objective symptoms was superficial. Only someone who failed to appreciate the depth and grandeur of therapy could propose such a thing.

It was all turned upside down. There is not a shred of evidence that Fraudian therapy works. The Fraudians aren't upset about this. Why? Because the impossibility of studying Fraudian therapy scientifically proves just how deep and wonderful it is.

Nobody came right out and said this straight. But this is what I was taught. Wrapped in Fraudian jargon and primitive tribal social signals. Only a superficial person would ever try to measure the effects of therapy. Or even think of trying.

There was one hitch. In order to get paid for Fraudian therapy, you had to bill the government health care system. In order to bill the government health care system, you had to be a medical doctor. You had to write a medical diagnosis on your billing card, before you mailed it in to get paid.

Medical diagnoses are based on symptoms. For shrinks, this meant DSM-III symptoms and diagnoses. Psychologists, who were not medical doctors, could only bill the government a total of $350.00 per patient per year for therapy. Why? Because they were not real doctors. Shrinks could bill any number of hours they wanted.

If a shrink had ten patients and saw each one four times a week, he could make about $150,000.00 a year off the government, if he took a few weeks of vacation.

This is why I got taught about *medical psychotherapy*. I was told that the difference between what shrinks do and what psychologists do, is that shrinks treat *the whole patient*. Because of their medical training, they can assess the physical causes of mental problems, and treat that too. They can spot when a patient is depressed for medical reasons, and pop them over to their family doctor. Psychologists don't have the training to do this.

It was complete baloney. The shrinks even published position papers about medical psychotherapy in journals. It was just a billing scam. There was nothing medical about the Fraudian therapy. There was nothing about it that required an M.D., and there was absolutely no reason shrinks were more qualified to deliver it than anyone else. Not one case in a thousand required the shrink to use his M.D.

If this was medical psychotherapy, how come there was no science around? Why was I actively discouraged from even thinking about studying the efficacy of psychotherapy scientifically?

Because science would expose the Scam. I recommend that the Canadian government stop paying for psychiatrists to do psychotherapy. It's a waste of money. You could get effective cheaper therapy out of Master's level therapists trained in cognitive therapy.

It is in fact perfectly straight-forward to demonstrate the efficacy of psychotherapy. The methodology is well known. In 1997 I published the first prospective psychotherapy outcome study for multiple personality, using standardized scientific measures of symptoms and diagnoses.

The False Memory Police wrote in to several journals to bash me for methodological limitations. The study did have limitations. The requirements for a tighter, more definitive study can be found in a commentary I published in response to the False Memory Police in 1999.

The point is, this is no mystery. It isn't rocket science. The rules are well known. It is perfectly possible to do scientific studies of therapy and show whether it works. The shrinks just won't get off their butts and do it. Instead, they coast on their personal belief in Sigmund Fraud and their confidence that they will continue to get away with the billing scam.

The problem is not simply that Fraudian psychotherapy studies have not been done, although that is a problem. The problem is the fact that the shrinks are actively opposed to any studies being done. It is an actively anti-scientific guild. The problem is not low scientific standards, although scientific standards are extremely low in psychiatry. The primary problem is a deeply passive-aggressive anti-scientific attitude, cloaked in jargon and a pose of science and medicine. In skate boarding terminology, the shrinks are *posers*.

Scientific and intellectual standards are kept very low in psychiatry for a purpose. Psychiatry cannot tolerate science. The emperor has no clothes. The shrinks need to have pretend science. Real science would expose the psychoanalysis scam.

"Well, what about biological psychiatry?" the shrink will ask.

"Psychiatry has become much more scientific in the last two decades. Most biological psychiatrists would agree with what you say about Dr. Fraud."

Here we have scam number two. Biological psychiatry is as deeply anti-scientific as psychoanalysis. The same habits of thought pervade. Habits of non-thought, really. Biological psychiatry doesn't come up in the shooting gallery for a bit.

It took me a long time to figure out how sick Fraudian theory is. Major league mega-sick. Off the scale sick. Wacko sick. Stick sick. Or dick stick. Or dip stick. I get confused.

I remember when card carrying psychoanalyst number two got recruited to the Department of Psychiatry. He came and gave a Grand Rounds lecture to the Department. Grand Rounds is the weekly lecture given in the different departments in the Faculty of Medicine. This talk wasn't very grand. But it sure was Fraudian.

Dr. Big Number Two showed slides of drawings by a boy he was treating. They looked completely normal. But Dr. Big Number Two could see deeply into them. He pointed to the outboard engine on the boat. Clearly a phallic symbol.

It was the most ridiculous talk I ever heard in four years of medical school and four years of psychiatry residency. It was like a Saturday Night Live send-up of psychiatry. Except it was serious. Very serious. No one blew the whistle.

I read a couple of thousand pages of Fraud before I went to medical school. In four years of psychiatry training, I didn't read one page. This was another amazing fact about the Fraudians. They hadn't read Fraud. At least we residents hadn't. Not as part of our training. In four years, I was never assigned any Fraud to read. We never went over any original Fraud in seminars. Never had any exam questions on Fraud. Were never shown a documentary film about him. Were never quizzed on how to define any Fraudian concepts. Nothing. Nada. The big goose egg. Zero. Zilch.

Fraudian psychotherapy dominated Canadian psychiatry and all talk about psychotherapy in Manitoba shrinkdom. But we never read Fraud in our training. Not a page. I have to make this point over and over so that I can believe it. Otherwise I might think I'm making it up.

But we heard about Fraud. We knew about the Oedipal Complex, all right. That's where little girls get horny. There was even a Fraudian called Karen Horney, who we heard about a little bit. She wasn't a bit, we heard about her a bit.

"Have a little respect, eh."

The Fraudian Professors taught me that little girls literally, consciously want to have intercourse with their fathers, around age four to six. This wasn't a metaphor. Literally. Anatomically. Vaginal penetration. Right through the hoola hoop. We're not talking phallic symbol here.

This was not taught to me as a theory. It was a known fact about human psychology. I heard about how Fraud had "shown" this and that. Fraudian theory was said to be scientific, by my Professors. One scientific fact we knew as medical doctors, who did medical psychotherapy, was that little girls want to get it on with daddy.

When convicted sex offenders talk like that, they fail their parole hearings. It's pedophile thinking. It's sick. My Professors explained to me what horny little bitches girls are. This was their deep theory. Their penetrating insight into girls. If a patient talked like that, the nurses would want to hang him.

The nurses didn't want to hang the shrinks because the shrinks dressed up their sick ideas in fancy jargon. Translate these ideas into plain English, and they make a decent person puke. The shrinks never got hung, or weren't hung, whichever is the correct grammar.

I remember one seminar where a really deep Fraudian came in from out of town to explain about Heinz Kohut to us. Kohut should be in the Guinness Book of World Records for most convoluted incomprehensible prose. You really had to be deep to understand Kohut. He is a Fraudian who developed his own shrink theory spun off from Fraud.

I remember at a break, one of my Professors explained to me that he understood the explanation for bulimia based on Fraudian libido theory. Bulimia was clearly caused by fantasies of wanting to throw up semen ingested through fellatio. Fear of oral impregnation. But he wasn't quite sure how to explain bulimia in Kohutian theory. What a Kohoot. I mean, what a hoot. Hoot. Hooters. Whatever.

My Professor was completely serious. He believed that women with bulimia are in conflict about their fantasies of oral impregnation. They want to get pregnant, but they are up tight about it, so they displace this onto a fantasy of oral impregnation, then they reject the orally implanted semen by vomiting it up. The food they binge on is clearly a phallic equivalent.

It's just sick. It isn't science. It isn't medicine. It's just a bunch of intellectualized pedophilia.

It's a disgrace being a shrink. I might change professions, if I can't change the profession. Which I can't. Might get some applause from the psychologists, though.

The real problem isn't with the content of Fraudian theory, sick though it is. The problem in psychiatry is with the thought processes and intellectual standards. Both of which are abysmal. Shrink readers of this chapter can define the issue. Colin Ross does not believe in Fraud. Colin Ross is against Fraud.

By the way, what do you call it when psychiatrists get together and sing? Shrink rap.

No matter what the subject matter, the tune is the same, in psychiatry. Take my comments on Fraud. They get reduced to a matter of personal belief. Colin Ross doesn't believe, Dr. Big does. It becomes a battle of personal belief.

But it really doesn't matter what the subject is. The intellectual process is the same. Whether it's drugs, Fraudian theory, genetics of schizophrenia, or multiple personality, the thinking all works the same. The not thinking. Everything is folklore, anecdote, and low levels of intellectual function. There is no real science. No disinterested intellect. No pursuit of data. There is a posture of science, but no real science. No real thought, by humane or scientific standards. Just a bog. A miasma. A swamp of despair.

"Careful. Don't fall in."

Colin Ross does believe in multiple personality. Colin Ross doesn't believe in the genetic basis of schizophrenia. I'm so sick of it I could scream. AARRGGHHH!!!

Could we make it be about data? How about evidence and argument, instead of personal belief and political motive? The problem with Fraudian theory is not that I disagree with it. The pedophile part needs to be taken out in the back forty and shot. But there's lots of Fraudian theory I personally agree with and believe in. I talk about the ego defenses a lot in therapy, using normal vocabulary. And I use the specific technical term *undoing* a lot in therapy. Cognitive therapy. Not Fraudian therapy. Wouldn't be caught dead doing Fraudian therapy. Or alive.

The problem is not that I personally disagree with Fraud. I do disagree with fraud, but that's not what I'm talking about here. The problem is that Fraudian theory is not scientifically testable as formulated. There are no scientific studies, data, or experiments to support it. There can't be.

Fraudian theory and therapy are not medical. It's a belief system, not a science. A confused, self-contradictory, inconsistent body of thought. It's obvious that Fraud was a genius. He has obviously had a huge impact on the twentieth century. But he isn't a scientist. His theory and therapy aren't medical. Nor is he a clear-thinking genius. I'd describe him as an intricate, ingenious creative dreamer.

In Canada, the biggest scam of all was the medical psychotherapy scam. The shrinks had it set up so that only they could bill the government for psychotherapy on a fee-for-service basis. They brought a lot of smoke and mirrors in to protect the guild. A lot of parade and posture of science and medicine. Because it was a sham, they had to keep real science out. Had to obscure the difference between real science and pseudoscience.

Had to create biological psychiatry. Biological psychiatry is just the flip side of the shrink coin. It's the same monetary system.

"Ssshh. Don't tell. The monetary system is bankrupt. Might start a panic. A run on the banks. Or the shrinks."

"Run, run as fast as you can. You can't catch me, I'm the shrinking head man. I'll eat up your money, I'll phallus your mind. I'll bill to the feds, I hope you don't mind."

"I do mind, Doctor. I'm on record with that. I'm clear. St. Michael, you watching? I cleared myself. I'm clean. I blew the whistle. Let The Great Psychiatry Scam be judged, when the Judge is in Court. I gave my expert witness testimony. I'm out."

"No, I'm in. Out. In. Out. Oohh. No, done. Out."

25

THE FECAL STICK

There is one Fraudian idea that really does make sense. It is so important, I wanted to give Dr. Fraud's brilliant, revolutionary idea a separate chapter. I'm talking about *the fecal stick.*

Dr. Fraud taught me some other things I didn't know before. He explained that little girls want to be fucked by their fathers. This isn't just a theory or a metaphor or a way of talking. Dr. Fraud taught me that little girls literally, consciously want to have their fathers' penises inside their vaginas. In psychiatry, this is called the Oedipal Complex. Everywhere else, it's called being horny.

Little girls get bummed out though, especially when they are grown up. They want to have a penis inside their vaginas because of penis envy. They realize that the penis is a big, powerful, magnificent thing (especially Dr. Fraud's), and they want one for their own. It's really a downer for the little girl when she realizes all she has is a pitiful little clitoris. She never gets over her penis envy, even when she's grown up.

All grown up, the little girl tries to get a penis inside her as much as she can, but the darn thing keeps going soft on her and falling out. She finally realizes that fucking her father, who has by this time been replaced by her husband, a sorry substitute for the real thing, isn't going to get her a penis on a long term basis. She thinks about it real hard. It's like she gets her own hard-on.

She realizes she can have a penis inside her by getting pregnant. That's smart. In the unconscious mind of this woman, which Fraud could see into deeply (a woman's unconscious mind is located somewhere underneath her panties), a new equation is set up. Baby = penis. The woman realizes she can have a penis growing inside her for a long time by having a baby inside. The baby is her own personal hard-on. Great! Problem solved!

But bummer of all bummers. She gets a real bad stomachache after nine months and loses her penis. Back to depression, inadequacy and inferiority. She wants Dr. Fraud's penis more than ever now. Thank goodness this woman is really smart. She sets up a new equation. Now penis = baby = shit in her rectum. Dr. Fraud was very polite, so he didn't say shit in her rectum, or even less, shit up her ass. He said *the fecal stick.*

Dr. Fraud was really smart, even smarter than his women patients. He figured out for the first time in the history of the human race that little girls try to solve their missing penis problem by making the shit up their asses be penises, in their subconscious minds. Now they can keep the penis forever. Except, oh, oh, it falls out even faster than the penis baby.

This is Dr. Fraud's explanation for anal-retentive behavior in women. They are trying to hold onto the fecal stick in order not to give birth to the baby that is really Dr. Fraud's penis. I'm sure Dr. Fraud would have been willing to give the stick to his patients if they had asked. For strictly medical reasons.

Whacked out sicko crap like *the fecal stick* would be grounds for putting somebody in an insane asylum, you would think. It's sicker than anything I have ever heard from any patient. But no, instead, such theory ruled psychiatry for most of the twentieth century. Approximately one hundred years ago, psychiatry lost its fecal stick, I think, or its penis, or its baby, or its mind, or something. Hard to tell what. But something.

26

SHAKESPEARE ON ACID

By far my favorite rotation in psychiatry was general adult inpatient, which I did for six months in the second half of my first year. The 23-bed ward was a theater of incredibly intense pain, drama, misery, hilarity, perversity, self-destruction and madness.

I remember the three patient phones on the wall across from the nursing station. I would stand behind the desk and watch. You could write a book about the dramas played out at the phones. The depths of human tragedy and the heights of comedy, all played out at the phones.

There was the elderly man brought in for diagnosis of Alzheimer's disease. He could function all right in the familiar environment of home. But bring him to a strange place, and disaster struck. I watched him walk up to the phone, take out some change, take the phone off the receiver, then become confused and panicked. He couldn't figure out what to do next.

He looked frightened. A few moments of agitation, and another patient arrived to help him. It was a life dying in front of me. No one could do anything. There was no hope. In a while he would no longer recognize his children. The only question was how long. I thought about what it must be like, to watch a loved one get worse and worse. Dementia.

We talked about dementia at medical school in detached clinical language. But on the ward it was a real person, a real life, joys, sorrows, hopes and accomplishments. All dying. All preparing to be forgotten. Not by others, but by the man himself.

We hope to live on in others' memories. I hope for that. It is one reason I write. It is why we have children, in part. Why we have gravestones. History. Real history. The dead living on in our hearts, our minds, our memory. Not just in books, but in the living present, still part of life, not utterly dead.

With dementia, you don't even live on in your own memory. You die before you die. It is the most horrible anonymity possible. Not even known by yourself. No longer there. No one there to know. I saw it in front of the phones.

Then there was the middle-aged mother and homemaker, an immigrant from a Mediterranean country. She was a depressed hypochondriac. She controlled her family through the sick role. Everyone and everything revolved around her aches, pains, nausea, and headache. She had strange feelings of something moving around her heart, like a wind, like a coldness around her heart, something moving in her veins, a great tiredness in her, and such a headache.

"Such a headache, doctor."

You couldn't hate her. But you certainly couldn't love her. For every problem, for every need, a physical symptom. She couldn't work, or cook, surely couldn't make love. Always too tired, and sore, and sick. And the doctors had tried so many medications. Nothing worked. There were side effects. Or she forgot to take her pills. Or threw them out.

There was nothing wrong with her, except that everything was wrong with her. Really, we had nothing to offer. Mainly, it seemed, the family needed a break for a few weeks while we obsessed about her diagnosis and fiddled with her meds. Nothing changed. Then she went home.

I watched her talking on the phone, reaching out to her absent family, telling her tale of physical misery. I imagine a thin tentacle of malignant energy traveling down the phone line, into her home, out through the receiver, into the brain of her family member, hooking on there, establishing the parasitic connection. Maybe she was an alien. Maybe this is what the Alien movies are about. I think science fiction movies are allegories about spiritual principles in our culture.

The borderlines came to the phones. This is where we kicked into high drama. Calls to boyfriends and uncaring husbands. Extravagant reactions, yelling, slamming the phone down. Calling back in tears. Manipulating and wheedling for a visit, or a McDonald's meal to be brought in, or for the loved one to tell the doctor to discharge her. Hanging up again. Highly dramatic monologues in the neighborhood of other patients, near the phone. Not conversations. Monologues with other people present. The other people were props in a personal melodrama, not real human beings.

The phone was another prop. As was the nursing station. The nurses. The doctor. All props in a theater of the absurd. This was before I figured out that borderline personality is a normal response to chronic childhood trauma. All I saw was the behavior. I couldn't see the pattern. A lot of theater, but no plot. No real theme. No purpose or direction.

Severely psychotic people sometimes wandered up to the phones, stared at them, and wandered away. They had a dim sense, it seemed, of a real world out there, somebody to call. But they couldn't connect. Couldn't connect on the phone, or in life, to themselves, to others, or to their own thoughts. I understood why schizophrenia used to be called *dementia praecox*, early dementia.

In psychiatry lingo we talk about *negative symptoms of schizophrenia*. Schizophrenia is like a kind of dementia. The person isn't there anymore. They walk, talk, eat, and take their meds. But they're gone. Androids. Our culture is full of them.

You can see the emptiness at the phones. No focus. No direction. No motivation. No suffering, even. Just endless mechanical function, going through the days, doing the routine, or the chaotic lack of routine. The meds didn't make any difference. There was no one there to take the meds. The android was less agitated, less hallucinatory on meds, often, but the person never came back. Not fully. Not like before.

And yet, there was a person there, still. An intense, deep, withdrawn suffering. You couldn't get to it, touch it, or talk to it, that spirit, but it was there, somewhere. I was taught that 10% of people with schizophrenia commit suicide. Therein lies the tragedy. A suffering human being is still present, somewhere. But you can't find him.

The shrinks knew what was wrong. Too much dopamine.

Why would a person's spirit go away because he had too much of something in his brain? The real problem in schizophrenia, it seems, is that there is too little of something. There is an English psychiatrist who has a theory about this. The positive symptoms, the hallucinations, delusions and agitation aren't the real problem. They are a side effect, so to speak, of the fundamental emptiness. The loss of soul. Or brain tissue. Or both.

Not loss of soul, really. Withdrawal of the soul deep inside. Like the sleeping people in the book and movie, *Awakenings*. Except nobody knows how to wake them, get them back, the schizophrenics. I read the theory in textbooks. I saw the human reality at the phones.

The manic patients would come by too. Wildly euphoric, elated, hilarious, expansive. Radiant with shining energy. Full of gestures and life and exuberance. If we had the right kind of meter, I'm sure we could measure a high intensity of radiation coming out of a manic. I'm sure there is a low level of energy in the depressed phase. I mean this literally as a principle in physics.

I think it's electromagnetic. But there is a real, physical energy that obeys the laws of physics. We just don't measure it.

The manics would make wonderfully happy phone calls. With great joy they would explain to whoever was listening how great they felt. Had never been better. They just loved to make phone calls. What could be better than being on a mental ward talking on the phone! What a life! What a day!

One manic patient explained to me that he could walk through walls. He got his energy directly from the City of Winnipeg power grid. He was in his mid forties and still lived with his mother. She was frail and kind and loving. She knew it was mania. And he agreed to come into the hospital, even though there was nothing wrong, and he felt fine. He knew. Couldn't say. But knew.

Another manic patient had come onto the ward in order to help the other patients.

He was very happy to have this opportunity for evangelical work. God talked to him on the television, and counseled him about what to do and say to the other patients. I wrote about him in another poem I published in the *Canadian Journal of Psychiatry* entitled, "On Leaving the Inpatient Service."

Sometimes there would be a power struggle at the phones between the nurses and a patient. The patient was being loud, belligerent, rude, even swearing on the phone. Slamming the phone down. Walking off in a huff. Storming back to make another call and blast the person on the other end. If the patient pushed it too far, there was a take down, a trip to the quiet room and 20 mg of haldol in the butt.

What an empire! What territory! The patient was in charge of this great expanse, this kingdom. No one could tell him or her what to do. He would God damn well say whatever he wanted on the phone. It was his dime. Until the nurses asserted control, backed by the doctor. Then the powerful patient was deposed, and the iron hand of the law ruled.

I completely agreed with the need for the take down and the haldol. My agreement didn't make the drama any less intense, tragic, comic or insane. That a human being should feel so powerless, insignificant and out of control. So down trodden and without value. Then should compensate by being in control of nowhere and nothing. It's a tragic tale. The final scene was 20 mg of haldol in the butt.

Others would stand at the phones genuinely tearful, lost and lonely, reaching out to a world that did not reach back. They did not make a performance. They were not on stage. They were just small and lonely and lost and sad and hopeless.

The shrinks knew what was wrong.

"Not enough serotonin. Or noradrenalin. Hard to tell which."

The shrinks played the *role* of medical scientist on the ward. But there was no real science going on. The shrinks were just another group of actors in the psychodrama. Their lines were more dialogue in the play. They weren't above the action, more conscious of the play's theme than the patients, or in any way superior. They were a lot less interesting. The purpose of the shrinkiatric theory was to reduce everything to a simple, mindless formula.

"Depressed? Low serotonin. Giver her an antidepressant."

"Psychotic? Too much dopamine. Give an antipsychotic."

The complexity, the nuance, the humanity, were all gone. Replaced. Not by science. Replaced by MCQ thinking. Not real thinking. A cognitive checkers game with simple rules. An intellectual token economy for the mentally retarded. I'm talking about the thought patterns of the shrinks, not the patients.

Consider the profound complexity of the field of observation. Infinitely far beyond the capacity of any physicist, chemist, biologist, sociologist or social psychologist to fathom. Or even describe.

"No problem. It's a chemical imbalance. Low serotonin. Caused by a gene."

The fact that there was no scientific proof of low serotonin or a gene mattered nought. The shrinks needed a formula. There was a formula for every situation.

"Acting out? That's attention seeking. Punish it."

"Psychosis? High dopamine. Medicate it."

"Borderline personality? Untreatable. Discharge it."

"Alcoholism? Send them to the Alcoholism Foundation of Manitoba or the Chemical Dependency Program. We don't deal with that here."

"Mania? Lithium."

"Posttraumatic stress disorder? We never diagnose it or talk about it, ever. Never, ever. Not even once a year."

"Childhood sexual abuse? We don't talk about that here. That's for outpatient therapy."

"Primal scream therapy? We don't do that."

"Who gives out the meds? Nurses."

"Who writes the orders? Doctors."

There was no real thinking or analysis. It was a matter of moving a few tokens around on a two dimensional intellectual playing board. The decision tree was simple and repeated over and over and over. There were only a few legitimate diagnoses. And only a few treatments.

The diagnostic categories were psychosis, depression and mania. Anxiety floated around everywhere. Psychosis got antipsychotics. Depression got antidepressants. Mania got lithium and antipsychotics. Anti-anxiety drugs got sprinkled around to everybody. For all other diagnoses there were no real treatment decisions.

If you couldn't figure out whether it was psychosis, depression or a mixture, you gave all of the above on the checklist of drugs. There was no real therapy for anything else, except a few groups. No real individual therapy. The groups were run by well-meaning nurses with almost no education in group or any other kind of therapy. The doctors didn't really know what went on in the groups, weren't intellectually interested in them, didn't attend them, had no input on the content of the groups, and regarded them as Mickey Mouse.

The patients sat around most of the time, saw the doctor briefly, watched TV, talked to each other, slept, and went to a few groups. Got their meds and had their vitals checked. Got dealt with if they acted out. That was it.

It wasn't that the individual nurses were bad people. It wasn't that the doctors were callous or mean. The rules of the game were just too simple, and the level of expertise too rudimentary.

I hadn't grasped a basic fact yet. The problem is, the field of shrinkiatry can't do any better. The shrinks are maxed out. That's all they've got to offer.

I used to think it was personal problems, or resistance, or laziness, or bad theories, or the wrong philosophy. All those factors are present. But the basic problem is, the shrinks can't step it up. They just haven't got it. Haven't got the intellect, the energy, the motivation, the grasp of science, or the education. Haven't got the inner drive. The fire in the belly. Or the loins. Or wherever. Just aren't bothered enough by the status quo.

I understood the problem with the shrinks, years later, while watching some of my sons' hockey teams. There was enough raw talent there to do better. The coaching could be better, but it was good enough. Volunteer dads doing their best. Good, motivated fathers with knowledge and love for the game. The boys just didn't have it. Most of them.

Didn't want it bad enough. Didn't work hard enough in practice. Didn't dig hard enough in the corners. They were good recreational athletes. But they didn't have it inside. The drive to excel. Be the best you can. Push yourself. Do the extra skating. Listen carefully to the coach. Learn from every mistake.

Too many boys just fooled around. Weren't focused. Weren't really serious athletes. Which is fine. When you're a boy. But it isn't fine when you're a shrink. You're paid too much, you get too much social status, and you have too much control over people's lives, too much control over dangerous medications to be goofing around in the locker room. Or coasting through the skating drills. You should be in house league if that's your attitude.

Psychiatry is one big house league with the odd travel player scattered around the landscape. It's like hockey in Texas. Too many of the best athletes go into football, baseball and basketball in Texas. Soccer is drawing more and more. There's golf, tennis and swimming too. Hockey is just too new and too far down on the totem pole. There isn't the money in it, or the public support.

Psychiatry is to medicine as hockey is to youth sports in Texas. Hardly any top athletes go into hockey or psychiatry. It's just a fact of life. If you kicked all the psychiatrists out of psychiatry, and forced internists and surgeons to become psychiatrists, things would improve. It's a difference in mind set, attitude and character style. Not so much I.Q. Though I.Q. is a problem too.

Let's be real. How many people think that the best minds in our culture are going into psychiatry? Take a look at business, science, the arts, computers and data processing. There you have lots and lots of brilliant, gifted people doing really impressive and amazing work. What about in psychiatry?

"Yeah, right."

I learned on M3 that shrinks don't really do any analytical thinking. They aren't scientists. They aren't doctors. What are they? Witch doctors masquerading in the garments of western medicine. This is true despite the pills and the drug company studies.

I've learned since, in the remaining years of the twentieth century, and the first years of the twenty-first, that the subject matter doesn't matter. The shrink can't think. Sing this to the Marine Corps tune, as you march along:

"Head shrinker is one smart man. He will screw you if he can. He will slander, he will lie. He will leave you wonderin' why. Why the system's down on you. There ain't nothin' you can do."

"One and one and one is three. You're psychotic, can't you see?"

It doesn't matter if the subject matter is the cause of schizophrenia. The answer is so simple someone with an IQ of 65 could memorize it.

"Too much dopamine."

Everything got boiled down to absurd simplifications.

"The cause of multiple personality disorder?"

"Iatrogenesis."

"The writings of Thomas Szasz?"

"Antipsychiatry."

It was infuriating to hear everything reduced to such simplifications. By the way, *iatrogenesis* means *created by the doctor*.

The problem wasn't whether I agreed or disagreed with any particular proposition. It was the level of intellectual function. I realized that psychiatrists are truly uneducated. They simply aren't intellectuals. At least not on M3, or anywhere else in Winnipeg, that I could see. There wasn't a single shrink in Manitoba who was seriously studying something, doing research, or writing about their work. A few people cranked out a few papers, mostly in low level journals.

But nobody had a body of published work. Original thought, research or observation. The shrink conversations were all derivative of stuff done in the United States or England.

Am I being an elitist? No. Why? Because I am only holding psychiatry to the standards prevailing in the rest of the University of Manitoba. Not Harvard. Not Oxford. The University of Manitoba.

What do you find in other Departments? Really serious work. Sure there's lots of mediocrity. But there are really excellent people. I met them among my undergraduate professors, in English, Physics and Genetics. In medical school I met them in Immunology and Biochemistry. I mean met them personally and intellectually. Got to know their work. And admired it.

There was no work to admire in psychiatry. This was true at both academic and clinical levels. On M3, in six months, I never saw one shrink do one impressive, clever or creative thing with or for a patient. The patients were fascinating. The shrinks were boring, in comparison. Sure there were some people doing good bread-and-butter clinical psychiatry. But mostly I saw a complete absence of any real therapy, ridiculous polypharmacy and incredibly sloppy diagnostic practices. It was a disgrace to medicine.

Once you start medical school, your education stops. What you get is *training*. Unless you do original research, you are not taught scientific thinking in medical school. You don't learn how to evaluate or analyze data. How to design experiments. How to weigh observation, data, and argument.

You are taught a lot of facts and a very simple basic thought pattern, called differential diagnosis. The subtleties of creative science are completely absent. Unless you do a Ph.D.

Psychiatry training is just more of the same. It is an apprenticeship. You get thrown on the wards at the beginning of first year. Thrown into the ER on call. Dealing directly with patients with tiny sprinkles of supervision. You learn on the job. Why? Because you don't really need to know much to do psychiatry. You can do 90% of the work with less than ten drugs and ten diagnoses. On M3. I did it. Better than the shrinks. In first year. I was a more competent psychiatrist before the end of first year than a lot of my Professors.

Why? Is this bragging? Narcissism? Grandiosity? No. It's an indictment of psychiatry.

I could have become an internist. I could even have been an OK surgeon. Not a brilliant surgeon. An average surgeon, at best. There is absolutely no way that first year surgery residents are more competent than half their Professors. It just doesn't happen in Surgery. But it does in Psychiatry. Lots.

At the end of first year, if I had to refer someone I loved at random to either a fully trained psychiatrist or a resident, I would have chosen the resident hands down. Much higher competence levels. Take me out of the equation. It isn't about me. It's about the shrinks.

The nurses used to come and beg me to change my Professor's medication orders, diagnoses, and chart orders. They talked about his incompetence behind his back all the time. One time a Visiting Professor gave us Grand Rounds (not very grand) on calcium metabolism in manic depression. The next morning my Professor told me to order a 24-hour urinary calcium test on a patient, to see if she was manic-depressive.

I refused. I told him this was completely unscientific. I told him that if he wanted the calcium ordered, he would have to write the order himself. There was no way a 24-hour calcium could be used as a diagnostic test. The shrink never ordered the test. It was like I had gotten sucked into a parallel dimension where all the psychiatrists were mentally retarded.

It wasn't really an IQ problem. I imagine the average IQ among the shrinks was probably 120. Nothing to write home about, but at least enough to be sensible. The problem was a lack of sense. Common sense. Medical sense. Street smarts. The shrinks just weren't regular people. There was something wrong with them. They weren't right in the head. Or the solar plexus. They were maladjusted. They just weren't right. I think it's a chakra problem.

Shrinks don't want to develop the science of chakra electroencephalography because they know, unconsciously, that they would come up abnormal. It shows in their cognition, writing, behavior, body posture, gait, and facial expressions. Hypofunctional solar plexus syndrome. Managed care doesn't cover it. Western medicine doesn't diagnose it. Shrinks got it.

"The shrink can't think. The shrink can't think."

Another ridiculous theory in western psychiatry is the idea that the mind is linked only to the brain. Quite a lot of the mind is actually in the peripheral nervous system.

"The shrink can't think. The shrink can't think."

Not in an embodied way. In an embalmed way, yes. But not real thought. Rooted thought. Thought that arises out of the waters of creativity.

Hence, no real art, science, or religion, in shrinkiatry. Shadows of each. Essence of none. Maybe it's a deodorant problem.

27

GINSENG PSYCHOSIS

One patient was so memorable, I thought I would give her her own chapter. She was a middle aged Korean woman admitted in a manic state. She was flying high. She was euphoric, expansive, and very, very happy. Full of overflowing energy. Boundless energy, energy without limit. She had tapped into the Fountain of Youth.

I discovered that the Fountain of Youth is not in Florida. Ponce de Leon was way off course. The Fountain of Youth is a bottle of ginseng. I figured out that my patient had been drinking enormous amounts of liquid ginseng. This was long before ginseng became popular in North America. I even got hold of a paper on ginseng psychosis that had been published in an obscure medical journal. Suddenly, I was a leading expert on ginseng psychosis. No one else had even heard of it.

We didn't really have to treat her. She came down on her own over a period of a few days. Transformed into a shy, quiet, polite Korean woman with a bowed head. No more vigorous leaps in front of the nursing station. No whoops, yells or boisterous greetings. No martial arts kicks, either. She had performed numerous Tae Kwon Do kicks to the top of a doorway opposite the nursing station. Sadly, all this stopped.

I was struck by how fragile sanity is, in all of us. A little chemical can push us out of our minds. Micrograms even. And not just chemicals. Herbs, spices, plants, flowers. I realized that the health food nuts really are nuts.

A lot of stuff in forest and field can kill you. There are a lot of chemicals in health food.

28

MANIC MENTAL MANTRA MUTTERING, MOMMA

A person can't be held responsible for what he says in a manic state. It's the chemical imbalance talking, not the person. Creativity and madness. So say the shrinks. Say what? Say, the shrink says that? Say, what? The shrink ain't smart. Got no bulk in the think department, the Shrink Department. No bulk at all. No fiber, no fruit. They kicked the gays out of DSM-III-R, in 1987. Senator Shrink McCarthy got rid of 'em, the Commie pinko rats.

It used to be called a mental disorder. Homosexuality, I mean. In DSM-II. Then in 1980, DSM-III was brought down from the mountain. Just before I went into shrink training. Now it was called *ego-dystonic homosexuality*. You weren't mental just because you were gay. If you were gay and felt OK about it, you weren't mental. But if you were gay and didn't like it, then you were mental.

Until DSM-III-R came out in 1987. Then you couldn't be mental no matter how gay you were. Or how gay you were about it. The problem with shrinkdom isn't creativity and madness. It's no creativity and madness. What a drag. You could say psychiatry is medicine in drag. Not a real woman. Just a drag queen. Take off the clothes and the makeup and there ain't no broad there.

That's how it works. Gays were mental for almost 100 years because Sigmund Fraud said so. Then the political heat got too much. The shrinks got out of the kitchen. I think this is called integrity. Or science. Or DSM-III-R. Or something. Not sure which.

The shrinks tried to keep the gays barefoot and pregnant and in the kitchen. But they had to give it up. Great science! That's what I say.

You say 'Yes,' I say 'No,' you say 'Why,' I say, 'I don't know.'

29

WATCH OUT OR SHE'LL START HEARING VOICES

During the four years of my shrink training, like all the other residents, I carried two long-term psychotherapy cases. I had two supervisors, one for each case. At the end of each year, I was assigned two new supervisors.

In the second half of my first year, in early 1982, I picked up a new case from M3 at the time she was discharged. She turned out to be my second case of multiple personality. She has been integrated for over fifteen years now.

I started to explain the situation to my supervisor, who was heavily into Fraud. My patient was a married woman in her thirties with depression, agoraphobia and borderline personality disorder. She started to talk about a Little Self inside, using her first name. This is not to be confused with Mini Me in the movie *Austin Powers, the Spy Who Shagged Me*, which is a completely different phenomenon.

The five-year old held incest memories and came out to talk to me. I gingerly tip-toed into this arena with my supervisor, wary of his response. He told me not to go in that direction, not to acknowledge or talk to the five-year old at all.

"Watch out, or she'll start hearing voices," he said.

I had to spend the rest of the academic year faking my reports of the therapy sessions. I worked with the five-year old a lot. My patient's agoraphobia was cured. Her depression went into remission. She divorced her physically abusive alcoholic husband. She brought up her two children as best she could. Her multiple personality was cured in less than three years. On top of that, she never did turn into a serial killer.

But I couldn't talk about the therapy I was actually doing with my supervisor. I just left half of it out. Instead, I talked about the parts of the sessions that didn't have to do with the five-year old.

My supervisor never caught on.

This experience did not breed respect for shrinks in the mind of Colin Ross.

I picked up another case of partial multiple personality late in first year. When I started with my new supervisor at the beginning of second year, I presented the case to him. He refused to supervise me on it. Why?

He said she was too sick. He wanted me to get a nice light neurotic case. He absolutely refused to supervise me on the case, even though I had made a commitment to treating her under my previous supervisor.

When I told him this would leave the patient in the lurch, he said he didn't care. He told me to get rid of her. That is exactly the language he used.

On my own initiative, I went and found a different supervisor who agreed to supervise me on the case. I fired the shrink who refused to work with me.

Great. One year of training in psychiatry and I was already firing shrinks for ugly irrational behavior. The patient did well. I rescued her from a future of revolving admissions, polypharmacy and repeated suicide attempts for schizoaffective disorder. Rediagnosed her as dissociative disorder not otherwise specified. Kept her out of inpatient wards from 1981 till I left Canada in 1991.

The treatment only lasted two years. She contacted me by phone shortly before I left Canada in 1991 to update me on how she was doing. Seemed like she might be cycling back down. I've had no contact with her since.

In my fourth year, I arranged to be supervised by a psychologist in the Department of Psychiatry who did behavioral therapy. All I had had up to that point was generic Fraudian supervision. Needed a change. Wasn't learning anything.

With my behavioral supervisor I did some cognitive behavior modification of adult attention deficit disorder, based on the writings of Donald Meichenbaum. My patient made small triumphs that did lots for his self-esteem. In his late twenties, under my brief therapy, he learned to tie his shoes and remember phone numbers for the first time in his life. Then I put him on Ritalin, which helped a ton, and referred him out for ongoing care.

I tried to treat another woman with classical Wolpian desensitization. Set up hierarchies. Pumped her up in vitro. Did the deal. Her problem was she couldn't eat anything except tomato soup and plain yogurt. She slept in the attic in her parents' home with the door locked from the attic side. For safety.

She had no idea what she was safe from in the attic. But that was the only place she could sleep. This case was screaming out incest at me. But I didn't hear it. The behavioral treatment was useless. She stopped coming and I never saw her again.

Under the same supervisor I treated a man with several specific phobias with desensitization. It helped a lot. And I treated a woman for treatment-resistant depression with classical Beck cognitive therapy. Cured her based on Hamilton and Beck Depression Scale scores. At least for that episode of depression. I had learned cognitive therapy on my own and by studying in Dallas for two weeks. No shrink in the Province of Manitoba did any cognitive therapy at all during my residency years, from 1981 to 1985. Solo mio.

I learned not to tell the shrinks much about what I was really doing. It wasn't worth the hassle and shit. They just wanted to force me into bland useless Fraudian therapy techniques.

"Sorry, Fraud. I wanted to go there. Just couldn't. I know you're a drag queen, not a real doctor. Even with the white lab coat."

One supervisor kept telling me I was too active in therapy. I said too much and worked too hard. I should sit back, be more passive, just listen.

I told her that her advice violated the three cardinal principals of client-centered therapy, as preached by Carl Rogers. She had already agreed she supported these principals. Which are: genuine positive regard, accurate empathy, and congruence. Congruence means acting like yourself and being real.

I had a little trouble with the genuine positive regard part, until I realized I only had to feel that way about the patients, not the shrinks.

I told my supervisor that for me the passive style wasn't congruent. It didn't fit my character. She told me I needed to be more passive.

By the way, client centered therapy is the kind where the therapist says, "I hear you saying that you are angry with your mother."

Then, "I hear you saying that you're tired of hearing me saying that I hear what you're saying. How do you feel about the fact that I hear what you're saying about that?"

Followed by, "I'd like to share with you that _______." (fill in the blank).

Client centered therapy is regarded as an example of *humanist therapy*. It's real nice therapy.

I didn't find out for another ten years that while he was doing such nice therapy and writing such nice books about it, Carl Rogers was a mind control contractor for the CIA with TOP SECRET clearance.

The shrinks at the University of Manitoba forgot to tell me about Carl Rogers and the CIA. Oh well. What's it matter, anyway?

I wasn't sure if I was waiting to graduate from my psychiatry residency or waiting for Godot.

30

OVERDOSES AND BABIES

My second year was divided into two halves. Six months of child psychiatry, six months of adolescents. The child rotation was the most extreme Fraudianism of my entire residency. Off the scale. The main thing was I hardly did any work. There were hardly any patients. Nobody seemed to care about that, though.

I saw three children under ten years of age for psychotherapy twice a week. One boy refused to talk and never said more than five words per 45-minute session. I'm not sure what was supposed to be wrong with him. My supervisor told me just to wait until he started to talk. I did. He didn't. After a while he just stopped coming.

This was not defined as idiotic by my supervisor. The shrink spent a lot of time doing Fraudian interpretations about why the kid wouldn't talk.

The second case was a psychotic kid who was completely incapable of participating in any kind of therapy. But I was supposed to be doing deep work with him, twice a week. My work with him was totally useless. My supervisor thought I was learning a lot.

The third case was a girl whose father had died the previous year. She had been suicidal. I saw her twice a week for a while. All we did was goof around. There was no therapy at all. Once I tried to get her to do play therapy using a doll house and dolls.

She looked at me and said, "You're trying to get me to talk about my dad."

She wouldn't. But she improved a lot and wasn't morbid, depressed or suicidal anymore. There wasn't a single thing I did that required any training or expertise of any kind. Her mom wanted to date me. My supervisor thought I was doing good therapy. Working out the transference neurosis. Deep healing. I was just a Big Brother. Didn't need an M.D. to do the work, that's for sure. Fortunately, though, the Department of Psychiatry was able to generate revenue, because the supervisor billed the Manitoba Government under his name for all the therapy done by the residents.

Then, in the second half of the year, I was on call for psychiatry in the children's hospital. I took call every fifth night or so for six months. During this time I saw a couple of dozen identical cases. All girls age 12 to 17. All admitted to pediatrics overnight for stabilization and medical observation after overdoses.

The point of the consult was to give psychiatric clearance for the girl to go home.

In every single case, clearance was given after a brief interview by me. The supervision on the cases was over the phone and basically non-existent. I just told the shrink what I had done and he said OK.

Every time, I wrote a consult note saying that the girl was not clinically depressed, was not currently suicidal, suffered from an atypical personality disorder, and was ready for discharge. There was never any psychiatric follow-up. They never wanted it and shrinkiatry didn't want to offer it.

Why did the girls overdose? Every single time it was for the same reasons. Either to make people feel sorry for them, to manipulate a boyfriend, or to get attention. One girl explained to me that she overdosed every three to six months in order to make her mother be nice to her. After an overdose, her mother would treat her kindly for a while, then she would drift back into verbal abuse and neglect. Then the girl would know it was getting time to overdose again.

The girls also talked about getting pregnant. Many of them were deliberately planning to get pregnant, with no intention of marrying. They didn't even care if the boyfriend stuck around. Actually, they didn't even care if the guy was a boyfriend. As long as he knew the in vivo fertilization procedure, that was all she required. Fortunately, donors were not hard to find.

The reason for getting pregnant?

"To have someone to love me."

The girls were absolutely clear about what they were doing, and why. They knew their moms would help out. They would still be able to do teenager stuff. When they didn't need the baby, mom would do the chores. When they did, mom could take a hike, I guess.

I realized that plans to reduce teen pregnancy through education are a joke. At least for these girls. Most of them were native. Lived in shattered, chaotic families. No dad, lots of booze, lots of welfare, no future, no education. Just a plan to get pregnant.

The strange thing was, we sent these girls home and had absolutely no idea what happened to them after that. Nor did we care. Too busy. We had no idea whatsoever how many of these girls killed themselves, got pregnant, or what. And this wasn't a problem. We were all doing our jobs fine. We all talked down to the girls, and about the girls to each other. Smirked and sighed and went on being smarter and more important than them.

Every once in a while there was a girl who was plugged into five hundred social service agencies. I remember a meeting I went to about one of these girls. She was no different from any of the others. Just happened to be the one who was plugged into the care network. A lot of people cared about her.

There were at least 25 professionals at the meeting. Me, representing shrinkdom, nurses, social workers, welfare workers, native workers, housing workers, special this workers, special that workers. We all sat around talking for an hour. Everyone really cared a lot.

At the end of the meeting, the conclusion was nothing would change. Psychiatry would have no further involvement. The agencies would monitor things closely. It was a total farce. But everyone played it sober and serious. That meeting alone cured me of any thought I might do child psychiatry. Couldn't stand the meetings. All that caring. God, what a bore!

I was never actually taught anything about these girls. There were no seminars, readings, handouts or discussions about why they wanted to get pregnant, or what to do about this social problem. Imagine the burden these girls would place on pediatric services over the next twenty years. The number of kids who would end up with permanent hearing loss because these moms never got them antibiotics for their ear infections! That alone was a crime against humanity.

Psychiatry had absolutely nothing to offer these girls. But it had lots of knowing about them. We had all the Fraudian comments and rationalizations we needed to be able to walk away. And feel fine about it.

I realized that there were no data. The shrink thoughts, attitudes, theories, and behaviors towards these girls, were not supported by a single jot of data or science. It was the same thing for everyone we sent home from the ER. We had no idea what happened to them. No one in psychiatry was disturbed about this.

No one said, "Wait a minute!"

No one protested. Everyone was too busy. The worst part of it was, we received all kinds of "teaching" about how to handle patients in the ER. We got patted on the back for being tough, not getting sucked in, and sending people home. But no one had the slightest idea what the outcome of our smart interventions was. We just knew Sigmund was applauding somewhere up in heaven.

I had learned in first year that you take a lot of shit from the nurses if you admit too many people from the ER while on call. Get back-stabbed plenty. No way I was going to admit one of these girls after an overdose. Did I want to get ragged on? No. I knew the drill. So did the girls. Atypical personality disorder. I was done. I was out of there.

31

BAD, BAD BORDERLINES, WORSE THAN LEROY BROWN

If you want to know what kind of a shrink you're dealing with, ask him three questions: 1) what is the cause of schizophrenia? 2) what is the cause of multiple personality disorder?, and 3) what is borderline personality disorder? The answers will allow you to place the shrink in one of several categories: 1) biological phony 2) psychological phony, or 3) reasonable guy (or gal).

Your main problem will be trying to get a straight answer. It's a little like when the shrink is talking to managed care. The game has rules. Everyone knows there's a lot of phony bullshit going on. But no one blows the whistle. The shrink has two languages: 1) the correct answer language, and 2) the real answer language. This chapter is about the real answer.

Borderlines are to psychiatrists as witches are to Inquisitors. This is all laid out in my book *Satanic Ritual Abuse*. In that book I have a Table with three columns in it. The first column is a list of adjectives defining a witch. It is taken from the *Malleus Maleficarum*, the chief operations manual of the Catholic Inquisition, published in 1486. The list defines a witch. The *Malleus* provided strict guidelines for how to recognize witches and decide on their punishment.

The *Malleus* is to the Inquisition as DSM-IV is to psychiatry. *Malleus Maleficarum* means The Witch's Hammer. DSM-IV means The Patient's Hammer.

The second column is a list of adjectives defining a woman, taken from the German philosopher, Schopenhauer's 1851 essay, "On Women." The essay is the senior document in a Universal Theory and Principles of Male Chauvinism. Feminists would love to hate it, if they read it.

The third and fourth columns are the diagnostic criteria for histrionic personality disorder and borderline personality disorder from the American Psychiatric Association's *Diagnostic and Statistical Manual of Mental Disorders, Third Edition, Revised*, published in 1987. DSM-III-R.

The four columns cover the same ground. The Inquisition's definition of a witch, Schopenhauer's definition of a woman, and American Psychiatry's definition of two mental disorders, are all the same thing. Cover the same ground. There are a few minor variations in vocabulary. Otherwise the four columns are identical.

By the by, I place Dr. Fraud next to the late nineteenth century neo-Romantic English poets, like Swinburne, in my butterfly collection. With a little colored thread going over to the area where I've pinned up the German metaphysicians. And another thread, in another color, going over to Aubrey Beardsley. I'm considering linking Fraud to Baudelaire using a fourth color of thread. But Fraud is located nowhere near Pasteur or William Osler, in the butterfly collection. Nowhere near.

Nothing much has changed in the last five hundred years, except witches are now called borderlines. And, oh yeah, we don't burn them at the stake anymore. Now we admit them to hospitals and abuse them psychologically. We're more advanced now.

Like the Inquisitors, the shrinks both fear and lust after the borderlines. Walk into their webs with pointers erect, and try to escape and control them at the same time. It's some kind of arachnid mating ritual. I don't claim to fully understand it.

The most common scenario for sexual misconduct by a psychiatrist is an attractive young female borderline patient and a middle aged male psychiatrist.

Lots of shrinks don't have to have mistresses, or pay prostitutes. They've got borderlines. The borderlines pay *them* for therapy. What a deal! You can't tell me the shrink can't think. No way. It took brains to think up that scam.

There is a series of published papers in which doctors have done mail-out surveys. To doctors of all kinds, shrinks, and psychologists. Asking them if they have had sex with a patient currently in treatment. About 10% of doctors admit to having sex with current patients. Shrinks the same. 10%. This is just the ones who admit it.

As a medical student and psychiatry resident, I had no teaching on these matters. Not one lecture, handout, MCQ, case discussion, nothing, in four years of med school and four years of shrink teaching. Sexual misconduct by doctors didn't exist, wasn't talked about. Probably occurred in one shrink therapy out of a million, like the rates of incest quoted in the *Comprehensive Textbook of Psychiatry*. Sexual misconduct by shrinks isn't even a topic in the *Comprehensive Textbook of Psychiatry*, 1980 Edition.

Total denial. Major acting out. No plan for anything to change. Not surprising, considering nothing much has changed since 1486. We wouldn't want to move too fast on this. In 1992 the Catholic Church finally issued a formal apology for keeping Galileo under house arrest for years. His crime? Saying that the earth orbits the sun. The shrinks are working on change too. They just need a couple of more centuries. It's hard to get the Committees together, when everyone is so busy.

My money's with Galileo. Not the Inquisitors or shrinks. I felt a little better when I realized the shrinks are just fascists. Then all the abuse I took for being an expert on multiple personality didn't hurt as much. It's the opposite of that line you hear in the movies:

"This time it's personal."

The deal is, it isn't personal. Not at all. It's a cultural pathology, one that shifts in time frames of thousands of years. The twentieth century shrinks are just another wave in a big historical ocean. Four hundred years from now, there will be no institutionalized Inquisitors called Psychiatrists. The Inquisitors used to be called Inquisitors. Now they are called Psychiatrists. In 2486, they will be called something else.

Some of the behavior changes. The vocabulary. The surface philosophy. But not the underlying cultural dynamics. You still have a male power elite. It still persecutes the women it fucks. A few women buy in. We call them nuns or lady doctors. But they aren't really *the boys*. It's still the good old boys who run things.

The witches were sick in the soul, according to the Inquisitors. The borderlines are sick in the brain, according to the Shrinks. When the witches spoke unspeakable truths, demons spoke for them. When borderlines who also have multiple personality speak unspeakable truths, alter personalities speak for them. At least the Inquisitors acknowledged the existence and reality of the demons. The twentieth century shrinks have stepped up the game. The alter personalities aren't even acknowledged.

That's what the Inquisitor Shrinks say about multiples.

"They're really just borderlines."

Or, neighboring philosophy, "They're really just hysterics."

This means you can ignore what they have to say. And ignore their alters. Which is handy, because who wants to talk in bed anyway?

I was taught about borderlines in shrink training. Not anything scientific. Or medical. I was taught a lot of attitude. That's mostly what shrinks have to offer borderlines. A lot of attitude. Plus Fraudian psychoanalysis. Which is mental incest voyeurism anyway. My Fraudian psychotherapy supervisor told me to always ask about the patient's sexual fantasies in great detail. I didn't.

One of my Fraudian supervisors was absolutely obsessed with female patients who told him about doing blow jobs on their husbands and boyfriends. He had all kinds of psychoanalytical things to say about oral gratification and primitive defenses. Probably, his wife wasn't primitive enough for him. So he got it from his patients, mentally. It's called being an adolescent. The only thing is, when you're an adolescent, the Government doesn't pay you $83.00 an hour to read *Playboy Magazine* and jack off. That was the rate for psychotherapy paid by the Manitoba Government in those days.

I did a survey of the residents in the program in 1990. A medical student sat with them while they filled out a questionnaire. This was so they wouldn't cheat. Only a third of the residents could list enough DSM-III-R criteria for borderline personality disorder to actually make the diagnosis.

During day-to-day work, shrinks and shrink residents never actually read DSM-III-R to decide if someone is borderline. In Winterpeg, Manitoba, they had lots of attitudes towards borderlines when two thirds of them couldn't even define borderline personality. There were eight criteria for borderline personality in DSM-III-R, of which you had to have five. In DSM-IV, which came out in 1994, there are nine criteria, of which you have to have five.

In 1994 it got a little easier to be borderline.

Since there are nine criteria and you only have to have five, two people can both be borderline but only have one symptom in common. This makes sense to shrinks.

When I was in shrink training, from 1981 to 1985, there were basically no data on borderlines. No systematic studies. No scientific data on any form of treatment. Very little evidence shrinks could make the diagnosis with any degree of consistency. But I heard lots about borderlines.

"She's a borderline."

Translation: "She's a baby-eating Nazi witch with leprosy."

There were your average borderlines. Then there were your really heavy duty borderlines. They were called *bad borderlines*. This was an actual technical term I heard all the time: *bad borderline*.

"Bad borderlines are scary people. Really primitive. Will give you a blow job at the drop of a hat. If they don't sue you for malpractice. Or complain about you to the Head of the Department," the shrinks said to me in seminars.

These were attitudes and fantasies of the shrinks, not facts about the patients.

You didn't have to worry about complaints to the Head of the Department. Such complaints were called Giving Head, if I remember right. They caused a headache, which was strangely pleasurable. The borderlines were always talking head, or talking to the Head, or talking to the talking head, or something. Or giving the Head shit. Or no, that would be the fecal stick. Putting the stick to the Head, maybe. All this psychiatric theory is so confusing.

The Head might say, "Your borderline called me. I think she's trying to yank your chain."

We all wanted our chains yanked. The boys were clear on that. The rules were well laid down. The rules for getting down, or getting laid. I think it all had to do with floor linoleum. It's so confusing. Borderlines will do that to you, with all their projective identification.

Projective identification is a Fraudian defense. More disease can be found in the shrink minds. Not in the borderlines. That's not where the action is, in this psychodrama. Psycho drama. It's the shrinks' heads that are sick.

"Hare Hare Rama, Psycho Drama, Hare Hare."

No, you didn't have to worry about the borderline's complaints. I was taught they could always be ignored.

"She's a borderline."

"No wonder she's making up stuff. That's what borderlines do, the wily mischievous horny she-devils."

It was all set up so the borderline was discredited in advance. What I hated the most about the whole Scam was the smug, superior amusement on the shrinks' faces when they talked about borderlines. It was no different from my adolescent friends talking about the leading sluts in our neighborhood, in the early 1960's. The sluts were scorned and lusted after simultaneously. It was the whore-Madonna syndrome. Madonna knows about it. Made lots off it, too.

I now understand that the leading sluts were probably all incest victims. One for sure, who at twelve years of age was known to boys miles away in the North End of Winnipeg. Her father was a judge, too. You can bet he and the shrinks saw eye to eye on the rates of incest in North America in the early 1960's. This was before any of Eli Lilly's product, acid, started to arrive in Winnipeg. By the time acid arrived in Winnipeg big time, other entrepreneurs had accomplished a major market penetration. They were called criminals. Eli Lilly is called a drug company. Two entirely different things.

The shrinks who said incest was one family out of a million belonged to the same club that introduced LSD into North America. Which is the same club that coined the term *borderline*.

Herr Professor Paul Hoch had his full-page obituary in the *American Journal of Psychiatry* one year. In 1953, he killed a 33-year old tennis pro, Harold Blauer with an injection of U.S. Army mescaline at the New York State Psychiatric Institute. This crime was covered up for a few years, but eventually the widow was compensated by the State of New York. Hoch and the boys had told her Harold died from a reaction to a test given for diagnostic purposes. Straight outright lie.

Paul Hoch coined the term *borderline* in a 1949 article in *Psychiatric Quarterly*. You think it's surprising that these people have weird attitudes towards borderlines?

When I mentioned at Grand Rounds in the late 1980's in Winnipeg that Hoch and Polatin's definition of borderline personality left childhood trauma and dissociation out of the picture, I was angrily denounced by a Professor. He told me, in public during the question-and-answer period, that Polatin was one of his teachers. Whoops! I had broken an Old Boys' Club rule. This was the same Professor who told me to get rid of the long-term psychotherapy case at the beginning of my second year.

Questioning The Teachers was heresy. It was like a cult. I had offended God, my Professor and the Divine Ascended Master Teacher Swami. Worse, I wasn't sorry about it.

I heard about "my borderline" and "your borderline" and "the borderline." Borderlines this. And borderlines that. I just wish the shrinks had set it to music, so it was more entertaining.

I remember being at a real stuffed shirt psychiatry meeting one time, at a reception attended by wives. A distinguished shrink in his early sixties and his wife were talking to another shrink I knew. I was standing there listening. Right in front of his wife the shrink talked about "my borderline patient."

Maybe the wife couldn't hear because her diamond earrings were so heavy. Probably interfered with sound wave transmission in the vicinity.

It was the shrink's tone of voice that killed me. He talked about his borderline like he was talking about his mistress. You just knew the borderline was young and hot. And adored the shrink and needed him a lot and had lots of crises only he could understand and handle. Because only he knew and cared. So much. So much.

I remember being on call with a Fraudian shrink once when he got paged by his borderline. I got to listen while he talked to her on the phone. It was sickening. I'm sure if his wife had been there she would have hit him on the head with her purse. He talked in this weird syrupy voice, really, really nice and calm and soothing and caring. It was like he was talking to Lolita. Like he was talking to a child, telling her she would be fine, and everything would be OK, and she should just go to sleep, and he would see her in the morning.

It was sexual. She was in bed, trying to go to sleep. His tone of voice was sexual. Some kind of bizarre pedophile voice. Couldn't put my finger on it. Wouldn't want to. Might get contaminated.

The problem is not with theory, data, academic writings by shrinks or other "professional" aspects of the shrink-borderline relationship. It's the dance, which is carnal. It's a weird, distorted, sick dance. Of course, that's an over-generalization, but that's what we're talking about here. Generals over privates.

Generals in privates. Shrinks in privates.

“Sure does.”

Maybe they’re called shrinks because they have a complex about that.

A shrink once said to me, “You know those borderlines, always looking to chop it off. They’re bad, the baddest girls in the whole damn town. Which is why they need treatment. For a long time. Long term intensive individual psychoanalytical psychotherapy.”

Notice that “anal” is at the core of psychoanalytical. This has something to do with the fecal stick, but I’m not sure what.

I was taught that most shrinks only carry one or two borderlines in their practice at a time. The borderline is so demanding! You might get shrunk up permanently if you had more than one or two at a time. The Professors talked about *managing borderlines*. If you had two at a time, that would be a *manage a trois*, which could be a handful. You only have two hands. There’s only so much you can handle, as a shrink.

The borderline scam is one of the Chief Cons in Shrinkdom. And it’s usually done bareback, not with a condom. You have to admire those Old Boys, they’ve got it set up real good. Even have their wives scammed. Or maybe not. Maybe it’s a straight trade for diamond earrings.

Poppa Bear treats the borderline. Insurance Bear pays Poppa Bear. Poppa Bear buys Momma Bear diamond earrings. Momma Bear doesn’t blow Poppa Bear or the whistle. Poppa Bear penetrates the borderline’s defenses with well-timed interpretations. Until he terminates therapy and gets another borderline. Everybody’s happy. Except Borderline Bear, who has an 18% rate of completed suicide under the care of Poppa Bear. Or under Poppa Bear. On the couch. Youch.

“Aye, there’s the rub. Whether ‘t is nobler in the mind to suffer the slings and arrows of outrageous fortune, or take up arms against a sea of shrinks, and by opposing, end. To sleep, to die, perchance to dream. Aye, there’s the rub.”

Or rubber. Or whatever. You need special tools to treat borderlines. They’re so bad. Fortunately, shrinks have the equipment.

“It’s OK, Momma Bear. More diamonds coming. Since you’re not coming.”

That’s how the arrangement works. It’s called Women’s Not Liberation. Shrinkdom’s gift to borderlines is no longer to be burned at the stake. The borderline can get hot on the shrink’s stake, but not burned. The borderline is the Shrink’s Witch. The witch was the Inquisitor’s borderline. Shrinks cannot claim credit for the public health advance of no longer burning witches at the stake.

The last witch was burned in Scotland in 1797, before psychiatry existed. Too bad. I won't even mention the borderlines who got lobotomies in the 1950's.

Product Warning Label. Notice. This chapter has been an analysis and parody of the pathological, sexualized attitudes of shrinks towards women they call "borderline." It is not about the reality of the women.

My attitude towards "borderlines?" First of all, borderline is not an entity or category. Borderline personality is not something you either have or do not have. It is something you have to a greater or lesser degree. We are all a little borderline and we all get more borderline when stressed out.

The DSM-IV criteria for borderline personality disorder are a Trauma Symptom Checklist. The trauma consists of chronic childhood chaos, sick family dynamics, neglect, loss, and emotional, physical and sexual abuse, all mixed in a very disturbing cauldron. The borderline symptoms are the normal response of the human organism to this kind of trauma. I would be that way if I went through that childhood. It is only by the grace of God that I get to be the doctor.

There is absolutely no need to have the twisted, sexualized attitudes of the shrink towards the borderline, or the Inquisitor towards the Witch. A "borderline" who comes to the ER is a victim of trauma, as surely as the person brought in by ambulance from a car wreck. The healing of both requires consent to treatment and active participation in rehabilitation. The victim status of both justifies special entitlement in neither. Just good treatment. Signed, Colin A. Ross, M.D.

32

FORMULATION. WHAT'S THAT?

For my third year of residency I did a Teaching Fellowship. My topic? Formulation. One reason I decided to study formulation was nobody seemed to know exactly what it was, or how to define it. The word on the street was that formulation is a really high-powered function. Something probably only a fully trained psychoanalyst can do. Something deep and mysterious and hard to define.

Turns out, that wasn't true. Add one more scam to the list. Formulation means weaving a case together into a unified picture that helps you plan treatment.

During the Teaching Fellowship year, I developed the first objective scheme for grading formulations. I did inter-rater reliability studies on it and developed a nice structured package for it. Published it. There had been some previous schemes for doing psychoanalytical case formulation. But they had not been tested scientifically. And they didn't take biological and social factors into account.

It was good work. Not rocket science, but good work. I've been thinking ever since about writing a book on formulation, but haven't gotten to it.

During the Fellowship year I learned a couple of things. I got clear on one of the major shrink strategies. Obfuscation.

Everything is made so deep and ineffable that everyone has a license to be completely vague. I had heard about *milieu therapy*, for instance, in the first year of my residency. But I had only the vaguest idea what it was supposed to be. I talked to a Professor who had written a paper on it in a shrink journal, and read his paper, but I was no further ahead. He said that you use the milieu as a tool of therapy.

I never grasped what the milieu was supposed to be. It seemed to be the ward and the people on it. It sounded like some kind of therapeutic community. Maybe using patients as therapists on each other. The strange part was the strange way the word *milieu* was pronounced. Looking back, it reminds me of the way patients talk about *the cult*. Something big and powerful and hard to document. Something deep and secret.

The word for this way of thinking is *superstition*. It ain't science.

When the Professor said the word "milieu" he gave you one of those deep, knowing looks, like this was so deep you wouldn't really grasp it for another five years. There was always an insinuation that the shrinks had reached deep depths, and you couldn't follow them yet. It was a scam.

The truth was, milieu therapy was vague and undefined. There were no scientific data on it. Nobody in the Department took it seriously. Nobody talked about it much.

It was the same thing with formulation, except formulation got mentioned more. You knew it was deep and important, but you didn't know what it was. No one actually taught you how to do it. No one had any data. Nothing was systematized.

Imagine going to Microsoft and asking how they develop new programs.

"We process."

We heard about *processing* in therapy. You had to *process* the material, *work it through*. But no one had the faintest idea what processing consisted of, or how you did it.

When you go to Microsoft, I'm sure, there is a mega mountain of detail on what processing is, how it's done, where the manuals are, what the data look like. In psychiatry there's none of that. Formulation. Milieu therapy. Working through. Processing.

We knew where to plug these words into MCQs or conversations.

The Professor might ask a resident, "How would you handle that in therapy, doctor?"

"I'd work it through."

The Professorial head would nod, the points were scored. This resident really knew his stuff.

The Professor never asked, "But specifically what would you do?"

And the resident never asked the Professor. Didn't want to look dumb.

There was no manual. There was nowhere you could actually learn this stuff. I call it The Great Psychiatry Scam.

During this year I did lots of work on the social and psychological factors that go into formulation. I had to include biological factors in order to stay out of trouble. But in the entire year I never identified a single specific factor in a single case. I did lots of formulations of cases with other residents every week.

Biology was where the big prestige was. But there wasn't actually any biology going on in our patients. Not that we could identify. In four years of residency I saw maybe a couple of patients who had an identified specific biological factor related directly to their symptoms and treatment plan. Not counting drug toxicities and substance abuse problems. I mean an inborn or acquired biological problem that looked like a *disease.* A couple of examples at most, in four years.

But the heat was on me to have biological factors in my formulations. I was gasping for air. Fortunately, I did not drown.

I was frequently able to identify two biological factors in my patients: 1) stopping their meds without consulting their shrink, and 2) a family history of the disorder they had, e.g. depression.

Bad news. Stopping your meds is a *behavior*, not a biological factor. Speaking Chinese runs in families. That doesn't mean it's "biological."

The fact something runs in families provides zero evidence it is biological or inherited. It could be purely environmental, like speaking Chinese, or purely inherited, like eye color, or a mixture.

Not in the Department of Shrinkiatry in Winterpeg. Or elsewhere. Without question. Without question by one person once, a family history was accepted as evidence of a biological factor at work.

The patient is depressed. His mother or uncle or grandma was depressed. Or all of the above.

"The patient has a biological diathesis for depression."

We could never say it in plain English. There could be zero inherited component to the depression. Or it could be 100% genetic. You just can't tell from the fact it runs in the family.

But the shrinks knew. It was biology.

During my Teaching Fellowship year, I learned more about how shrinks know things. They know things because they know them. Not because of science or medicine or data.

Everyone "knew" that a family history meant genetic causation. The conclusion was certain and unquestioned. Absolute knowledge.

No one required any evidence. It was known. Being *poser* scientists and doctors, we had to make it look like we had evidence. So everyone referred to some studies no one had actually read that proved depression was genetic. Backup plan if we didn't completely have all the evidence yet? We were just about to get it. Any day now.

This was how the shrinks knew how to do formulation. Just because they knew it. Nobody was particularly thankful that I developed an objective method for making and grading formulations. It was never adopted in psychiatry at large. Why? Because it had flaws or was incomplete? No. The shrinks just didn't need it. They knew already.

I learned that there are politically acceptable pieces of knowledge. These are known without the need for proof or compelling data. An example is the gene for schizophrenia. Everybody knew it was there, although the evidence did not exist.

Then there was knowing in the opposite direction. Some things were not politically acceptable. Like multiple personality. Everybody "knew" that multiple personality was either very, very rare or completely bogus. This knowing was not supported by any scientific evidence. No one had done any scientific studies to see how often multiple personality occurs in the world. The shrinks just knew.

I also learned about setting the bar, dimly. The full understanding didn't come for another decade and a half.

If you were pushing a politically acceptable fact, like the genetic basis of schizophrenia, the evidence required was minimal or non-existent. The bar was set at zero or maybe one inch.

If you were pushing a fact, theory or position that was politically *verboten*, the bar was set at ten feet. This makes it a difficult high jump.

Rotate these rules 180 degrees. If you were arguing against a politically acceptable fact, the bar was set at ten feet. If you were arguing against a politically unacceptable fact, the bar was set at zero.

The game continues into the twenty-first century. The problem is not with the subject matter. Could be multiple personality. The gene for schizophrenia. Milieu therapy. Drugs for depression. The bar gets moved up and down for political reasons. Big time. All the time.

Moving the bar is not science. It's politics. In science, the bar stays at the same height all the time, no matter what the subject matter. Not in psychiatry. Why? Because psychiatry is not based on science. Psychiatry is a belief system posing as a branch of medicine.

These rules are hidden. You're not supposed to comment on them. If you do, it's trouble. In the Supreme Court of the United States of Shrinkdom. Which has jurisdiction over the entire western world. That's OK. I'm concerned with rulings in a higher court. Actually, two higher courts. The Court of Public Opinion and The Afterlife. The shrinks are at risk of frying in both.

"It's time to fess up, boys, and try for a lighter sentence. Or continue with the crime wave, and face execution. Your choice. I'm just here to define the options."

“You can take a shrink to water, but you can’t make him drink.”

The shrink can’t drink, the shrink can’t drink.

33

STANDARD DEVIATION. WHAT'S THAT?

During the four years of my residency, there were a couple of half-hearted efforts at having a journal club for residents. A journal club is a seminar in which you review articles from professional journals. Usually one resident summarizes an article, then there is discussion. It's supposed to be a forum for learning how to read the professional literature critically.

"The shrink can't think. The shrink can't think."

Here is a fact. Most shrinks are incapable of critical reading of scientific literature.

In one journal club we were talking about an article, I think from the *American Journal of Psychiatry*. The article had some data in it that included means and standard deviations.

Everyone in the room had an M.D. Except the journal club leader, who was a psychologist. Everyone had at least eight years of post-graduate education. Within a few years, all the residents would be earning over $100,000.00 a year. Most of them didn't know what a standard deviation is, which was amazing in itself. But the residents had not yet fully revealed their complete lack of scientific education, or their complete inability to think scientifically.

The journal club leader explained what a standard deviation is: several residents didn't get it. Then he put a diagram on the board. They still couldn't understand. The leader couldn't figure out how to get these residents to get it. He was stumped. They never did.

What is a standard deviation? Does it take a Ph.D. in mathematics to grasp the basic idea? Maybe. You judge.

Let's say you measure the height of 100 adults in your neighborhood. There will be some short people and some tall people. Most people will be in the middle somewhere. This is called a normal distribution. If you did a graph of the heights of these 100 people, it would come out as a bell shaped curve.

Now imagine a neighborhood somewhere near you. Take a deep breath. Relax. We are going to do a small exercise to help you understand standard deviation. Remember, this is not advanced mathematics. Consider a neighborhood near you. Or perhaps Mr. Rogers' neighborhood.

The average height of adults in the neighborhood is 5'7". Because the distribution of heights is normal, the number of people who are 5'11" - 6'0" is the same as the number who are 5'2" - 5'3". The number who are 5'7" - 5'8" is the same as the number who are 5'6" - 5'7". The curve has the same shape on both sides of the average.

Of course, in a sample of 100 people, in the real world, this won't work out exactly. But if you did height measurements on 10,000 people, you would get close to a perfect normal distribution. A bell-shaped curve.

What is a standard deviation? In a normal distribution, two thirds of the data is within one standard deviation of the mean. What does that mean? Now I assure you, I'm not going through this exercise just to be mean. There is a point. It's another aspect of the Great Psychiatry Scam. Let's say the standard deviation in our neighborhood height sample is two inches. This means that two thirds of the people are between 5'5" and 5'9". The mean or average is 5'7".

Since the distribution is normal, we know that one sixth of the people are shorter than 5'5" and one sixth are taller than 5'9". Two thirds of the people are between 5'5" and 5'9."

If a statistician tells you a subject is within one standard deviation of the mean, in this sample, you know he is between 5'5" and 5'9".

Two standard deviations means 95% of the data. In a normal distribution, 2.5% of people are two standard deviations below the mean and 2.5% are two standard deviations above it. If two standard deviations in our neighborhood was five inches, we would know that 95% of the people are between 5'2" and 6'0".

Why is standard deviation important? Because the size of the standard deviation tells you how much variability there is in the sample. Let's say the standard deviation in another neighborhood height sample from five miles away was 10". This would mean that two thirds of the people are between 4'9" and 6'5". There is a lot more variability in height in the second neighborhood, even though the average height in both neighborhoods is 5'7".

If you put these two groups of 100 people at two ends of a football field, and looked at them from the stands, you would see right away that one group has a lot more short and tall people, while the other has a lot more people who are roughly average. This would be easy to see at a glance. But just looking at the average height of 5'7" on your computer screen, where the data were analyzed, wouldn't tell you about the difference between the two groups.

As soon as you look at the standard deviation, though, if you understand introductory statistics, you get the picture. Just like you would by looking at the actual people standing on a football field.

Why does standard deviation matter? Imagine we are doing a study of nutrition. The first group of 100 people have received a nutritional supplement since birth.

The second group of people has had a regular diet.

We want to know if the nutritional supplement has affected the height of the people in the first group. Let's say the first group has an average height of 5'9" and the second group 5'6". It looks for sure like the nutritional supplement has worked. Not so. You have to look at the standard deviations.

For this example, I am ignoring all other factors that might have affected the heights of the subjects. I am assuming all these other factors have been controlled for or ruled out in some way. The only difference between the two groups is the nutritional supplement.

Let's say the standard deviation is nine inches in the supplement group and eight inches in the comparison group. This means there is a huge overlap between the two groups. Even though the average heights are different, there is so much overlap, and such a wide range of heights, that the two groups aren't really significantly different. A statistical test called a *t test* will tell you that the two groups are not different overall.

If you put these two groups of people at two ends of a football stadium, you wouldn't be able to see any overall difference between them.

But let's say the standard deviation is half an inch in the nutritional supplement group and three quarters of an inch in the comparison group. The average heights are still 5'9" and 5'6". Now there is a huge difference between the two groups. There is very little overlap and the nutritional supplement is really working.

If you put these two groups of people in the football stadium, you would be able to see the difference easily. This is why standard deviation is important. And why you have to have statistical tests to check things out.

The residents couldn't understand. They couldn't grasp the basic concept. I'm not talking about the mathematics of it. Just the basic idea. Absolutely could not compute it.

There were several residents who absolutely could not grasp the idea. The majority was pretty fuzzy on it. A few got it.

This is introductory undergraduate statistics. And it's the easy part of the course. Conceptually, standard deviation is simpler than a lot of high school mathematics. But the residents couldn't go there. This is what I mean when I say that shrinks are uneducated.

The shrinks and shrink residents maintain their self-esteem by claiming they are clinicians, not researchers. Problem is, their clinical thinking is no better. The claim to be clinicians, not researchers, is a defense against low self-esteem, not a viable argument. The reason the shrinks can bill the health care system for "medical psychotherapy" in Canada, when psychologists can't, is the shrinks are running a scam on the populace and the government. A plank in the scam is the claim that shrinks are scientifically trained medical doctors.

"Right."

"Scientifically trained but can't grasp the basic idea of a standard deviation. Uh huh."

"Anything else, doctor?"

What is the fix for this problem? If all shrinks were forced by the government to go to classes until they could explain the idea of a standard deviation, would the problem be solved? No. Why? It's like the Chihuahua in the Taco Bell ad who is trying to capture a lizard in a box. When he sees that the lizard is actually Godzilla, he revises his plan.

"Here, lizard, lizard. Oh, oh. I'd better get a bigger box."

The Chihuahua is outside the box, but he isn't thinking outside the box. Same with the standard deviation problem. Forcing shrinks to pass statistics courses would be a good idea, but it wouldn't solve the real problem. Why?

Because it isn't about statistics. Just like it isn't about multiple personality. Or the gene for schizophrenia. It's an all-across-the-board problem.

"The shrink can't think. The shrink can't think."

I've noticed that shrink discussions get reduced to simple yes-or-no disputes about belief. *Multiple personality is iatrogenic*, which means created by the doctor in therapy, versus *multiple personality starts in childhood as a way of coping with trauma*. I'm always getting pulled back to the level of psychological warfare by my colleagues. They want it to be a war about personal belief in one of two mutually exclusive options. The so-called debate about multiple personality isn't a debate. It's a dispute. The rules of engagement for the dispute are not the rules of science, debate or serious scholarship. They are the rules and tactics of psychological warfare.

One of the psychological warfare tactics is to pose as a scientist. But there is no real science. Why?

Because the shrinks can never rise to the level of real science. They just can't get there. They can never make it be about data or methodology. They don't exist and can't function at that level. I am not talking about a few oddball shrinks in Sudbury, Ontario. I'm talking about top people in the profession who publish in leading journals. Chairmen of major academic Departments of Psychiatry. Can't engage in a rational scientific analysis of the data about multiple personality. Can't and won't.

They always drag it back to the level of belief in one of two simple, diametrically opposed options. Belief A or belief B.

"Me and my friends believe A. You and your friends are incompetent idiots because you believe B. We are going to attack you with innuendo, slander, scoffing, black balling, phony arguments, whatever it takes. You're going down, pal."

They never engage in a rational analysis of the data. Never use the rules of debate or science or logic. Of course, they won't admit to that. But it's a fact. See the chapter in the *livre* you are currently reading entitled, "Top Brains in the Profession," for instance. *Livre* is the French word for book, not liver.

There are all kinds of specific tactics in the war. All disguised as scholarship and science. Problem is, the emperor is in drag. Ain't the real thing.

I have a theory. Colin A. Ross, M.D. has used more different types of statistical test in his published research than any other psychiatrist in the history of the human race. Check it out, scholars. The list?

T test, chi square, chi square with Yates correction, Bonferroni correction, Cohen's kappa, analysis of variance, Fisher's exact t test, z score, analysis of covariance, Kruskal-Wallis test, principle components analysis, discriminant function analysis, regression analysis, Pearson correlation, Mann Whitney U test, Chronbach's alpha, receiver operating characteristic analysis, Spearman correlation, Kolmogorov-Smirnov statistic, MAXCOV-HITMAX technique, Mahalanobis distance. There's probably a couple missing.

If I don't win, I've got to be in the top ten. Yet I have to take shit in professional journals from people who don't believe in multiple personality and can't grasp basic science. I really don't give a flying fuselage whether they believe in multiple personality. Nor do I care whether I believe in multiple personality. Personal beliefs don't matter. In science. It's the data.

"The data. The data. The data. The data."

"Eh, what's that?" queries the shrink.

"I said," I say, "Are we going to decide things in psychiatry based on a personal belief vote? Whichever belief gets the most votes wins?"

"Fine. But don't call it medicine."

Personal belief vote is how homosexuality got into DSM-II. Also how it got out of DSM-III-R. Neither move was based on data. Neither move was medical. It's the same intellectual process everywhere in shrinkdom. Whether it's believing in the gene for schizophrenia or not believing in multiple personality. Doesn't matter. It's not about multiple personality. The "debate" about multiple personality is just an *example* of the problem. The problem is, the debate isn't a debate. The additional problem is, the shrinks can't tell the difference. The difference between the rules and tactics of psychological warfare, and those of science and analysis.

It isn't about believing. Or at least it's not supposed to be. Not in medicine.

I believe that it isn't about belief.

Same for Sigmund Fraud. It doesn't matter. Sigmund could be right or wrong. Doesn't matter. The problem is twofold: 1) there are no data, and 2) Fraudian theory is not scientifically testable.

It doesn't necessarily matter whether Fraudian theory is scientifically testable. Neither is Christianity. But Christian pastors don't bill insurance companies for their sermons. Why? Because what they are doing is not medical. Neither is Fraudian therapy. It may be a wonderful thing. It just isn't medical or scientific.

If you are going to bill the health care system for Fraudian psychotherapy, you have to obfuscate. You can't be clear. You have to be a Fraudian. You have to practice intellectual Fraud. Or health care Fraud.

The average Fraudian shrink is two standard deviations below the mean for the general population on integrity and common sense. If patients want to pay for Fraudian therapy out of their pockets, that's fine. They can donate to the Fraudian of their choice, or the church of their choice. It's their choice. That's fine.

Just don't jack up my tax rates in Canada or my insurance rates in the United States to cover a therapy that can't even be tested scientifically, delivered by shrinks who can't explain the concept of a standard deviation.

"Standard deviation. What's that?"

Note to counsel: class action lawsuits against Colin Ross by psychiatry are not to be accepted. They are to be returned to the sender unopened.

The astute physical chemist might ask, "How will your lawyer know it's a class action suit from psychiatry in the envelope?"

My response? "He'll use an odor detector."

34

DUFFERENTIAL DIAGNOSIS

Real doctors do differential diagnosis. Let's say you go to your doctor with a sore left knee. The doctor makes a differential diagnosis. He comes up with a list of possible diagnoses. The problem could be a sports injury, arthritis, or an infection. The doctor has to narrow it down to one diagnosis, then provide treatment.

In real medicine, the treatment depends on the diagnosis. A knee infection requires antibiotics. A sports injury might require rest, physiotherapy or surgery. A sore knee is not a diagnosis. The sore knee is the *chief complaint*, *presenting problem*, or *entrance complaint*. The patient "complains," the doctor diagnoses.

Psychiatrists are very close to being real doctors. They are off by only one letter.

"Damn! So close. Yet so far."

Shrinks don't do differential diagnosis. They do dufferential diagnosis. They try to act like real doctors, but they're off by one letter.

"Damn! So close. Yet so far."

How does it work in shrinkdom? It doesn't. Real doctors deal with separate diseases. An infection of the knee is a separate disease from arthritis of the knee. Separate causes and separate treatments. Similar symptoms, maybe, but separate diseases. Everything isn't always neat and tidy in real medicine, but the single disease model predominates.

Shrinks copy real doctors. So they have a single disease model too. They do differential diagnosis too. Problem is, the single disease model doesn't work in psychiatry. The shrinks are doomed to dufferential diagnosis, because their diagnostic system, DSM-IV, is based on a single disease model. Depression and schizophrenia are separate diseases. You have one or the other. Not both.

DSM-IV came out in 1994. Back in the ancient past, in DSM-III, which came out in 1980, you were not allowed to have a diagnosis of depression if you had schizophrenia. Not major depressive episode, which means heavy duty clinical depression. The single diseases of schizophrenia and depression were so separate, you couldn't have both at the same time.

This was a very silly rule. About 15% of people get a clinical depression at some time in their lives. So why not 15% of schizophrenics? Do we think schizophrenics are happier than the average person?

This kind of rule is called an *exclusion rule*. You can't have a given diagnosis if you meet an *exclusion criterion*. Schizophrenia was such a ridiculous exclusion criterion for depression that even shrinks noticed the problem. The schizophrenia exclusion rule for depression was dropped from the diagnostic system by DSM-IV.

The single disease model in psychiatry is approximately 97.43% ridiculous. Sorry I can't give a more exact estimate. Real patients don't have single psychiatric diseases. Not in mental hospitals. Not on this planet. The average psychiatric inpatient meets DSM-IV criteria for a bunch of different psychiatric disorders. Way too many patients with way too many disorders way too often. Can't be separate diseases. Ain't possible.

Trying to squeeze psychiatric patients into a medical-style differential diagnosis then squeeze them all the way down to a single diagnosis is not hard to do. All you need is a good trash compactor. The patients may bleed a bit, but hey, it's a hospital.

OK. There's the other 2.57% of patients. Rough estimate. For them, differential diagnosis works good enough.

"Go for it, shrinks."

I'm talking about the other 97.43%. They just ain't got single diseases. Single disease differential diagnosis don't work for 'em. Hence my diagnosis of the differential diagnostic practices of shrinks: dufferential diagnosis.

I go into this in big academic detail in my book *The Trauma Model: The Problem of Comorbidity in Psychiatry*. Here I just want to go on record with my diagnosis of shrinkdom logic structures, pseudo-medical activity, scientific posturing, general scam behavior and insurance company billing patterns. It ain't pretty. And it ain't medicine.

35

AMERICAN COLLEGE OF SHRINKS FELLOWSHIP

I was at the American College of Psychiatrists Annual Meeting one year, when Bessel van der Kolk was a speaker. He gave the same talk he had given at a multiple personality meeting the previous year. To a standing ovation. At the American College of Shrinks Meeting he got a cold reception. People were ruffled and offended. Bessel actually brought up some controversy, and made a couple of critical remarks about the Holy DSM-IV Process.

“Bad, Bessel, bad. Not at the Club. Get with the rules.”

After his talk, I went up to say hello.

Bessel gasped with astonishment and exclaimed, “You belong to this organization?”

Who is Bessel, what is the American College of Psychiatrists, and why was Bessel flabbergasted?

Bessel is a psychiatrist who studies the biology of trauma and posttraumatic stress disorder. He has done lots of research and teaching that doesn’t fit with Club Rules.

The American College of Psychiatrists is a limited-membership power club in American Psychiatry. It’s prestigious and hard to get into. If I applied today, as an expert on multiple personality with my political status in psychiatry, I highly doubt I would get in. Hence Bessel’s respiratory crisis.

How did I get in? In my fourth year of residency I won a Laughlin Fellowship from the College. Each year, each medical school in North America gets to nominate one resident for a Laughlin Fellowship. The nominated resident submits a copy of his resume, his C.V., through his Department. The C.V.’s are ranked by members of the Laughlin Fellowship Committee and the fifteen top residents get a Fellowship.

This includes a free trip to the Annual Meeting and guaranteed later Membership in the College. All you have to do is apply. It’s an inside track. This isn’t corrupt because former Laughlin Fellows are always qualified to be Members. If you want to look at it that way, which I do.

I got in as a Member before my multiple personality specialty was set in stone, and because I was a former Laughlin Fellow. Whew!

If I had never studied multiple personality, and had the same number of grants and publications on other topics, I would be OK politically. But that isn't me. I try not to mention my specialty at the Meeting. It just makes people uncomfortable. I try to talk about the other people's interests. Or maybe mention trauma but not multiple personality.

A big chill goes over the table when I mention dissociative disorders. It's kind of like farting in church. Not good form. You get in trouble with your parents.

"Sorry, mom. Sorry, dad. I'll never do it again."

Ffftt.

36

BUSPIRONE TAKES ME TO DUSSELDORF, FLORENCE, DALLAS, NEW YORK, CALGARY, TORONTO

Buspirone is the biggest gold mine I ever hit in psychiatry. It is an anti-anxiety drug developed by Bristol Myers, before Bristol Myers merged with Squibb.

"Thar's gold in them there anxious people."

When the Bristol Myers people came to Winnipeg looking for *investigators*, I ended up being the man. "Investigators" is the term drug companies use for the shrinks who do drug studies for them.

No shrink in Winnipeg had ever completed a drug study for a drug company. It's fair to say we were a little provincial in the Peg. A Professor got the contract and I did all the work. Ten people got buspirone, ten got diazepam (Valium) and ten got placebo for three weeks each. Everyone got placebo for a week to start off. I did all the recruiting, assessments, record keeping, organization, and writing of the paper based on the results, published in the *Canadian Journal of Psychiatry*.

This yielded *beaucoup* dollars. I couldn't put the dollars directly in my pocket, but I set up a research fund I used to pay for a lot of later research. And I got perked big time major league.

Bristol Myers paid for me to fly to Dusseldorf, Florence, Dallas, New York, Calgary and Toronto. The Dallas trip covered two weeks I spent studying cognitive therapy in 1985. All I had to do was give a talk on buspirone to members of the Psychiatry Department. The Calgary trip was to give a talk on buspirone to some family doctors. Got to visit my parents there and got paid a fee on top. The Toronto trip was to attend a small conference on buspirone for shrinks and give a talk on the Winnipeg data and experience.

The New York trip included a stay at Leona Helmsley's hotel and a visit to the Bristol Myers headquarters in Connecticut. It was pure perk.

Dusseldorf was a conference attended by about 400 shrinks and family doctors from all over Europe, a bunch from North America and a couple from Africa and South America, if I remember right. It was the marketing launch for buspirone in Germany. Germany was the first country in the world to get buspirone on the market.

We stayed at the Hilton, went on a private riverboat cruise on the Rhine, and ate out all the time. Flew over and back Business Class on a 747. My airfare was over $2000.00, in 1985. Went to the Conference in a big fancy amphitheater style hall with simultaneous translation in a number of languages. Every penny picked up by Bristol Myers.

The cost of this conference had to be more than the $800,000.00 the University of Manitoba transferred to the Department of Psychiatry each year in Winnipeg, to support the academic functions of the Department. Probably equal to the annual incomes of ten or more shrinks in Winnipeg. One conference. One drug. One country.

A few years later I got an offer from Bristol Myers to go to a conference all expenses paid in Japan. For family logistical reasons I had to decline. The woman with the company said not to worry. As backup I would get to go to Florence the next year. Which I did. All expenses paid. Dr. Ross and spouse. To attend a Biological Psychiatry conference.

The hotel room was $340.00 U.S. a night. One dinner up in the hills overlooking Florence must have cost Bristol Myers three grand.

You're really one of the boys when you get to say, "Hi!" to another shrink over in Florence, and drop the info that a drug company has picked up the tab.

A funny thing happened on the way to the forum in Dusseldorf. Actually in the forum. I was sitting beside a psychiatrist from Ottawa, George Fraser, whom I had never met. He asked me what I was interested in. It was safe to say anxiety disorders. I was scheduled to finish my residency in a few months and become Medical Director of the Anxiety Disorders Clinic at St. Boniface Hospital in Winnipeg. Anxiety was cool. Nobody got anxiety about anxiety in shrinkdom.

Of course, anxiety is known to be Mickey Mouse compared to depression, in shrinkdom. Panic disorder isn't really heavy duty in the shrink universe. Not like depression. But then again, depression doesn't cut it like psychosis. Psychosis is the big cheese. Schizophrenia is number one. Manic depression number two. Regular depression number three. The psychiatric disorders have clear rankings. All shrinks know the rank order.

But anxiety is OK. It's an approved subject. Not like - my God! - dissociative disorders. At a drug company meeting, surrounded by biological psychiatrists, the last thing you want getting out is that you're interested in dissociative disorders.

"Are you insane? There's no drug for that."

I really didn't want to tell George I was interested in multiple personality. But I decided to take a chance. Making sure no one else was listening, I let it slip out that I was interested in dissociative disorders. I didn't let the big fart out, being in church and all. Didn't say multiple personality. But I came close. Let George know I had a gas problem.

Miracle of miracles! George treated multiple personality too. We have subsequently published together, spoken together and met at far too many multiple personality meetings to remember. I consider it hilarious that I met George courtesy of a drug company. What a hoot! I think it's called divine justice.

I met a lot of drug company employees I liked. Many of them had worked for different drug companies and many had sold many different kinds of medical drugs, not just psychiatry meds. They were regular people. Some of them did incredible amounts of international travel.

I also got a free dinner at the most expensive restaurant in Winnipeg one night, plus a $500.00 honorarium. This was to attend a trial marketing presentation for another drug, then give the company feedback. It was a drug for panic disorder. There were about fifteen shrinks. We had a four star dinner then watched a slide presentation. The shrinks gave feedback after the presentation. This is called singing for your supper.

Being a polite chap, I waited till a private moment to give my feedback. One of the slides showed that although the company's drug was as good as the standard drug manufactured by a competitor, both drugs were no different from placebo. I suggested they might want to drop that slide and de-emphasize the placebo data. They thanked me kindly.

This is what I found in my buspirone study. The two drugs were very effective at reducing general anxiety levels. But placebo was just as good. One of the Canadian drug contract gurus commented on my results to me. This was a shrink who did dozens of this kind of drug company studies, for ultra beaucoup dollars.

The shrink explained that the reason I was unable to separate drug from placebo was because I was a beginner. He had seen this in other young investigators. He said I probably spent too much time talking with the subjects. This increased the placebo effect too much. In the future I would learn not to be reassuring or supportive, to be more distant, and to spend less time with the subjects. Then my placebo response rate would drop down.

Placebo response is an ugly enemy in drug studies. From the perspective of the drug companies. Therefore from the perspective of the shrinks who test the drugs. Therefore I needed counseling on how to minimize it.

I learned in the buspirone study just how powerful placebo can be. One woman dropped out because she couldn't stand the side effects of the medication. At the end of the study, when we broke the code and found out who was on which drug, it turned out she was on placebo. The people on placebo in drug studies always have side effects. The company hopes there is no difference between the level of side effects on placebo and those on their drug. Usually, there are a couple of side effects for which this isn't the case.

The point is; placebo causes side effects. Clinically, you can't tell a drug side effect from a placebo side effect, unless it's extreme. The same is true for benefits.

I had people in the buspirone study I swore must be on buspirone. They had no side effects but had over an 80% reduction in symptoms. Hadn't been so well in years. But they were on placebo.

I also learned that psychiatrists have no creative scientific input on drug studies. The design of the experiments, how they are set up and the rules you have to follow, do not come from shrinks. The protocols are standardized around the world and set up by the drug companies in response to federal government requirements in the various countries. Shrinks have no real input.

Shrinks contribute zero scientific thinking or creativity to the development of psychiatric drugs. They are not scientists. They are contract technicians. Lab technicians. Not scientists. Not thinkers. Not creative.

"How many ways can I say I love thee?"

An individual drug is developed by chemists working for the drug company. They play a game they call *chemical roulette*. The chemists invent thousands of new molecules in the test tube. Their method is a mixture of random chance and educated guess. The structure of the drug molecule has nothing to do with understanding how the brain is structured or works.

If you look at the chemical structure of different types of antidepressants, they are very different. Not one of them is based on a scientific understanding of the structure of brain molecules with which the drugs interact.

Two points: chemical roulette is played blind, and shrinks have nothing to do with it. After a drug is synthesized in the test tube (strictly speaking, it isn't a drug yet, it's just a molecule), it's tested in animals. If it affects a mouse's behavior in a certain way, it may be an antidepressant in humans. The behavior in the mouse has nothing to do with depression.

It's blind again. The lab rat people have figured out by testing godzillions of mice or rats or rabbits that a certain behavioral effect in a lab animal increases the odds the molecule might be an antidepressant in humans.

If the drug passes this hurdle, big doses are given to animals for years to see if it causes cancer. Once this hurdle is passed, there is safety testing in human volunteers. A few shrinks might show up at this point on the assembly line, but probably not. You really want real medical doctors for this stage.

We have now finished what the drug companies call Phase I trials. Basic safety and initial dosage testing. Phase II involves checking the drug out in depressed people to see if it seems to have any effect. Phase III is the full-tilt trials with placebo required to get permission from the federal government to put the drug on the market.

Phase III is big business for shrinks. But I didn't contribute any science in Phase III. What I contributed was entrepreneurial hustle. I had to have a medical degree and shrink training. I needed a shrink supervisor on site because I was only a resident. But no thinking was required. No creative science. In this or any other drug company study.

It's a simple game with simple rules. An important and lucrative game. The drugs are clearly more effective than placebo alone. But it isn't a scientific game. Drug contracts are industrial contracts. Not scientific research grants. Two totally separate categories.

The development of psychiatric drugs has required zero creative scientific input from psychiatry. This is not a criticism of the drugs or drug companies.

The motivation for the studies comes from the drug companies. It is called the profit motive. There is nothing wrong with the profit motive, in my philosophy. I am not criticizing capitalism. I'm talking about The Great Psychiatry Scam.

A major plank in the Scam is the claim by shrinks that they are more scientific because they prescribe meds. Not so. They are just technicians. Not scientists. Why has so much money been put into drug research compared to psychotherapy research? Because drugs work better than psychotherapy? No. The data clearly show that cognitive therapy is as effective as antidepressants.

Psychotherapy is not big business. Drugs are. Simple as that. It has nothing to do with science, medicine or intellectual curiosity about nature. It's just market forces. Which is fine, in a way. Our culture gets what it pays for.

The problem is with the shrink propaganda. Why is there so much data on drugs compared to psychotherapy? Financial reasons only. Is it more medical or scientific to write a prescription than do psychotherapy? No. It's all propaganda, not science.

How much gray matter does it take to write, "Prozac 20 milligrams in the morning, thirty tablets, renew x 3 at one month intervals?" You don't even have to write it. You can have pre-stamped prescription pads for your favorite meds.

The idea that psychiatry has gotten more scientific in the last thirty years because of drug development is a lie. A marketing lie. Bought into by the drug companies and the shrinks. The shrinks are in the drug company's pocket. No problem there.

"Wait a minute," some shrink will protest.

"The drugs do work and have relieved much suffering."

That is a standard evasive strategy. The fact that the drugs work is beside the point. It's the propaganda that's the problem. The Scam. I had to let go of drug company involvement with regret. I blew off a lot of future trips when I moved to Texas and dropped drug company contracting from my portfolio. I was set up to be the man in Manitoba, probably in western Canada. The go-to-guy on all drug contracts.

I could have set up my own consulting company probably, and earned seven figures a year. I was on track. Oh well. The weather's better in Texas.

37

THE DRUG SCAM

In the last chapter I let the drug companies off the hook. I'm leaving them off. The shrinks are still on.

There are several Subscams to the Drug Scam. The shrinks are the Marketing Department and also the suppliers for this operation. One lie, which I have heard far too many times, is the idea that since the drugs work, we can conclude that the cause of mental illness is biological. That's bull.

Another lie is the claim that the drugs have been shown to work for real patients. The lid blew off that many chapters ago. The really ill patients who really need shrinks are excluded from the drug studies because they're too ill. We don't have any data on them.

Eyeball this little mathematical equation:

drug works = evidence the mental illness is biological

It's a cute equation endorsed by shrinks all over the world. You don't find many shrinks blowing the whistle. You don't find them emphasizing the need for more research on psychotherapy. When the shrinks say a mental disorder is "biological" they mean the basic cause is biological. Which means genes. And means the treatment is biological. Which means drugs.

"If it ain't biological, it ain't a real disease."

Due to this equation, everybody is happy. In Dusseldorf and Florence.

Consider some simple arithmetic. I'll use round figures.

Any given antidepressant works for about 50% of patients. Placebo works for about 30%. You would think the drug is almost twice as effective as the placebo. Not so. Why?

Because 30% of the people who got better on the drug, say Prozac, would have gotten better on placebo. We know that for a scientific fact.

What does this mean? Let's say that in this drug study there were 100 people on Prozac and 100 people on placebo. Fifty of the people given Prozac got better, but only 30 of the people given placebo.

"With me so far? This too complicated for you yet?"

Of the 50 people who responded to Prozac, 30% would have gotten better if given placebo. This means that only 70% of the 50 people who got better on Prozac had a response they could get only with Prozac.

"Need a calculator yet?"

In my universe, 70% of 50 is 35 people. So let's augment the placebo response by 5% by adding a whiff of therapy, like I did in my buspirone study.

Now 35% of people get better on placebo. But only 35% of the Prozac responders had a response that required the drug.

All around the world, when you average all the data on Prozac, you only have to boost the placebo response by 5% to get the placebo effect equal to the unique drug effect.

Check the cute equation again. The data do not support the scientific conclusion that drug response proves biological causation. All you need to prove this fact is junior high school arithmetic. The gap between drug and placebo is too small in psychiatry.

When Prozac is compared to cognitive therapy for depression, it's a tie. Do the shrinks conclude that drugs are unnecessary? Does the equation melt away? Do the shrinks adopt a new equation (cognitive therapy response = evidence the mental illness is not biological)? No way, Jose. Not in a million years.

Why don't the shrinks acknowledge the problem with their equation? I see two options: 1) they're too stupid to do junior high school arithmetic, or 2) it's a scam.

In the Sixties, the hippies promoted Better Living Through Chemistry. The original acid heads from the forties and fifties were shrinks. These shrinks became the fathers and grandfathers of late twentieth century psychiatry. Pre-hippie hippies. They turned themselves onto LSD, then turned the populace onto Prozac.

The motto changed from Turn On, Tune In, Drop Out to Turn On, Tune In, Stay In, when the drug of choice switched from LSD to Prozac. The neurotransmitter stayed the same, though - serotonin. This is called Colin Ross' Radical History of Psychopharmacology.

Why is it better to take drug than placebo? Not because the chemical in the drug is superior to placebo. The chemical effect of the drug, which can be obtained only with drug and not with placebo, is equal to the placebo response rate. The advantage of the drug is that it combines both the true chemical response and the placebo response, which is better than placebo alone.

"Go ahead and dope up. Thing is, if you feel better, it doesn't prove you had a *chemical imbalance*."

"Chemical imbalance. Chemical imbalance."

It's the mantra of biological psychiatry. I think some evil doctor in an underground lab has hypnotized all the biological psychiatrists. They keep reprogramming themselves and each other with the mantra.

The shrink can't think. The shrink can't think.

"Oh, oh. It's the war of mantras."

This is different from the War of Roses.

The only proof that mental illness is caused by a chemical imbalance is the fact that shrink drugs work. There is no other good, consistent scientific evidence that mental disorders are caused by chemical imbalances. None. Nada. Zero.

Humpty Dumpty and his equation and his proof just fell off the wall. All the shrinks' horses and all the shrinks' men, will never put Humpty together again.

I hope my remarks aren't too off the wall. I wouldn't want to be down there with Humpty, slipping around in all that egg white. Might get trampled by horses. Or the shrinks' men. Scary!

"Scary stuff, boys and girls. The Great Psychiatry Scam."

Talk about loose associations. Try the American Psychiatric Association. Loose cannons. Maybe it was a shrink cannon that shot Humpty.

Maybe psychiatry is on a self-destruct countdown. Maybe. Could we count faster?

III. SHRINK IN CANADA

38

HERE'S AN INTERESTING CASE

When I finished my residency, I took a full time job as an Assistant Professor of Psychiatry, Department of Psychiatry, University of Manitoba, starting July 1, 1985. I was based full time at St. Boniface Hospital. Half time I was responsible for 6 beds on M3, the inpatient ward. Half time I was Medical Director of the Anxiety Disorders Clinic, which was all outpatients. Mostly people with panic disorder.

I got scammed right away. Several of my colleagues offered to refer very interesting cases to me for treatment. They played the game serious and straight. They claimed I'd learn a lot. I had the special skills these people needed.

In medicine this is called a dump. It was a con. They were trying to unload their most unpleasant, stressful, difficult, annoying cases on me. I didn't fall for it. But I reset my hypocrisy gauge. I had grossly underestimated the levels of hypocrisy in the profession.

Later, when I had become the local multiple personality expert (actually, the local multiple personality nut), I experienced a twist on the con. The Interesting Case Scam, Variation Number Two.

"Come on baby. Let's do the twist. Come on, and it goes like this. Round and around and up and down."

Several shrinks offered to transfer the care of their worst borderlines to me. They told me it would be fine with them if I re-diagnosed the patients as having multiple personality. These shrinks didn't believe in multiple personality. They would neither diagnose it nor treat it themselves. But as long as I wanted to take the patients, I could call them anything I wanted.

It was a dump. I call it, The Little Psychiatry Scam. The shrinks didn't care about the patients, the correct diagnosis or the proper treatment. I could have treated the patients with extract of Argentinean horse urine, they wouldn't have batted an eye. As long as the patients bought it. Drank it.

"Get this case off my case, Colin. Whatever it takes."

I didn't. This was not my worst experience with snakes at the University of Manitoba. But it does get an honorable mention.

39

MPD CASE NUMBER THREE

Within a couple of months of starting work at St. Boniface Hospital in July, 1985, I diagnosed my third case of multiple personality disorder (MPD). This was a woman I saw in consultation as an outpatient. I had now diagnosed more cases of multiple personality than all the other psychiatrists in western Canada combined.

Over the first year of working on the inpatient unit, M3, I kept track of every case assigned to me. I excluded people already diagnosed with multiple personality. All these people were admitted through the Emergency Department and assigned to me at random.

In a paper published in the *Canadian Journal of Psychiatry*, I reported that I diagnosed multiple personality in 3 people out of 68 admitted under me in that year (4.4%). Where did I go from there? In 2001, I was notified that a research paper was accepted for publication in a professional journal. In the research project I studied patients admitted to the general adult inpatient service at a hospital in Dallas.

A table in this paper summarizes nine studies in five different countries involving a total of 1407 patients. In each of these studies, conducted in Canada, the United States, Norway, Switzerland, and Turkey, patients were studied with standardized interviews. Overall, 4.8% of the 1407 patients had previously undiagnosed multiple personality. My clinical diagnoses in 1985-86 were accurate.

Two of these nine studies were by me, one in Winnipeg, one in Dallas. Instead of sitting back and being content to be the only doctor in western Canada diagnosing and treating multiple personality, I decided to study the subject systematically. And I decided to write about it. Twenty-two years later, I am still at it. And still taking shit from my colleagues.

Here's what I did. I noticed that there was no standardized method of diagnosing multiple personality. In psychiatry research, we use what are called *structured interviews*. These are standardized lists of questions for making diagnoses. There are structured interviews for anxiety disorders, depression, schizophrenia, most of the mental disorders. In 1985, there was no structured interview for dissociative disorders, which include MPD.

In the summer of 1986, I started developing The Dissociative Disorders Interview Schedule (DDIS), with help from a medical student doing summer research under my supervision. Since then, the DDIS has been the foundation for dozens of published studies.

Once the DDIS was developed, I got a grant from the Manitoba Health Research Council to study the frequency of undiagnosed MPD at St. Boniface Hospital using the DDIS. DDIS combined with clinical interviews. The answer, published in *The American Journal of Psychiatry* in 1990, was 5.4%.

I have been studying this question with increasingly tight scientific methodology for twenty-two years. Over that time period I have been scoffed at in professional books and journals for claiming that undiagnosed MPD affects 5% of general adult psychiatric inpatients. I don't mean that I have been criticized scientifically. I mean scoffed at.

I have been treated like a nut who pulled the number 5% out of the air. The scoffers pay no attention to the science or the data at all. There is no scientific debate going on in the profession about MPD. It's a psychological warfare campaign. Abuse. Shit. Crap. Baloney. Garbage. Moronic. Stupid. Ugly.

Here's what ain't involved. Science. Analysis. Integrity. Scholarship. Decency. Intelligence. Medicine.

The idea that undiagnosed MPD affects 5% of general adult psychiatric inpatients is not a personal belief of Colin Ross'. It's the data. The data. The data. The data.

I'm hoping if I write "the data" a few hundred more times, the shrink might get it. The question of how common undiagnosed MPD is, is a *scientific* question. It can only be answered by studies and data. The rules for these studies are exactly the same rules that apply to all other psychiatric disorders. You would think. But that's not how it works in shrinkdom. Scoffing passes for scientific argument in that clubhouse. In that clubhouse, MPD patients and their doctors get treated like shit. It's very upsetting and hurtful.

Am I bitter? No. Why? I wrote this book, and got the shit out of my system. You can have it back, colleagues. Puke. Fart. Belch.

Psychiatry brought some humanity to the mental hospitals when Pinel removed the chains from patients' legs in the nineteenth century. There is still a lot of abuse of patients going on in psychiatry at the beginning of the twenty-first. It's a little more subtle, but just as barbaric. Things have changed, but not that much. I have spoken with professionals who were directly involved in cases in Dallas in which adolescents were kept in restraints continuously for six months or longer. These hospitals settled huge fraud cases with the Federal Government.

There are people living in Dallas today who grew several inches while in restraints in psychiatric hospitals. This happened in the late 1980's. The shrinks treat the patients like that. They treat multiple personality experts like shit too. Since I'm not a patient, I don't get to sue. I just get to whine and complain and suffer and be victimized.

That would be true, except for several facts. I have successfully treated many cases of multiple personality. I have published more original research data on multiple personality than anyone else in the world. I have been running a program for treatment of multiple personality in Dallas for fifteen years. I wrote this book. The knockout blow to the Department of Bullshit Psychiatry. KO or TKO? TKO. Why? The opponent isn't even in the ring. It's a virtual reality fight. I'm a legend in my own mind.

"Who shot Liberty Vallance?"

"Colin Ross."

The shrink can shoot. The shrink can shoot.

What is The Great Psychiatry Scam? It has many elements. One is the lie that psychiatry is being run by Cro-Magnon man.

Note to shrinks in the readership: that was a clear example of derailment. Let me get back on track now. On the Freedom Train. I removed my chains myself. Auto-removal. Is that against the rules? Do I need a doctor's order for that? Would it be sufficient if a medium channeled approval from Abraham Lincoln?

The DDIS is included in a book about structured interviews and symptom questionnaires published by the American Psychiatric Association in the year 2000. Called the *Handbook of Psychiatric Measures*. It was a difficult book to get into. A real stamp of approval by the powers that be in psychiatry. The editors are not MPD believers. But they were willing to look at the data. That's all I ask.

I'm not asking for the moon here. I have a simple request.

"Colleagues. Could you please stop acting like abusive morons. At least pretend you're scientists. Look at the data. Talk about the data, rationally. You got it in you?"

A few shrinks have made the grade. Thank God for that.

Here's the deal. Option 1) undiagnosed MPD affects about 5% of psychiatric inpatients in North America. The anti-MPD propagandists are idiots. Option 2) undiagnosed MPD is extremely rare among psychiatric inpatients in North America. Colin Ross is an idiot.

There is no middle ground. I have been blackballed, insulted, squeezed out of academia, ostracized, and scoffed at. It isn't a scientific debate. It's abusive professional conduct. It's unethical. A moral crime against medicine. A disgrace. Petty office politics. No different from any other office or business. Except the shrinks are claiming to be *analyzed*. What a joke.

Take your pick. Ross is an idiot. The False Memory Police are idiots. I'm up for it. Roll the dice. Let's see how the data turn out. The data. The data. The data. Not the political war. The science. The research. The medicine. More later.

Thank you, Robin Williams, for the structural tip. The organizational principle. The stylistic device. The shrinkdom vice. Head shrinker squeeze. Oh, oh, watch out. Pus coming out. Whose vice? Their vice, but I have the vice, the tool, the squeezer. I've got the juice. I make the noose. Sorry colleagues. This lobotomy is for your own good. It hurts me more than it hurts you.

Ever watch a movie of a lobotomy? The shrinks used to do a couple of hundred a day. At the psychotherapy level, a lobotomy is the best they have to offer multiple personality patients. Today. Or borderlines. Or people with PTSD. Current standard mainstream hospital treatment for multiple personality, borderlines and PTSD is as barbaric as lobotomy. As barbaric as Bedlam in the nineteenth century.

Bad news, general public. The treatment you are getting from psychiatry at the beginning of the twenty-first century is in the dark ages. If you have a trauma-based disorder, or set of disorders, and you go to a regular, mainstream hospital program, you get nothing. Nothing helpful. With abuse added on top. That's my profession. Those are my colleagues.

Anybody who offers anything better gets treated like shit. Ignored. Ostracized. I am so sick of those Neanderthal grins and comments, I could almost get there. Where? Wishing I would be abducted by aliens. The problem is not whether aliens exist and are abducting people. The problem is if they aren't. Then we're stuck here with just ourselves. And the shrinks. How depressing. How angry that makes me! People wonder why America is such a violent society. People treat each other like shit here. Canada is just as bad, with a veneer of British politeness.

It isn't an intellectual debate. It's a series of drive-by shootings. At the professional conferences, in the journals, in the corridors of academia, in the textbooks. The adolescent shooters in the schools are copying the behavior of the shrinks. After a school shooting is over, the shrinks mind fuck the shooters by making psychiatric diagnoses, if the shooters are still alive. It's a cover up. The kids are just copying the way adults treat each other in this culture. The way my colleagues treat me. Case in point. It isn't about me. I am just an example. I'm just another shooter. Have been since Mrs. Parkinson's class. Don't plan on changing.

40

MALPRACTICE BASE RATE 25%

I worked at St. Boniface Hospital in Winnipeg, Manitoba, Canada for six and a half years. I never kept an exact count, but I'd guess that there were about 5000 admissions to M2 and M3, the two adult wards, during this time period. I estimate that 25% of these patients were victims of clear malpractice. Water-tight malpractice cases that could be won by any good U.S. plaintiff's attorney.

Not a single one of these malpractice cases involved psychotherapy, talking about the patient's childhood, multiple personality, or memories of sexual abuse. They were all regular mainstream psychiatry cases. Come to the University teaching hospital. Get your meds. Stay two or three or four weeks. Go home. This malpractice had nothing to do with any unusual theories, fringe beliefs by the shrinks, or anything out of the ordinary. It was standard government-issue psychiatry.

I'm not talking about my personal opinion, although I just gave it. I mean successful malpractice cases based on the objective documentation in the medical records.

While I was on staff at St. Boniface, there was some rumbling and grumbling from the outpatient shrinks about the inpatient shrinks. The shrinks working on M2 and M3 were not writing notes in their patients' charts often enough. So the rules were changed. Things were tightened up.

Under the new rules, psychiatrists were required to write a note in the chart at least once a week. Once a week! This was tightening up! Problem was, there was no enforcement. A patient could be in the hospital for three weeks, and there would be fewer words written in the chart by the shrink than there are on this page, by a considerable amount.

The first component of the malpractice was the fact that the psychiatrists weren't doing much psychiatry. Too busy doing psychiatry.

I remember one case that did involve multiple personality. So happened it was a case in which the patient probably made the multiple personality up herself. She was in the hospital for six weeks. The shrink saw her on the day of admission and again on the day of discharge. When she complained to her therapist about this, the shrink was incensed. He called her an entitled narcissist.

Dr. Fraud is a helpful guy. You can always rely on him for a piece of jargon to screw the patient over with.

When a shrink did see an inpatient, it was usually for four microseconds. Nobody felt bad about this. Or apologized for it. Guess what happened when I started diagnosing multiple personality and seeing my inpatients for an hour of psychotherapy several times per week?

The other patients started to complain to their doctors.

“How come Dr. Ross spends so much time with his patients, and you hardly spend any time with me? I never get to see you.”

The solution to the problem? A diarrhea dump on multiple personality. It wasn’t about multiple personality. It was about laziness. The system was set up to rationalize and protect laziness and mediocrity. In this system, excellence is malpractice and malpractice is standard treatment. The myth of the busy doctor was used to justify being too busy to be a doctor for anyone. It was all about the doctor’s time and income. Not about the patients.

I saw dozens and dozens and dozens of cases in which you couldn’t tell from the chart what was going on. Couldn’t tell what the problem was, how the patient was doing, or what the treatment plan was. The information just wasn’t there.

The symptoms being treated were not described in any detail. The symptoms often did not match the diagnosis. There was no documentation of the response of specific symptoms to medication.

Medication. Oh, my God! Wild, crazy, irrational polypharmacy was the norm. People were on eight different psychiatric meds at the same time *routinely*. This was common, everyday practice. With zero scientific support. There isn’t one scientific study looking at these kinds of drug combinations.

One ridiculous event I remember clearly. One of the polypharmacists had it in politically for one of the others. He got incensed that this psychiatrist had his patient on four different tricyclic antidepressants at the same time. On a University teaching ward with a resident and three medical students. In full view of everybody. And without remorse. With much grumbling, the shrink was forced to stop two of the tricyclics.

I was assigned a patient one time who was being treated by an old shrink who was away on vacation. The patient was older too. She was on some ridiculous combination of six or eight or ten psychiatric drugs. I decided to be a scientist. I sat down with her and explained how this combination of many different drugs could cause side effects and drug-drug interactions, and in any case did not fit her diagnosis or symptoms.

She was insulted. Her doctor had been working with her for years, and had gotten her balanced out just right, she said. She was in a mental ward when she made that statement. There was nothing I could do. I just had to back off. I, the young shrink who knew nothing compared to her doctor who had been in practice for years.

There was nothing I could do systemically either. The corporate culture was completely tolerant of this kind of practice. The number one rule was not to rock the boat. Follow the rules. Play the game.

There were some really bad borderlines in the Department. A small collection of forlorn, demanding women who had been admitted dozens of times each. Who had made over 100 visits to the Emergency Department each. One of them had been an inpatient in the adolescent program for a couple of years before coming of age and graduating to the adult wards. Everyone knew her. Everyone had seen her on call.

The staff was completely burned out and sadistically angry at her. Everyone talked really bad about her, in a mean, condescending, blaming fashion. One time I saw her in the Intensive Care Unit on call. She had overdosed on a huge pile of pills and was being monitored for cardiac arrhythmia. This was the old days of tricyclic antidepressants, which could cause cardiac arrest in overdose.

The young woman had been discharged from the psychiatry ward about three weeks earlier. I was not her regular doctor. I never changed her diagnosis when I saw her on call various times and had no input on her treatment. She did not have a dissociative disorder. She had a horrendous abuse history and believed absolutely that it was her fault, that she was bad, and that she deserved to die.

I talked directly to the psychiatrist who treated her whenever she was an inpatient. She had overdosed on the meds he prescribed for her on discharge. Which was a mountain of different drugs. I spoke with him about how he had prescribed a lethal amount of medication. To a woman who had overdosed and attempted suicide by various methods countless times. Whom he knew very well. He had given her a month's supply of six or eight different drugs, several of which could kill her by themselves, let alone in combination with the others. I told him the only reason she survived was that she had taken the overdose late in the month, so there wasn't much left.

I even talked to him about the hostile counter-transference involved in writing a prescription like that. Talked to him about how it was an expression of the staff's anger at the woman. He agreed with me on all these points. Accepted the feedback in a professional manner. Agreed with me that it was crucial to simplify her med plan and only give her a week's supply at a time as an outpatient.

A few months later she killed herself with an overdose. The same psychiatrist had given her a prescription for a month's supply of a whole bunch of different meds. This time she overdosed early in the month and died. Exactly as I had said would happen. It was murder by counter-transference.

What happened? Nothing. No investigation. No peer review. No change in Department policy. The patient was blamed. Everybody went back to work.

Really, they were relieved she was dead.

That was an unusual case. But not so unusual. We sent suicidal people home from Emergency all the time with no follow-up. And we had no idea what happened to them.

There was no real review of clinical practice in place. There was a so-called Audit Committee in the Department. But all it looked at was whether everything was in the chart. Was there a history and physical? Were the med orders signed? Was there a discharge summary?

Nobody looked at the quality of care. There was no outside insurance company reviewing the charts. The government, the hospital administration, nobody looked at quality of care. It was up to the doctor. The individual doctor-patient relationship. The doctors were out of control. Even if they practiced sound, careful, conservative psychiatry, they were out of control.

I made a couple of efforts to change things. I tried repeatedly to initiate a system for chart review based on objective criteria for prescribing drugs. I did a literature review. What was my scheme? Nothing fancy.

I tried to set up a system that had the basics of psychiatry in a systematic format. The first step was the diagnosis. There would have to be an adequate history to support the diagnosis based on DSM-III diagnostic criteria. If the diagnosis was depression, an antidepressant was required. If an antidepressant was prescribed, it had to be given for long enough in a sufficient dosage to see if it worked. No one could get two drugs from the same class of psychiatric meds at a time.

It was simple basics derived from the literature. The facts in the literature were not in dispute. What's the average dose of amitriptyline? 150 milligrams at bedtime. Simple.

What reception did I get? Obfuscation, huffing, puffing, avoidance, passive-aggressive resistance. I heard paragraphs of baloney about *clinical judgment* and *complex cases*. I heard about how much experience the shrinks had. I heard an un-climbable mountain of excuses and rationalizations for why we could never have standardized protocols based on research. And we never did. The shrinks didn't want it. They actively fought it.

In Canada, there was nothing I could do. There was no managed care. The corporate culture was set. It was a system to protect and foster malpractice, laziness, and sloppiness. A good, conscientious psychiatrist could work within the system. So could a buffoon. Both were tolerated. Some of the Professors of Psychiatry went home at 4:15. Not the surgeons. There was a reason for them to stay. They had real work to do.

Then there were the nurses. The nurses were assigned to five patients for each shift. An eight-hour work day is 480 minutes. Five patients. Let's give the nurses 80 minutes for charting and meetings. That would leave 80 minutes for face-to-fact contact with each patient per day. To do some nursing.

OK. I admit it. I'm being unreasonable. Let's give the nurses 180 minutes for charting, meetings and other duties. Three hours. Now there are 300 minutes left, a full hour for each patient. I met with hostile resistance when I requested that the nurses spend 15 minutes a day talking face-to-face with each of my patients. They never did do it. Except for a couple of really dedicated nurses who worked hard and took heat from the other nurses for it.

The problem was both individual and systemic. The lazy, mediocre people had control of the system. They were individually responsible for their own sloth. But you could never solve the problem at an individual level because it was a systemic problem. Interventions at the system level were also futile.

I survived in that climate for 5.5 years. Starting January 1, 1991, I no longer did inpatient work. Couldn't stand it anymore. Couldn't stand to see the crappy care day in and day out, the hypocrisy and malpractice. Near the end of my tenure on M3, I tried to get myself transferred to M2, for a change of atmosphere and to get away from the two worst polypharmacists. We discussed this option at a Medical Staff Meeting.

Everyone refused to take a turn on M3. They defined the problem as a *personality conflict*. They said I was having a personal problem working with one of the shrinks. They all refused to work with him. But I was the one with the personal problem. These people are *psychiatrists*? Their job is helping people deal with reality in a more healthy fashion? I wonder why none of the patients ever get better.

I'm trying to keep my estimate of the rate of malpractice low and conservative at 25%. I don't want to come off as a radical. If you want the real estimate, let's not talk about legal malpractice. Let's just talk about crappy mediocre psychiatry. Let's talk 75%.

41

HEY MAN, CHECK OUT THIS CARBON DIOXIDE!

The training I had in psychiatry was based on folklore. There was some science floating around. But it was mostly anecdote, attitude, myth, and inherited dogma. One lie was focused on Russian psychiatry. The Cold War was still hot while I was a resident, from 1981 to 1985, and for the first few years of my career as a fully trained shrink. We knew Russian psychiatry was bad.

How did we know? Just because we knew. We never actually talked to a Russian psychiatrist, visited Russia, read any Russian psychiatric literature, or listened to a lecture from someone who had been to Russia. But we knew for a fact that the political abuse of psychiatry was a serious problem in Russia. Psychiatrists were being used as instruments of the State. People were being locked up in psychiatric hospitals based on bogus diagnoses, when they were really political dissidents.

How did we know that? We were told. Told by whom? Experts. The American Psychiatric Association. Big shots. Everybody knew it. It was a fact.

There is a twist in the logic here. Follow me, if you can. The irony is, it was true that political abuse of psychiatry was going on in Russia. Dissidents were indeed being locked up for phony psychiatric treatment. But how did we know? The fact that we were right was just luck. It was hit and miss. The problem in psychiatry is with the *process of knowing*. I don't know much about pissing, not being a urologist, but I think the study of knowledge is called *epistemology*. I get pissed when I think about shrink epistemology. And pissed at when I write about it.

We knew Russian psychiatry was bad because we bought the dogma. We didn't know scientifically. We didn't know as scholars. We just bought the propaganda. It so happens that on this subject the propaganda was accurate. It was a blind hit. Not real knowing or seeing.

We knew that Russian psychiatry was behind North American psychiatry. They were losing the Psychiatry Race, as well as the Space Race. We were proud to be doing our part for freedom and democracy.

The Russian shrinks believed in all kinds of crazy unscientific treatments. I was instructed that we were scientific, while the Russians were superstitious. I was given specific examples, during my residency. None of this propaganda was organized structurally. It wasn't planned out or delivered at seminars. It was all gossip. There was no conspiracy. You have to be conscious of what you are doing to run a conspiracy. The epistemology was unconscious, in the shrinks. They just knew because they knew. Like lemmings do.

“Time to head out, boys.”

“Russian psychiatry is in the dark ages.”

The little feet ran in the right direction. Consider this book a warning about cliff edges.

The Russians, I was told, practiced strange, superstitious, barbaric psychiatry. Stuff we never do in the West. Like sleep therapy. They would put people to sleep for days with drugs. Then when they woke up, the patients were supposed to be better. Sleep therapy was scoffed at as obviously stupid. It was self-evident that this was a ridiculous idea. The Western shrink facial expressions told you what to think, and you were socialized to conform. Nobody questioned the dogma. No one asked if there were any data. You would be regarded as an idiot if you asked such questions. No one did.

The Russians, I was told, had another dark ages treatment method. They gave people carbon dioxide to treat mental illnesses. Carbon dioxide? How absurd! Carbon dioxide therapy in Russia was laughed at as obviously unscientific.

A few years later, in the same Department of Psychiatry, I participated in a research study, which had been reviewed and approved by the Faculty of Medicine Ethics Committee. I was treating panic disorder with carbon dioxide. Carbon dioxide therapy went from obvious evidence of dark ages psychiatry to the subject of a research study in less than half a decade.

It turns out that inhalation of a 35% mixture of carbon dioxide is a perfectly scientific treatment for panic disorder. A North American professional literature on it exists now. It can be studied scientifically. It's safe and cheap. Not all that effective, but better than Fraudian therapy.

There's even a little scientific theory behind it. If you breathe air containing 35% CO_2, your CO_2 levels in your blood will go up. This will stimulate your respiratory drive. You will feel panicky, or suffocating. You will hyperventilate to blow off the CO_2. This will mimic a panic attack. But it is controlled and created on purpose in the lab.

The experience teaches you that panic attacks are not mysterious catastrophes. They can be provoked by many means. And controlled. The carbon dioxide is just a device to make the cognitive therapy more powerful. The fact that cognitive therapy for panic disorder is highly effective, is completely proven scientifically.

Carbon dioxide therapy never really caught on. For one thing, it's a lot of hassle getting the compressed air bottles containing a 35% CO_2 mixture. There's a lot of red tape for purchase orders, hospital inspections and so on.

It doesn't matter whether carbon dioxide is an effective therapy or not. The point is epistemological. It's how shrinks know things. Not by science.

My shrink teachers forgot to mention that in Canada, two decades earlier, Dr. Ewen Cameron had been putting patients to sleep for weeks at a time. Dr. Ewen Cameron. At various times, President of the Quebec, Canadian, American and World Psychiatric Associations. Ewen Cameron. TOP SECRET MKULTRA mind control contractor for the CIA. Ewen Cameron, whose sleep patients later sued and were compensated financially by both the CIA and the Canadian Government, which also funded the good doctor.

The Western shrink pot was calling the Russian shrink kettle black. Or, more accurately, red. They forgot to mention that Ewen Cameron gave his patients high doses of LSD. Fried their brains with hundreds of times the normal amount of electro-shock therapy. In Canada. Put them to sleep with drugs for weeks or months at a time.

Here is another fact. If not for the CIA, I would have died in Gulag decades ago. If not for the CIA, I couldn't write this book. If the Russians had won the Cold War, it would have been game over for Colin A. Ross, M.D., dissident doctor. Refusenik. I refuse the Great Psychiatry Scam. In Russia, a lot of the refuseniks were physicists – in Russia, they were persecuted, while in North America they were applauded. I'm a psychiatrist, not a physicist, and I'm waiting for my applause, here in North America. Waiting. . . Waiting. . . Still waiting.

In Russia, politically incorrect radicals like me got a one-way trip to Gulag.

It's not about the CIA. It's about the shrinks. There has been way more political abuse of psychiatry in North America than in Russia. Check it out in my book *The CIA Doctors: Human Rights Violations By American Psychiatrists*. A book I had to publish myself, through my own publishing company, in *samizdat*, one might say. Gulag is more subtle over here. More deniable. More virtual.

42

ON BECOMING A MULTIPLE PERSONALITY NUT

I'm leery about mentioning multiple personality. If I mention it even once, the False Memory Police will pounce on that and make everything be about multiple personality. The False Memory Police are commonly known as the Professional Advisory Board of the False Memory Syndrome Foundation[1]. I prefer my title. The Police have waged a relentless propaganda war against multiple personality disorder. In the media, the courts and the professional literature.

"Colin Ross is bitter because we don't buy his theories of multiple personality."

Not so. That's not the problem. The problem is not that the False Memory Police disagree with my theory. Whatever my "theory" is supposed to be. The problem is the tactics they use. The tactics would be despicable even if they were used to campaign *for* me, instead of against me. They are the tactics of negative campaigning in politics. It's propaganda, not science. Propaganda posing as science. The False Memory Police are propaganda experts, not scholarly analysts. (Legal note: I'm talking only about the propaganda war against multiple personality here, not about other aspects of the Police Officers' careers).

Consider the Branch Davidian siege. Psychological warfare consultants used the same tactics on the Branch Davidians as the False Memory Police use on me. Harassment. Psychological warfare. Intimidation.

The term the FBI spokesman used on TV during the Branch Davidian siege was *ratcheting up the pressure*. On TV we were told that John Rambos within the ATF and the FBI were running the operation. Trying to bust David Koresh on weapons charges. They brought in the tanks, the helicopters, the guns, the uniforms. Set up a perimeter. Ratcheted up the pressure. The vocabulary was straight out of a Sylvester Stallone movie. Rambo in action.

Consider this scenario. John Rambo and friends are sitting outside the Branch

---

1 Historical note: The False Memory Syndrome Foundation was formed in 1992 as a support group for people, mostly fathers, who claimed they had been falsely accused of incest. I'm sure there were members who indeed had been falsely accused, and I agree that they deserved support and a political voice. However, the Foundation also waged a campaign against multiple personality disorder, recovered memories of sexual abuse, therapists and various other targets of their psychological warfare operations.

Hysterical note: The Police are really, really mean people and I hate them hate them hate them.

Davidian compound perimeter, planning strategy.

John Rambo says, “Let’s nuke ‘em.”

Good old boy number two says, “Torch the joint.”

Good old boy number three says, “I think we should play Tibetan chant music over a loudspeaker. And sounds of screaming rabbits being killed.”

Tibetan chant music? There is no way John Rambo would choose Tibetan chant music. Tibetan chant music was in fact played over loudspeakers to the Branch Davidians during the siege. This is the work of a psychological warfare consultant. Nice job. Slick operation.

I remember a patient coming into my office a couple of days after the Branch Davidian compound burned. She was a real handful of a case. Lots of false memories and ridiculous claims about cult surveillance going on in the present. Very manipulative. Lots of phony symptoms. I liked her.

She made one statement.

“David Koresh was going to turn 34 in August.”

I knew what she meant. She knew I knew. We had never spoken about the Branch Davidians. I made a non-committal comment and we carried on with other subject matter. We never spoke of it again.

I say Koresh had to kill himself at age 33 in order to open the Seventh Seal. He had to die at the same age as Jesus in order to become Jesus. If consulted, and given some time and resources, I would have figured this out before the fire. The ATF and FBI strategy, then, would have been to wait until after David Koresh’s birthday in August, 1993. Then he could have been negotiated out.

I realize that hindsight is perfect. The point here is not to criticize the ATF or FBI. I am making a point about the False Memory Police. I’ll get to it.

In psychological warfare operations, you have to go inside the belief system of the client, or the target, in order to dismantle it from within. This is standard psychological warfare operating procedure. There are lots of books about it at Border’s or Barnes and Noble. It’s what I would have tried to do as a consultant on the Branch Davidian siege. It’s what I do with my patients who have been brainwashed by their therapists. Who believe they ate babies in Satanic cults as children. Go inside the system and dismantle it from within.

Simple instructions to wake up just don’t work. They don’t work for brainwashed cult members and they don’t work for multiple personality patients who’ve had bad therapy.

In family system theory this strategy is called, *aligning yourself with the resistance*. It is a principle used in several types of short term and cognitive-behavioral therapy. There are lots of precedents for it. The strategy is also used in Kung Fu.

I get beat over the head by the False Memory Police for not telling my patients their Satanic cult memories are bogus. Why? Because the Police are making a reasonable criticism? No. Because they are beating me up.

I ask, "You think someone could have gotten David Koresh to come out of the Branch Davidian compound by telling him his belief system was delusional?"

The False Memory Police reply, "Sure. Simple. At the Mickey Mouse School of Counter-Intelligence, we do that in simulation exercises all the time. Works like a charm."

I respond, "If the CIA is run by people with your brains, we're in serious trouble."

Members of the False Memory Police claim that I am using the mind control methods of destructive cults on my patients. Brainwashing them into believing they grew up in Satanic cults. I'm not. There is zero evidence that I am.

If the patient has already been brainwashed by a colleague before I meet her, I get beat up for not getting the person out of my colleague's belief system. I am supposed to explain that none of the memories are real. Then they are supposed to melt away. So simple.

What about the risk the patient will slash her wrists, bang her head on the wall, hang herself, or overdose if you tell her that her memories aren't real? Talk about armchair quarterbacks!

The False Memory Policemen who make this attack, are experts on the brainwashing techniques of destructive cults. But they use the same techniques themselves. Relentlessly. It's what they know. It's a propaganda war, not an analysis.

The False Memory Police include former CIA and military consultants with TOP SECRET security clearance. They studied, taught and carried out brainwashing experiments for the CIA. In the early fifties. This includes Dr. Louis Jolyon West, contractor on MKULTRA Subproject 43, who also killed an elephant with Air Force LSD at the Oklahoma City Zoo. Margaret Singer, who interviewed brainwashed U.S. pilots who had been POWs during the Korean War. Brainwashed by the Communist Chinese. West published with Singer. Singer published with Ofshe. Ofshe is the Chief Prosecutor for the False Memory Police, the one who brings the charges of brainwashing against Colin A. Ross & Co.

The big experts on cult mind control are testifying against Colin Ross, because when he gets a brainwashed victim of crazy therapy, who believes she ate babies in a Satanic cult as a child, he doesn't pop them out of their delusions by giving them a lecture on false memories.

"Uh, huh. Sure. Like it's so simple."

These big experts have never treated a case of multiple personality themselves.

"OK. I get it. If we could just have gotten hold of the Heaven's Gate people in advance, we could have explained to them that they had been brainwashed. We could have explained that the alien ship behind Hale-Bopp comet was a delusion. Then they wouldn't have committed suicide."

"Gee whiz, Professor. It's so easy when you say it. Ever done it?"

At this point, the Professor coughs and splutters but has nothing coherent to say.

"Say, Professor, tell me about the cult deprogrammers who had to kidnap people and hold them in hotel rooms against their will for days to break the cult programming, in the 70s and 80s. Why did they have to go to such extremes if deprogramming is so easy? Deprogramming Heaven's Gate members, or deprogramming the patients referred to Colin Ross."

See the absurdity of it? It's a Mad Hatter's Tea Party, not a scientific debate. The experts on cult brainwashing developed their expertise studying mind control for the CIA and military. Fact. Martin Orne, TOP SECRET MKULTRA mind control contractor. Louis Jolyon West, ditto. Margaret Singer, Defense Department debriefer of brainwashed U.S. POWs from the Korean War. Richard Ofshe, protégé of Singer. Co-author of Singer. Singer, coauthor of West. West published in a book edited by Orne. Orne, author of a laudatory essay on West. On and on it goes. They all belong to the same Club. All are on the Professional Advisory Board of the False Memory Syndrome Foundation.

The False Memory Police set themselves up as experts on cult brainwashing. Then they accuse me of being a cult brainwasher. They beat me up for not deprogramming my patients, or the patients referred to me by my colleagues. Any expert on cults knows that such Mickey Mouse deprogramming has no effect on brainwashed cult members. It just doesn't work. The task is much more subtle and complex.

Are the False Memory Police stupid? Do they believe their own propaganda? Or is it disinformation? I can't decide. Can't decide. Can't decide.

"Once you're in, you're never out. That's what this is all about."

"Now who said that? Who butted in here with that remark?"

There is no way you can take a brainwashed cult member and deprogram him with a little simple education about memory and therapy. Even if the cult brainwashers are Colin Ross' colleagues. I get attacked for not doing something that is impossible to do.

Even Officer Ofshe failed as a deprogrammer. In Lawrence Wright's non-fiction book *Remembering Satan*, Ofshe spent lots and lots of time with the Ingram family in Washington state. Paul Ingram had made a false confession of incest due to coercive police interrogation methods. He had been brainwashed. Ingram was never in therapy. But he recovered memories of sexually abusing his daughters during the interrogation. Ofshe worked on the Ingram family as hard as he could and had lots of direct access to Paul Ingram. Paul Ingram has not recanted his false confession to this day. He is still in jail.

"Nice going, Officer Ofshe. You can't deprogram these people either. So why do you beat me up? You got the track record to be holier than thou about it?"

"Say, Officers, where is the scientific evidence that your recommended course of action works? Oh. Got none. Sorry. Didn't want to embarrass you. If I had known, I would never have asked."

Officer Elizabeth Loftus is another member of the False Memory Syndrome Foundation Advisory Board. Unlike many of the others, she does real science. But she has gotten sucked in by the propaganda machine. She did a set of experiments in cognitive psychology called The Lost in the Mall Study. She convinced subjects that they had been lost in a mall as children, when it was known for a fact this never happened. In response to suggestive questioning, the subjects developed compelling subjective memories of trauma that never happened. The subjects were normal college students.

Interesting. The False Memory Police use The Lost in the Mall Study to beat up therapists. For implanting false memories. They forget to emphasize one fact. Many of the subjects in The Lost In The Mall Study refused to believe the memories were not real. Even when they were fully debriefed about how the memory had been deliberately implanted. And this is one simple, mildly traumatic memory in a normal college student.

Try talking severely disturbed psychiatric inpatients out of complicated memories reinforced by hours and hours of therapy.

According to the False Memory Police, I am supposed to accomplish this feat with simple explanation and education about memory. It's complete bullshit. It's humanly impossible. The False Memory Police themselves fail at simple versions of the task.

The False Memory Police attack me for using mind control methods on my patients. OK. But their attack is based on the rules and procedures of psychological warfare, not science. They blame me for what they themselves do. They attack a Colin Ross who doesn't exist. They create a propaganda image of Colin Ross, and then make fun of it. They invent a therapy I am supposed to do, and give it a name. *Recovered memory therapy.*

Before the False Memory Police invented the term *recovered memory therapy*, no one had ever heard of it. There were no professional articles about it. No one claimed to practice it. No one endorsed it. The Police created a straw man then made it be the entire field. Sure. Some therapists fit the recovered memory profile. I never did.

There are crazy therapies for arthritis and cancer. Everything from copper bracelets to pyramid power to extract of apricot pits. Does the existence of these crazy therapies prove all treatment for arthritis by all doctors is equally crazy?

The Police continuously use arguments that would be laughed out of court if used against any other diagnosis in medicine. If they wrote to the *Journal of the American Medical Association*, arguing that laetrile therapy proves cancer is a bogus diagnosis, they would never get published in a million years. Make exactly the same argument against MPD, and you get published in a top shrink journal.

"The shrink can't think. The shrink can't think."

Or worse, the shrink can think, but deliberately decides not to for fascist political reasons. Take your pick.

The False Memory Police invented a theory I don't hold and gave it a name. *Robust repression*. Robust repression is when you 100% block out years of horrible abuse and have complete amnesia for it. I have never seen robust repression in an MPD patient. My published research demonstrates that MPD patients report extensive childhood trauma in the same interview as the initial diagnosis is made.

The Police never get confused by the facts. They make MPD depend on the theory of robust repression. Which it doesn't. Then comes an additional slight of hand. They make dissociation be a synonym for repression. Which it isn't. Then they make repression be an unproven theory. A trick within the trick is the fact they are correct about repression theory. Then, since repression = dissociation, the foundation of the dissociative disorders is proven to be unscientific. The foundation of the treatment, which they call recovered memory therapy, is unscientific. Colin Ross is out in the cold.

It's a Cold War. And it'll be a cold day in Hell when I wave the white flag.

Here's what is true. Repression is a Fraudian concept. It is unscientific and untestable. I am not a repression theorist. I don't treat or observe repression in my MPD patients. Never have.

By the way, in order to be scientific, a theory does not have to be correct. It only has to be testable. This is Philosophy of Science 101. Fraudian theory is unscientific not because it is wrong, but because it is not scientifically testable as formulated. In my book, *The Trauma Model: A Solution To The Problem Of Comorbidity In Psychiatry*, I present a highly intricate, scientifically testable body of thought, based on the lessons I have learned from MPD, but extended far beyond MPD.

The word repression has several meanings in Fraud's writings. This is a source of further confusion. The Police use the confusion to their advantage.

One meaning of repression is that it is an unconscious ego defense. It is used by the ego to defend against unacceptable wishes and impulses coming from the id. This has nothing to do with the outside world, external events, memory, childhood trauma, or objective reality.

The second meaning of repression is that it is an ego defense used to cope with traumatic events. The memory of the events is split off and buried in the unconscious mind. This is a scientifically untestable concept because you can never prove that the unconscious has the properties attributed to it by Dr. Sigmund, or that the Fraudian unconscious even exists.

The third meaning of repression is a synonym for suppression. This is the everyday mental habit of putting things on the back burner. You consciously put them out of your mind.

Meanings one and three have absolutely nothing to do with MPD, dissociation or me. Meaning two might, but doesn't. Why?

First, the difference between dissociation and repression. The False Memory Police make repression and dissociation be synonyms so they can blow dissociation out of the water. But what is dissociation? Dissociation has four meanings.

In one, it appears to be a synonym for the second meaning of repression. But it isn't really. The first meaning of dissociation is a defense against trauma where memories, thoughts, and feelings are split off from consciousness. Let's look at that. If repression and dissociation are synonyms, why do Fraudian psychoanalysts rarely or never diagnose MPD? One of the False Memory Policemen died in a private plane crash in 1994. Nicholas Spanos. Besides being a personal tragedy for his friends, family and colleagues, this was bad news for me professionally. Why? Because Spanos had half a brain. It might have been possible to engage him in a real scientific conversation, to pull him up out of the level of propaganda. The other Policemen can't make the jump to light speed.

Spanos wrote in his book, *Multiple Identities and False Memories*:

> *Following Freud's lead, psychoanalysts rejected the concept of dissociation with its implication of two simultaneously existing states of consciousness. . . Psychoanalysts did not encourage patients to personify their conflicting attitudes and beliefs as alter selves and implied that such practices constituted poor therapy. Consequently, the patients of psychoanalysts, and others influenced by psychoanalytic ideas, rarely manifested MPD.*

Officer Spanos believes that 100% of cases of MPD are iatrogenic, which means created by the therapist. He says that dissociation theory and Fraudian repression theory are distinct. The Fraudians are protected from creating iatrogenic MPD because they follow Fraud and repression theory, and reject dissociation.

Great. Officers Ofshe and Paul McHugh make the opposite charge. Officer McHugh writes in his intro to the propaganda treatise of Officer August Piper, in Officer Piper's book *Hoax and Reality* (all these characters are False Memory Syndrome Foundation Advisory Board Members) that:

> *A major misdirection of concept and practice has plagued psychiatry for over a decade. It has misaligned psychotherapy, disrupted families, and burst from the clinics into the law courts. This misdirection rests, first, on the wholesale overemphasis on a psychological mechanism - repression - that demands no proof of its presumptions. . . And yet none of these claims are new. Rather, they are discredited and discarded ideas from almost a century ago, resurrected with no fresh evidence and defended by shabby reasoning and blithe dismissal of criticism. . . [August Piper] has studied the flimsy evidence and the twisted logics that have produced this decade-long disciplinary craze. . . a major folly, a folly astonishing in its wild presumptions. . . a threadbare business. . .*

Officer McHugh squarely puts the blame on discredited unscientific Fraudian theory. Fraud is the foundation of the MPD fraud. If so, what's with Officer Spanos' comment? And why does Colin Ross show so little respect for Dr. Sigmund? Does it add up? Only at the Mad Hatter's Tea Party.

Just to be clear, let's check what Officer Ofshe has to say, from his book *Making Monsters*, where he says that 100% of MPD is iatrogenic. Remember, Officers Spanos, Piper, Ofshe and McHugh are on the same team.

> *Many of the theoretical and practical mistakes committed today by recovered memory therapists were made by Freud a hundred years ago. . . Without Freudian props and backdrops, recovered memory promoters would not likely have been tolerated. . . . their notions and methods lack scientific backing. . . All in all, Freud cut the very figure of a recovered*

memory therapist.

The False Memory Police need to decide whether Dr. Siggy is the problem or the cure. As it stands, they say I'm bad because I am Fraudian and because I am not Fraudian. Other Officers have written that recovered memory therapy is the work of feminists who do not understand or practice the principles of good psychoanalytical (= Fraudian) psychotherapy.

Back to dissociation. Dissociation has three other meanings. Meaning two. Dissociation is a technical term in cognitive psychology. Dissociation has been defined in experimental cognitive psychology for decades. It is one of the most locked down, proven concepts in all of cognitive psychology. There are hundreds of experiments on *repetition priming*, *task interference* and related phenomena that demonstrate the reality of dissociation in normal psychology.

It is a totally proven scientific fact that memory is composed of at least two subsystems. The False Memory Police agree on this point. These are called *procedural* and *declarative memory*, which, roughly speaking, correspond to unconscious and conscious memory. Repetition priming proves that there can be a dissociation between procedural and declarative long term memory. In the normal human mind.

Accurate information about real external events can be stored in procedural memory, and can affect verbal and behavioral output in a measurable fashion, in the complete absence of declarative memory for that information. This is an absolute scientific fact. There is no doubt about it. Humorously, the False Memory Police Corps includes many cognitive psychologists who ignore their own science and cover it up with the phony equation, dissociation = repression. This allows them to pound the point that since there is no scientific proof of repression, dissociation goes out with the bath water.

Third. Dissociation is defined operationally in the published measures of dissociation such as the Dissociative Experiences Scale (DES), Dissociative Disorders Interview Schedule (DDIS) and Structured Clinical Interview for DSM-IV Dissociative Disorders (SCID-D). These three measures appear in the American Psychiatric Association's *Handbook of Psychiatric Measures*.

The rules for measuring dissociation are exactly the same as those for measuring anxiety, depression or psychosis. There are lots of data. Data. Data. Data. Data. Data. Data. Data. Data.

Four. Dissociation is a general systems term. Dissociation between two variables is observed in all branches of science under numerous conditions. I learned about dissociation in physical chemistry in pre-med.

Of the four meanings of dissociation, only one is remotely close to being a synonym for repression. But even here the False Memory Police are full of shit.

The word repression does not appear in DSM-IV. The word dissociation does. The word dissociation does not appear in a huge glossary of psychoanalytic vocabulary I looked at in a bookstore. Repression does.

There are Fraudian theories for every disorder in DSM-IV, including substance abuse, stuttering, sexual perversions, depression and schizophrenia. Do the False Memory Police attack depression because it depends on Fraud. No. Why? Because they aren't against depression and they couldn't get away with the strategy if they used it on depression. They would be laughed at and not given the time of day.

The False Memory Police are lousy Fraudian scholars. Dr. Siggy Butt started off with a trauma-dissociation theory. He assumed that the childhood sexual abuse described by his female patients was real. That real trauma was the cause of their real symptoms decades later. This is called *the seduction theory*. The symptoms included the formation of dissociated compartments within the ego.

Then, in the late 1890's, Dr. Sigmund decided the abuse stories were false memories. The abuse never really happened. He developed repression theory to explain why his female patients had false memories of childhood sexual abuse. It is when the memories are false that repression theory applies. Fraud explicitly rejected the word dissociation when he rejected the seduction theory. He rejected the theory of the splitting of the ego into dissociated identities when he rejected dissociation in favor of repression, and when he rejected the reality of the abuse.

It's a package. Abuse is real. Dissociation is real. The ego splits into separate compartments.

The Fraudian package goes like this. The abuse memories are Oedipal fantasies. Dissociation is not real. The ego does not split into separate compartments as a natural defense. MPD is rare or non-existent. Repression rules.

The False Memory Bozos can't even get their Fraud straight. This would be amusing if these people weren't so dangerous politically. Domestic terrorists.

According to Ofshe, Piper, McHugh and Spanos, there is no real splitting of consciousness. There is no real repression. Therefore no real MPD. Error alert! Error alert! Scholarship violation!

Repression doesn't involve a splitting of the ego. Repression involves unconsciously pushing traumatic memories down into the unconscious. Out of the ego. Out of conscious awareness. They become *repressed memories*.

According to the False Memory Police, the alter personalities in MPD are not real. The patients are just acting. The actor doesn't realize she is acting, but there is no real amnesia barrier in the conscious mind. There is no real split in the ego. The ego just takes on different roles to please the Nutty Professor, Dr. Colin Ross. Part of the role enactment is to pretend you have amnesia, but you don't really.

OK. Fine. There is no real split in the ego. No real dissociation. No real amnesia barriers between alter personalities. No alter personalities, really. Fine. In that case, there can be no recovered memory therapy. No memories were ever lost. They were held in the ego the whole time. Dr. Ross must be innocent as charged.

Dr. Ross claims that the memories were held by alter personalities, which are compartments in the ego. Repression theory is not required by Dr. Ross because, in his patients, nothing was unconsciously pushed down into the unconscious, the id. In his patients, the information has been held in the ego all the time. If the alters are just acts put on by the ego, then there are no recovered memories. The memories have never left the ego.

"Get it, colleagues? Can you follow the logic? Or does it seem, "twisted" to you, Officer McHugh?"

Let me repeat, if MPD is not real, then Colin Ross' patients have never repressed any memories. They do not recover memories in therapy and are not treated with recovered memory therapy. The memories have been held in the ego all the time. This is the case if MPD is not real.

On the other hand, if MPD is real, there still are no repressed memories. Repression theory is not relevant. There are no repressed memories to recover. Recovered memory therapy cannot be relevant to the treatment of MPD. Either way.

It does not matter if MPD is real or not real. Either way, the memories have been held in the ego all the time. They have never been repressed and therefore cannot be recovered.

"Give it up, boys. Give it up. Your propaganda is threadbare."

"Threadbare. Threadbare. Nyah, nyah, nyah."

"Paul McHugh's grandmother wears Army boots."

In psychiatry, that last remark gets rated as juvenile if it's made against the False Memory Police. As a persuasive argument if it's made against MPD.

Yet another problem. Officer Spanos makes a differentiation between *role enactment* and *simulation*. The other Officers and Spanos himself ignore this distinction when pounding on MPD. Simulation is conscious, deliberate, done on purpose, under full control. If asked, I could simulate believing in the stupid arguments of the False Memory Police, for instance.

Role enactment is more subtle. It has the quality of being "unconscious," one might say. The person absorbed into the role enactment actually believes it himself. The rules for the enactment are provided by the culture, context, cues of others present, and even deliberate training by others. But simulation and role enactment are different things.

Spanos believes that iatrogenic MPD patients (= all of them) actually believe they have MPD. So do their deluded therapists. The iatrogenic MPD patient is not *simulating*. On this point Spanos and Ross are in agreement.

The Police trot out the Spanos experiments on college students as proof that MPD is iatrogenic. What did Officer Spanos do?

Being a Psychology Professor, he did experiments on normal college students. He got a bunch of college students and asked them to act like they had MPD. They did. So what? What does this prove?

Nothing. Zero. Goose egg.

Why? Because the psychology students did not *role enact* MPD. They *simulated* it. None of the college students actually believed they had MPD. None had symptoms after the experiment was over. They were perfectly aware of what they were doing.

So here is the brain wave logic. Spanos sets up a distinction between simulation and role enactment. He gets college students to simulate MPD. In his mind, this proves that 100% of cases of MPD are role enactments. The False Memory Police give him a standing ovation.

How do you deal with people like that? Can they be that stupid? No. What is going on, then? How can such ignorance get published and applauded in the shrink literature?

I have the answer. It's The Great Psychiatry Scam. Psychiatry does not work by the rules of science or serious scholarship.

"I am going to count backwards from ten to one. When I get to one, you will be wide awake and fully alert. You will be able to think rationally. You will stop all these trance logic arguments against MPD forever. And you will feel calm, happy, and confident."

"Ten, nine, eight, seven, six, five, four, three, two. . ."

"Sorry, boys. Guess you'll have to wake up on your own."

Let's take one more peek at Officer Ofshe's tactics. *Making Monsters*, page 72.

One of the sub-strategies of the Police Attack is to beat therapists up for saying that sexual abuse causes eating disorders. More evidence of therapists' stupid beliefs, theories and practices. More reason for therapists to dig for non-existent abuse memories, and in the process create false memories.

Officer Harrison Pope and his pal, James Hudson published a paper in the *American Journal of Psychiatry* in 1992. In it they review all the studies on rates of childhood sexual abuse in eating disorders and show that the overall rate isn't very high. The data are clear. The overall rates of reported childhood sexual abuse in eating disorders are not that high. Fact. Fact not disputed by Dr. Ross.

Pope and Hudson are heroes and False Memory Club Members in the Cold War against MPD. According to Officer Ofshe, the Pope and Hudson analysis shows that:

> *In other words, sexual abuse was no more likely in the life histories of eating disorder patients than it was in the histories of other patients.*

Dr. Ross agrees. Officer Ofshe continues:

> *Remarkably, a second study that compared patients diagnosed with eating disorders to three groups of patients with panic disorders, schizophrenia, and multiple personality disorder, respectively, made the same mistake. By not ensuring that the control groups were matched for gender, the slight increased rate of sexual-abuse histories among the bulimic and anorexic subjects became meaningless.*

Seems reasonable. There's a teensy weensy tiny problem, though. I'm almost too shy to mention it.

The study of eating disorder, panic disorder, schizophrenia and multiple personality patients was published by me in 1989. Although Officer Ofshe references me in his book, he leaves out this reference and doesn't mention that the study is by me. My study is quoted in the 1992 Pope and Hudson paper where it forms part of the foundation of the Officers' conclusion that sexual abuse isn't that common in eating disorder patients.

In one paragraph, my study supports Ofshe, Pope and Hudson. In Ofshe's next paragraph, it is dismissed for failing to find any increased rate of sexual abuse in the eating disorder patients.

Hmmm.

What was the title of my paper? "Differences between multiple personality disorder and other diagnostic groups on structured interview."

What was the point of the paper? The MPD patients had much higher rates of dissociative and other symptoms than the other three groups. And much higher rates of reported childhood physical and sexual abuse. The whole point of the paper was that the MPD patients reported more abuse and more symptoms than the other three groups, which did not differ from each other.

The numbers? There were 20 subjects in each group. All were interviewed with the Dissociative Disorders Interview Schedule. Rates of reported childhood sexual abuse were: eating disorders, 20%; schizophrenia, 10%, panic disorder, 10%; MPD, 80%. That was the point. The MPD patients were high. The other three groups were low and not significantly different from each other.

The percentage of subjects in each group who were female were: eating disorders, 100%; schizophrenia, 30%; panic disorder 85%; MPD 100%. The only group that differed significantly from the other three on gender was the schizophrenics.

"Come on baby, let's do the twist. Come on, and it goes like this. Round and around and up and down."

What do Officers Pope and Hudson have to say in their 1992 paper?

> *By contrast, a structured diagnostic interview of established reliability, the Dissociative Disorders Interview Schedule was used by Ross et al. in the second controlled retrospective study we reviewed.*

That's nice. When the DDIS supports the desired conclusion, it gets to be a "structured diagnostic interview of established reliability." Not when it supports a forbidden conclusion, though. Like the validity of MPD as a diagnosis. No, then the DDIS is the work of Satan.

Pope, Hudson and some other pals published another paper in the *American Journal of Psychiatry* in 1999. It was a survey of shrinks for their opinions on MPD and the other dissociative disorders. Of the 301 shrinks who answered the mail out questionnaire, 40% "rated their theoretical orientation as psychodynamic-psychoanalytic." Which means Fraudian. Which means idiot in Officer Ofshe's opinion.

So, when opinions against MPD are solicited, it is fine to be Fraudian as long as you slam MPD. When you're slamming MPD, though, it is good Police procedure to slam and blame Dr. Siggy.

This makes sense. At the Mad Hatter's Tea Party. By the way, in the survey,

78% of shrinks said MPD should be included in future editions of DSM. Seven per cent said, "No Opinion" and 15% said it shouldn't be included.

What do the data say?

15% 15% 15% 15% 15% 15% 15% 15%.

Fifteen per cent of shrinks responded, "should not be included at all." This is called a small minority. In politics, a 78% Yes vote is called a landslide victory.

What do the False Memory Police conclude from their data?

> *In any event, our findings suggest that DSM-IV fails to reflect a consensus of board-certified American psychiatrists regarding the diagnostic status and scientific validity of dissociative amnesia and dissociative identity disorder. This finding is perhaps not surprising, given the existing evidence of controversy surrounding these disorders. This evidence includes the growing literature acknowledging this controversy (1,2,7), the recent closure of several major dissociative disorders treatment units, the sharp shifts in the features of these disorders as described in successive editions of DSM, and published arguments that dissociative amnesia and dissociative identity disorder lack the degree of empirical support normally required for most other entities in DSM-IV (8,9).*

References 1, 2, 8, and 9 are by False Memory Policemen. Eight is Pope, Hudson and colleagues. They are saying that their own conclusion supports their own conclusion.

Reference 9 is Officer Piper's book *Hoax and Reality*, published in 1997. In that book Officer Piper says that MPD, now called DID (dissociative identity disorder) is not supported by scientific evidence concerning its reliability and validity.

There are two structured interviews for diagnosing MPD/DID. The DDIS, developed by me. And the SCID-D, developed by Marlene Steinberg. Marlene Steinberg isn't even referenced in *Hoax and Reality*. The SCID-D isn't even mentioned. Marlene first presented the SCID-D in public in 1987, first published about its reliability in the *American Journal of Psychiatry* in 1990, and published an entire book about it at the American Psychiatric Press in 1995. Her research on the SCID-D has been funded by the National Institutes of Mental Health. She was a Professor at Yale when she had the NIMH grant.

"Officers! Come on."

"Step it up. You can do it. I see better scholarship in high school reports about multiple personality."

"Come on. Think positive now. You can make it."

"No? OK. Take a break. Try again later, maybe."

This chapter is the story of being the target of a vicious psychological warfare campaign. One designed to destroy my reputation. Take away my license. Reduce my net worth to zero. Reduce my children's college fund to zero. This is the desired outcome when the False Memory Police take their dog and pony show into the courtroom. A jury award far above my malpractice insurance policy limits. Meaning I would personally owe millions.

That's how drive-by shootings work in psychiatry.

"I'd rather be a multiple personality nut. I'd rather starve to death than sink to the level of the False Memory Police. I spit in your faces. Poop on your porch."

I remember one day in Norman Wells in 1971, I was lifting up some sections of wooden sidewalk with a forklift. They needed to be replaced. I was in front of the home of one of the oil company employees.

A four-year old boy I knew well ran out of the house and started yelling at me. He was very angry that I was tearing up his beloved sidewalk. You could see the anger, resentment and upset building up to explosive levels. All of a sudden he unleashed his ultimate invective.

"Chicken head!"

In psychiatry, that would be considered a good argument against the validity of multiple personality disorder.

43

90% OF ACADEMIC PRODUCTIVITY

I edited the Research Newsletter of the Department of Psychiatry, University of Manitoba for a number of years before moving to Texas in late 1991. I kept track of all grants, publications, grant agency reviewing and journal reviewing by the one hundred or so psychiatrists in the Province of Manitoba.

When I started out as an Assistant Professor in 1985, my University of Manitoba salary was $1,500.00. This was the amount of my salary contributed by the University of Manitoba to support my academic activities. These could include research, teaching, writing, and administration. The University of Manitoba gave the Department of Psychiatry an annual block grant of $800,000.00 out of the entire University budget. This was allocated internally by the Department of Psychiatry.

The rest of my salary came from a draw from the Fee Pool at the Department of Psychiatry, St. Boniface Hospital. The Fee Pool was funded by the joint clinical billings of the Medical Staff. None of the clinical income went directly to me or the other shrinks. From 1985 to 1991, I generated more revenue for the Fee Pool than I was paid.

From 1985 to 1988 I received 0.001875 of the Department of Psychiatry's University budget. During this period, I produced 90% of the professional papers in peer-reviewed journals. Ninety percent of the reviewing for professional journals and grant agencies. Ninety per cent of the research grants and drug company contract dollars.

In 1998, I received a job offer from the former chairman of the Department of Psychiatry at St. Boniface Hospital, who had moved to Calgary. As a result of this offer, I was able to negotiate an increase in my University money to $30,000.00. I continued to generate 90% of the academic output of the Department of Psychiatry and now received 0.0375 of the revenue.

The University money did not affect my personal salary. Its purpose was to free up time for academic work. To free me from the obligation to generate fee-for-service revenue for the Fee Pool. During my years at St. Boniface I did as much teaching as anyone in the Department. Except for 1991, I did as much clinical work as anyone.

I discussed this situation with both the Chairman of the Department of Psychiatry and the Dean of Medicine. Both agreed that my figures on academic productivity were accurate. Neither did anything.

During this time period, a bright resident decided to spend two years doing research at the National Institutes of Mental Health in Bethesda, Maryland. Which he did. To support the two years, he applied for money from sources within the Province of Manitoba and from the Medical Research Council of Canada. He wanted to measure brain electrical activity in people with schizophrenia.

This resident received over $100,000.00 in overlapping grant funding, including full salary support from the Medical Research Council. He had to turn down money, he was offered so much. He had no publications and no Ph.D. While in Bethesda, he completed one research subject in his EEG protocol and published nothing.

When this man returned to Manitoba to become a full-time Staff Member in the Department of Psychiatry, he was given an undisclosed but generous University salary support, equal to or greater than mine. The Department of Psychiatry bought him a special research EEG machine. He never used it, never did any research, and went into full-time clinical private practice a year later.

I have nothing against this guy personally. All power to him. He is a bright and pleasant individual.

But I got the message. The value the Department of Shrinkiatry, the Dean of Medicine and the University of Manitoba placed on my work. Got it loud and clear.

Howdy, Texas.

44

STRANGE EVENTS IN CHICAGO

The International Society for the Study of Multiple Personality & Dissociation was formed in 1984. Its first Annual Meeting was in Chicago in the fall of 1984. I have presented a paper at the meeting every year from 1984 to 2006. In 1984, however, I couldn't afford to go to Chicago, so someone had to present my paper for me.

The Chicago meetings were like journeys to Mecca. At first. There I was in Winnipeg, Manitoba, Canada, the only shrink west of Ontario diagnosing and treating MPD. Alone in the frozen North.

When I went to Chicago, suddenly I was surrounded by hundreds of like-minded colleagues. People who took the diagnosis seriously. It was an oasis in a barren professional world. I got to meet people whose papers I had read. When I was President in 1994, I shortened the name of the organization to the ISSD, the International Society for the Study of Dissociation. This change in name was supported by a 95% 'Yes' vote from the membership.

The Chicago meetings provided a major boost to my career. I formed research collaborations, learned a lot, networked, and visited the Chicago Art Institute. It was great. A number of medical students were funded by the University of Manitoba to present their summer research in Chicago. The studies were later published.

In 1988 something started to go wonky. SRA raised its ugly head. Satanic Ritual Abuse.

I remember sitting in the hotel banquet room in a crowd of eight hundred people, watching the hysteria. Female therapists stood up at the plenary session and denounced the male chauvinist pig, high-degreed professionals who were running the meeting. Denounced them for not doing anything about SRA.

The women shouted out that Satanists were kidnapping and murdering our children. Satanists were in the hotel and had infiltrated the Meeting. Some groups of women were holding meetings in hotel rooms to talk about it. The male chauvinist pigs were doing nothing. It was an outrage. You had to believe the children.

It was full-tilt hysteria. A lot of uteri in the room were wandering.

1988 was the year Geraldo aired a two-part special on Satanism, which was his highest rated program ever. The tidal wave had come in. The SRA craze was up and running.

I had heard about SRA for the first time in 1986 when a patient claimed to have been involved. She claimed the cult was monitoring her by ESP from British Columbia and had recently mailed her a human hand. Cult members watched her in drug stores and gave her secret hand signals to reprogram her. Her therapist believed all this 100%.

I tried to work with this woman for six months. She was the most stressful person I ever worked with. Her therapist used to dream about her. She dreamed about her therapist. Thing was, they told me they had the same dreams. Together, both confirmed that they met in common dreams, which both remembered the same way the next morning.

The woman fired me as a consultant after I set some limits on her manipulation. She didn't like it when I told her and her therapist, at the same time, that their dreaming the same dreams was a boundary problem. Evidence of over-involvement by the therapist.

A couple of other patients had made vague, half-hearted efforts to cook up some SRA fantasies and offer them to me. By the time I left Canada at the end of October, 1991, I had still not seen a full-tilt SRA case. As of October, 1991, no patient of mine claimed to have eaten a baby. The hysteria never hit the Canadian mid-West the way it did the United States. I treated MPD before the SRA hysteria wave, during it, and continue to do so after it has pretty much fizzled out.

Many, many therapists went completely off the deep end on SRA. Not a few. Lots. I met therapists who had post-traumatic stress disorder from listening to their clients' SRA stories. They believed absolutely that their clients had been the Brides of Satan in Satanic ceremonies, and had eaten babies. Estimates of the number of babies sacrificed by Satanists in North America per year ran as high as 50,000.

There was no evidence, of course. I noticed a habit of thought in my colleagues. Cattle mutilations became part of the hysteria. I learned that the cattle were not being mutilated by aliens or the CIA. It was Satanists.

My colleagues solved a problem concerning cattle mutilations. How was it that the surgically dissected cow corpses were found in fields with no tracks, surrounding mess, or blood spillage? Could be aliens. There were no crop circles around, though. The solution? It was brilliant, really.

There were two answers. One, the cult had slung the cows in from other locations by helicopter. Two, the cult had a special truck with a boom arm several hundred yards long which they used to deposit the cows in fields.

You can't fault my colleagues for lack of imagination.

I had noticed the same habit of thought in Catholic theologians, when I read Bertrand Russell's *History of Western Philosophy*. When Galileo invented the telescope, he looked through it and noticed there were mountains on the moon. This observation threatened the structure of the medieval universe. Why? Because according to Ptolemy, all heavenly bodies and their motions are perfectly spherical. This is part of God's plan. Dislodge one micro-detail, and the whole structure might collapse.

The Catholic Church did not sit by idly, watching the collapse of the universe. Heroically, they intervened. Theologians forbade Catholics to look through telescopes. Demons surrounding the telescope were distorting the light, making it appear that there were mountains on the moon when there weren't. Therefore if you looked through a telescope, you were willfully consorting with Satan. This is not a good plan if there are Inquisitors in the neighborhood checking up on you.

As a back-up strategy, a Father Clavius invented a transparent crystalline substance, gave it a Latin name, and said it fills up the valleys on the moon. The moon, therefore, is in fact perfectly spherical. Ptolemy, God and the revenues of the Catholic Church were saved.

Father Clavius was an early psychiatrist.

I noticed reading the *Malleus Maleficarum* that the Inquisitors were more hysterical than the witches. One Bishop described a case on which he consulted. A witch had put a spell on a young man, resulting in his genitals vanishing. The Bishop reported to the Inquisitor, who reported it to the authors of the *Malleus*, who reported it to me as fact, that the Bishop had looked in the man's pants and observed that his genitals were missing.

The Bishop told the man to go confront the witch. Which he did. This broke the spell. The Bishop then checked the man again, and his genitals were back.

A few hundred years later, Dr. Fraud called this *castration anxiety*. He renamed the witches. Now there were hysterics.

I'm confused. Which witch is which? Which witch needs a hysterectomy? For hysteria. Hersteria. The therapist or the client? Inquisitor or witch? Dr. Fraud or patient? It's so hard to tell. Oh, well. What the Hell. Meet you there. At the Meeting. Of minds and souls. Down there in Hell. I mean Chicago. Dante was there, once, I think. Long ago. Not so long, really.

I got it out of my system by writing my book, *Satanic Ritual Abuse*. Writing that book was not a Satanic ritual. It was just regular bulimia. Vomiting up the evil energy inserted in me by the hysterical shamans. Or witches. Or Master's level therapists. Or whoever they were.

You have to admire these people for extravagance. Over the next few years I listened to far too many women tell me they had been in training to be a High Priestess in the Cult.

I never did meet anyone who was in training to be a Low Priestess.

The False Memory Police were thrilled to death by the SRA craze. It gave them ammunition to pound on MPD for over a decade.

During the 1990's, I'd say it was a 50:50 split between the ISSD people and the False Memory Police. Each side was equally dangerous. Together, they put on a little party that could have killed MPD as a psychiatric diagnosis. I don't know which was a greater threat, the fascist propaganda of the Police, or the ridiculous hysteria of the therapists. Both groups were equally block-headed. No science. No scholarship. Hysteria and counter-hysteria. Witches and Inquisitors. It's the same old dance.

The Police needed the therapists to be as extreme as possible. Many therapists obliged. The therapists needed the Police to be as brutal and fascist as possible. The Police obliged. It was a dance. Both sides were deaf extremists. The absurdity of each side affirmed the moral outrage of the other. The deafness. The holier than thou-ness. Which is typical of Inquisitors. Each group was the other's Inquisitor and simultaneously the other's Witch.

The researchers with data ran for cover. A couple quit the ISSD. Got out of Nam altogether. I stayed deep in country. It was an interesting tour of duty.

On www.amazon.com, once upon a time, not long, long ago, were two reviews of my *Satanic Ritual Abuse* book. One right after the other. One reviewer criticized me for not believing the survivors and accused me of being a false memory syndrome advocate. The other reviewer lambasted me for being a typical recovered memory therapist causing false memories of SRA. This is a true memory of actual stupidity in polarized fanatics. The dance is polarized, ugly, and destructive, no matter how much SRA is actually going on in North America. Or Vietnam.

45

THE BOOK PUBLISHING LOTTERY

I decided to write a book about multiple personality. It was published by John Wiley & Sons in 1989 as *Multiple Personality Disorder: Diagnosis, Clinical Features and Treatment*. The second edition came out in 1997. Since MPD was changed to DID in DSM-IV in 1994, the title of the second edition is *Dissociative Identity Disorder: Diagnosis, Clinical Features, and Treatment of Multiple Personality.*

Not many doctors write textbooks that go into a second edition. I'm proud of that fact.

When I started writing the book, I sent proposals to a dozen academic publishers. Only one editor at one house was interested. Herb Reich at Wiley. Thank you 1.2 million times over, Herb. Herb also edited my other book, *Pseudoscience in Biological Psychiatry*. I increase my thank yous to 3.8 million.

It was just luck. If I had not included Wiley on my list, the book might never have been published. I remember Herb telling me that 90% of Wiley's professional texts sell between 3000 and 7000 copies. I would be doing well if I entered that range. So far the two editions have sold around 22,000 copies. Yet a dozen publishers declined it.

The first edition came out just before the 1989 Chicago Annual Meeting. I told Herb the book would probably sell at least 300 copies, maybe over 500. He said that about 1% of attendees at a conference buy a given book. If there were going to be about 800 people there, one hundred copies of the book would be way more than enough. These one hundred copies were all sold by the end of coffee break on the first morning of the Meeting.

I was lucky. I caught the wave at the right time. There are only two comprehensive textbooks on diagnosis and treatment of MPD, mine and Frank Putnam's. Both came out in 1989. The need for the book would have been minimal a decade earlier. Actually, I couldn't have written the book a decade earlier. Not just because I hadn't finished medical school yet. There wasn't enough literature or clinical experience to support such a book.

Critical mass was required. It was reached in the second half of the 1980's. A critical mass of readers, an Annual Conference, a Professional Society, a professional literature. A decade earlier, none of this existed. MPD wasn't even an official separate diagnosis until DSM-III hit in 1980. I finished medical school in 1981. Finished psychiatry training in 1985. Was one of the leading experts in the world on multiple personality by 1989. Seems like I was doing something right.

How did I find time to write the book? The McEwen Building that housed the Department of Psychiatry at St. Boniface Hospital flunked its government air quality inspection. It was shut down for the summer of 1988 for renovations. During this period I did no inpatient work and had no other duties to pick up. This gave me the free time to do most of the writing.

I used my $2,500.00 royalty advance to buy my first computer, which I used to write the book.

People think I am wealthy because of my books. My earnings per hour from my books are less than I would get paid for doing therapy. Take *The Osiris Complex*. It sells for about $20.00. Of this, the publisher gets 60% and the bookstore gets 40%. The publisher gets $12.00. Of this, I get 10%, $1.20. It took me hundreds of hours to write and has sold about 6000 copies. You do the math.

Nevertheless, the career spin-off from the books has been phenomenal. In terms of speaking engagements, professional contacts, research collaborations. Thank you, thank you, thank you, Herb Reich. And thank you, thank you, thank you Virgil Duff at the University of Toronto Press. Virgil guided *The Osiris Complex* and *Satanic Ritual Abuse* through the labyrinth of academic review and committee approval. Herb and Virgil. May the Inquisitors pass by your houses and the houses of your children.

In the current millennium I have added another name to my list of editors: Bob Geffner at Haworth Press. What about Bob? His children too should be passed over by the Inquisitors.

46

THE SQUEEZE PLAY

There was trouble in Denmark. Or Canada. Or wherever I was. By early 1988, the squeeze play had begun. I was the main squeeze. When I discussed the political situation at St. Boniface Hospital with the Chairman of the Department of Psychiatry in 1991, his comment was, "You're being squeezed out."

He didn't do anything about it. But that was his comment.

In case of confusion: The University of Manitoba, Department of Psychiatry had a Chairman. He was Head of the overall Department. He was based at the other major teaching hospital, the Health Sciences Centre. Normally, this would be the Health Sciences Center, but Canadians can't spell too good.

The Head of Psychiatry at St. Boniface Hospital reported to the Chairman of the University Department of Psychiatry. Two separate people. The Chairman also filled the position of Head of Psychiatry at the Health Sciences Centre. This was cool, because he got to report to himself.

I founded the Dissociative Disorders Clinic at St. Boniface Hospital in 1988. At the same time, I stopped being Medical Director of the Anxiety Disorders Clinic. People thought the Dissociative Disorders Clinic was some kind of big official entity. Not quite.

The Dissociative Disorders Clinic consisted of half of myself, one full time research nurse, Geri Anderson, and stolen pieces of the M3 Social Worker, Pam Gahan. That was it. Geri was funded entirely by the Fee Pool for a number of years, then I got her on grants. These covered about half her salary.

Each year, we found out in late June whether Geri would be funded again starting July 1. In 1989, I applied to the Government of Manitoba for funding for one full-time nursing position. This application went through two levels of Committees within the Department of Psychiatry, then through Committee levels in the hospital as a whole. From there it was submitted to the Government. Shortly before I left Canada in late 1991, the Director of Nursing estimated that it would be another three years before I got a decision. She said the answer would be, "No."

This is the value the medical system and the Government of Manitoba put on my work. Compared to a surgeon, who has a bunch of OR nurses paid for by the Government so he can do his work. I'm not whining. These are just the facts.

The first research grants I received were small ones from the Manitoba Mental Health Research Council. I also reviewed grants for them. From there I stepped up to a larger grant from the Manitoba Health Research Council. From there I stepped up to a national level grant from the National Health Research Development Program. Then one element of the squeeze play started.

The Provincial funding agencies regarded themselves as start-up funders. They supported researchers early in their careers. You were expected to graduate to the Medical Research Council of Canada. My Provincial money was going to dry up in the early 1990's. I knew that. My Federal money would never come on line.

There was no way in Hell I would ever get money from the Medical Research Council. For research on MPD. Are you kidding? Or from other Federal sources. It wasn't coming from the Hospital or the University.

When it comes to medical research grants, psychiatry is at the bottom of the totem pole. Way, way down at the bottom. Within psychiatry, biological research is at the top. Psychosocial research is at the bottom of psychiatry. Way, way down. Within psychosocial psychiatric research, MPD is at the bottom. Way, way down.

"Give it up, already, Colin."

I got the message.

In 1988, Pam Gahan went away with her Professor husband to Europe on a sabbatical year. Chop one arm off the Dissociative Disorders Clinic. The amount of Clinical Service we provided patients on M3 peaked in 1988, and was down to 10% of 1988 levels by 1991. Pam was never allowed to devote time to the work when she returned. It was blocked, fought and discouraged through myriad little social mechanisms. I was not able to solve these system problems.

For instance, one day I referred an MPD inpatient to the Outpatient Department for follow-up. The shrink who was Director of the Outpatient Department handed the written referral back to me and told me the Outpatient Department was no longer accepting MPD cases. If I diagnosed these people, they had nowhere to go. There had been no prior discussion with me on this change in policy.

When I tried to discuss this unilateral change in policy at the next Medical Staff Meeting, I was given condescending education on the fact that this was not a change in *policy*. Policy change requires a series of Committee meetings, resolutions and written changes in Department policy. So I should stop complaining that a policy had been changed. No policy had been changed.

When I said, OK, an operating procedure has been changed, I was told there was no more time to discuss the matter. I pointed out that all I had to do was diagnose the depression and not mention the MPD, then these people would be accepted.

No one cared. Or got upset. It was my fault. I caused the problem. On to other matters.

The people with MPD were admitted by other psychiatrists in the Department while they were on call at the ER. They had not been seen previously by me and had never received an MPD diagnosis before I met them. They were admitted to M3 and assigned to me. I was stuck with the ethical responsibility, the liability, and the referral problem. The psychiatrists on call got the cases off their hands by admitting them. I couldn't dump them back. It was a squeeze play.

You might think it unpleasant to speak of dumping patients. That is the vocabulary doctors use.

Later, the Outpatient Department expanded their non-acceptance policy to include borderline personality disorder. Or no, not policy. Operating procedure. Surgery without anesthesia. I did not experience these developments as encouragement for my work.

For a while, I admitted MPD patients from other Provinces to St. Boniface. This too was shut down and forbidden. My resources to do my work were dwindling. At the beginning of 1991, I got off M3 altogether. It was too stressful dealing with all the political shit there. And watching the professional incompetence.

I got squeezed all the way to Texas. I left Manitoba at a considerable ejection velocity. No one had sued me in the six years I worked there. I was not kicked out. No one had the balls to directly dismiss me. I was squeezed out. The shrinks engineered it with complete deniability.

Canadians like to lament the fact that there is a brain drain from Canada to the United States. No one is moving from Harvard to Winnipeg to reverse the flow. In my case, it wasn't a brain drain. It was a brain expulsion. Right down the toilet, out the sewage system of St. Boniface Hospital, and onto a commercial jet aircraft.

Winnipeg is a third world country. But it has a very efficient sewage disposal system. In sixteen years I have not been invited back to give Grand Rounds at the Department of Psychiatry, Faculty of Medicine, University of Manitoba, Winnipeg, Manitoba, Canada.

True fact: I published as many papers in *The American Journal of Psychiatry* in the 1990's than the boys at Harvard and Yale. Second true fact: the shrinks in the Peg don't want to hear from Colin Ross.

"He ain't got nothin' they want. He ain't got shit."

"No, no, no, Cecil. Can't use that language at the Club. Simply can't. You know the official facts in the case. Colin Ross left Winnipeg because he wanted to."

"Yes, quite, Basil. Jolly good thing for Winnipeg it was, too."

"Don't worry, Cecil. There is a backup strategy in place. The False Memory Police will start a rumor he left in disgrace."

"Jolly good, Basil. Disgrace for what?"

"Doesn't matter, Cecil. Doesn't matter."

"Quite."

"You know what I always say, Cecil?"

"What's that, Basil?"

"Walk softly and carry a fecal stick."

"Quite. It's jolly handy for beating Colin Ross with, I must say."

Fading, fading. Go to black. The End.

The Great Psychiatry Scam was filmed on location in Winnipeg, Manitoba. Any resemblance of the characters portrayed to real people is purely coincidental. Why? The shrinks aren't real. Or can't get real. Or won't.

"It ain't my problem anymore."

"Quite, Basil. Quite."

Fade to credits. Out-takes of Winnipeg in mid-January, 34 degrees below. Cut to Dallas at 67 degrees Fahrenheit. Colin Ross sits by a creek watching the water. Fade to black. Up music. The Rolling Stones song, *Paint It Black* is heard.

47

SPEX EXAM, FLUNKING THE JURISPRUDENCE EXAM

There are two private companies that provide MCQ exams for medical students and interns. Both companies are based in the U.S. One exam is called FLEX. The other is called the National Boards. These two companies provide standard MCQ testing that is used by State Medical Boards in the U.S. for licensing. You have to have either National Boards or FLEX in most states in order to get a license from the State Board of Medical Examiners in that particular state. This applies if you are emigrating from Canada.

You have to get a Visa from the State Department to work in the U.S., but you are not classified as a Foreign Medical Graduate if you're Canadian. So you don't have to take the USFMG MCQ exam. If you're coming in from any other country, you have to take this much tougher MCQ exam.

The LMCC exam is the Canadian MCQ exam you do to get your medical license in Canada. It is a national Canadian exam. You also do MCQ exams internally within your own University to get your M.D. But you have to get your LMCC in order to practice medicine in Canada. An M.D. alone isn't enough.

At the University of Alberta, everyone took the National Boards. Hardly anyone took FLEX. I passed my National Boards, which are in three stages. End of second year med school. End of med school. Part way through internship year, also called Post-Graduate Year I, or PGY-I.

Just my luck. Only three state Medical Boards in the U.S. required FLEX in 1991. Texas, Louisiana and the Virgin Islands. In all other states my National Boards were OK. Because I was also looking at a job offer in northern Virginia at the same time, I applied for Virginia and Texas licenses simultaneously. I got my Virginia license in three weeks. Texas took me five months.

I passed the SPEX exam first try. The SPEX is a sub-version of the FLEX that asks only about clinical medicine, not about biochemistry and other arcane material from first year med school. None of which real doctors can remember. I could get away with just the SPEX because I had been out of medical school for ten years. The full FLEX would have been a torture rack.

The SPEX was three half-days of MCQs on all of medicine, surgery, obstetrics-gynecology, pediatrics and psychiatry. I studied several hundred hours for the SPEX and answered about five thousand practice MCQs from booklets you can buy. Sailed through. I passed the SPEX again in 2003, I am pleased to report

– you have to redo it every ten years to keep your passing status current.

Not so with the Medical Jurisprudence Exam. The Jurisprudence Exam is 50 MCQs on all aspects of medicine and the law. The Texas State Board of Medical Examiners administers it. For study, they send you a pamphlet and information for ordering two Jurisprudence Exam Study Guides, both prepared by Texas law firms.

I ordered one and studied my butt off. Flew to Austin. Sat the Jurisprudence exam. Flunked. The woman who told me I had flunked asked me which Study Guide I had used. She told me to get the other one on the way back to the airport, and gave me the address where I could buy it.

It turned out there were numerous questions on the Jurisprudence Exam, the answers for which are in the second Study Guide but not the first. Armed with the necessary info, I passed on my second try.

During four years of med school and four years of shrink training in Canada, I received zero education on Medical Jurisprudence. No seminars, lectures, handouts, readings, textbook passages or MCQs. Medical Jurisprudence didn't exist. I relied completely on the pamphlet and the Study Guide.

The Jurisprudence Exam includes MCQs such as: The Board of The Texas State Board of Medical Examiners consists of which of the following:

A. Six MDs, 3 DOs, 3 lay people.
B. Nine MDs, 3 DOs.
C. Nine MDS, 3 DOs, 3 lay people.
D. Six MDs, 6 DOs, 3 lay people.

DO = Doctor of Osteopathy, a category that doesn't even exist in Canada.

The lawless wild west! Every man for himself! Turns out there's a lot of law in Texas. A lot more than there is in Canada. Or Virginia. Virginia didn't have a Jurisprudence Exam. Not that a Jurisprudence Exam is a bad idea. Studying for it is the only education in medical jurisprudence I have ever received from a medical institution.

Failing the Jurisprudence Exam is a little stressful when you are just about to put your house on the market in Winnipeg, and have already resigned your position as an Associate Professor of Psychiatry, Faculty of Medicine, University of Manitoba, Winnipeg, Manitoba, Canada.

When I handed in my resignation in June, the Chairman of the Department of Psychiatry said he was going to force me to give him six months notice. I called his bluff, and left in five. Without consequences. Never to be invited back.

The beat goes on.

IV. SHRINK IN TEXAS

48

A TRIP TO MACON

In four years of shrink training at the University of Manitoba, and five-and-a-half years as a Professor, the Chairman of the Department of Psychiatry never once called me to his office for any reason. Never initiated a contact with me of any kind. Despite the fact I published more as a resident than any shrink in the Province of Manitoba. Despite the fact I generated 90% of the academic productivity of the Department.

On November 1, 1991 I started work as Medical Director of the Dissociative Disorders Unit at Charter Hospital of Dallas. Which was located in Plano, Texas, not Dallas. The first thing I did was give a presentation at the Annual Meeting of the Texas Psychological Association in San Antonio. There were more presentations on trauma and dissociation at that meeting than in national meetings of the Canadian Psychiatric Association and the Canadian Psychological Association. By far. Also, the restaurants served better Tex-Mex food.

The next weekend, Charter Medical Corporation flew me to corporate headquarters in Macon, Georgia. The Administrator of Charter Dallas and I flew to Atlanta, then drove a rental car to Macon. There I met personally with three VPs, the CEO and the owner of a corporation with a billion dollars annual revenue. I talked to them about my vision for the future of trauma and dissociation, from clinical, research and business perspectives.

All the people I met at Charter Corporate were friendly and cordial. They welcomed me aboard personally. Shook my hand. Told me I had a good administrator.

At Charter Dallas I had a fully staffed specialty Unit with personnel I could train. I trained them. They responded well. I had doctors who believed in MPD and were willing to treat it. Patients came from all over the United States. I earned more than I did in Canada and paid way less taxes. The weather was great. The CEO of a corporation traded on the New York Stock Exchange knew me by first name, was aware of my work, and, after I sent it, had a signed copy of my 1989 textbook.

Some people called it Texas. I called it Paradise.

49

WHAT KIND OF INSURANCE POLICY IS THAT?

When I first arrived in The Republic of Texas, I came down with culture shock. Either that or the flu. They have their own language down here. Texans claim to speak English, but they don't.

For instance. In Texan, a liquid material used to lubricate car engines is called *awl*. In Texan, *oil* rhymes with *ya'll*.

In Texas *vehicle* is pronounced *vee hickle*. With a big emphasis on the "h." Weird. Garbage is trash. Holidays are vacations. Serviettes are napkins. The bathroom is the restroom. Cowboys are football players.

There is an almost complete absence of the expression, "Eh," in the speech of Texans. Texans couldn't pronounce "out and about" correctly if their lives depended on it.

At first I was confused by the insurance system. There were so many different kinds of policies with so many different rules. It was bewildering. Some policies had annual caps, some had lifetime caps. Some were indemnity. Some were managed. There were behavioral carve-outs. HMOs. PPOs. Capitated contracts. Cost-based reimbursement. All-inclusive per diems. Medicare Part A and Medicare Part B.

There was pre-certification and retro-review. Case management and utilization review. EAPs, out-of-network providers, DRGs and EMTs. You had to call the EMTs to take you to the med-surg hospital to get your brain straightened out, after listening to all this jargon. There were free-standing psych hospitals, for-profit psych hospitals, not-for-profit psych hospitals, and psych units in med-surg hospitals.

Patients admitted to psych wards in med-surg hospitals did not have their inpatient days deducted from their lifetime Medicare days. Then there was the Medicare Tefra limit. Totally incomprehensible. There was TDH and HCFA and JCAHO. Federal regulators and state regulators. Marketing issues and regulatory issues.

There was market penetration. Then came the management services organizations, the physician networks, the CON states, the non-CON states, Stark I and Stark II, safe harbor provisions, and The Corporate Practice of Medicine Act. The C-Corp and the S-Corp. The PA, the LLP, and the Inc. SEPs,

RIAs and 401Ks.

There was differential managed care penetration in different states. Projections on all of that. Analyses. Five minute plans and five-year plans. FTE ratios, cost-shifting, media buys, disproportionate share reimbursements, RTCs, certified beds and decertified beds, and, every once in a while, a concept you could grasp, like incremental revenue. There were arguments for and against hospitals entering into management services contracts based on incremental revenue, and corporate postures regarding incremental revenue during contract negotiations.

Census-driven contracts are a problem, I learned. Despite the fact that everything in the private for-profit sector is driven by census. ALOS, ADC, payor mix, reimbursed days and non-reimbursed days.

I had to learn this language, in which I am now fluent. It is never spoken in Canada. I have learned concepts like the negative impact on the hospital of managed care patients on cost-based reimbursement, and the consequent necessity of limiting non-Medicare patients to 10% of census in cost-based med-surg psych units.

I was relieved, in my second week at Charter, when I figured out that the Americans didn't understand the system either. I was at a team meeting when one of the shrinks said he didn't understand how a patient's insurance policy worked. The utilization review woman couldn't figure it out either.

I didn't feel like such a fish out of water. Or Canuck out of water. Or Canada. Canuck out of Canada. That's me. The boy from the wheat fields. Down in Dallas trying to figure out the American health care system. Trying not to blow a gasket.

Doing OK so far. I'm a gringo now, a dual personality. I mean citizen.

50

MKULTRA ULTRA PARANOIA

I remember how the CIA stuff started. A little door opened. I looked in. I have not looked back.

I was in the cafeteria in Charter early in 1992. Or maybe December, 1991. Not sure. A patient came up to me with great theater and drama, and an air of paranoia and secrecy. In hushed tones, she asked me to take a document from her. She was scared to have it in her possession. I looked at it, took it, thanked her, and walked away.

I had in my hands a memo from J. Edgar Hoover to the Director of the CIA, Richard Helms about the CIA's mind control program, MKULTRA. This was the first I had heard of MKULTRA. Or CIA mind control programs period. I had never read a spy novel or a book about the CIA. I had heard of the movie, *The Manchurian Candidate*, but I had it confused with the Marlon Brando movie, *The Ugly American*.

I had never been to a lecture about CIA mind control or heard about it from a patient or colleague. I had seen James Bond movies, that was it. I was a total naïve beginner on the subject of CIA mind control.

In the year 2000, I published a book entitled *BLUEBIRD: Deliberate Creation of Multiple Personality by Psychiatrists*. I am now the leading civilian expert in the world on the creation of Manchurian Candidates by intelligence agencies. It has been a long journey.

I am the first person to document that the Manchurian Candidate is not fiction. Previously thought to be fiction, the Manchurian Candidate is now fact. Documented. Proven. Locked down beyond dispute.

Another Winnipeger who looked into intelligence is William Stephenson, the Man Called Intrepid. Also known as The Quiet Canadian.

"Ssshhh. I am trying to be quiet too."

There is a large file on me at the CIA. How do I know? Because I have filed dozens of Freedom of Information Act requests with the CIA. Am I paranoid? No. I make jokes on the phone for the benefit of the people tapping it. I have to do something for them. To relieve their monotony.

Tapping Colin Ross. What a bore. Anyway, I have nothing to hide. I decided a long time ago not to be paranoid. I just decided. It's my policy. Not because there is nothing to fear. It's just that there is nothing to do. What? I'm going to out-fox the CIA? Right. Left. Right. Left, right, left, right. Wrong.

I rely on what I call *The Three Days of the Condor Strategy*. The best security system is to have nothing to hide.

You can run, but you sure can't hide.

51

WACKY THERAPISTS

When I arrived in Dallas, I thought I was in dissociative disorders Paradise. It wasn't till later that I would write *The Inferno*, also known as *The Great Psychiatry Scam*. Joseph Campbell told me not to worry about things. Every hero receives a return ticket to Hades from the Fates. It's part of the job description. As Conductor Campbell reminded me, it is a return ticket. Problem is, while you're in Hades, you can't be sure you'll catch the last train out.

In my case, the last train out is the last sentence of this book. That makes sense, because I wrote the book and I'm a legend in my own mind.

"Want to come in?"

Within a few months of arriving in Dallas, I was under the impression that there were dozens of therapists in Dallas I could refer multiple personality patients to, and who would refer into my program at Charter. Why did I have that delusion?

There were in fact dozens of therapists willing to treat multiple personality. They came to lectures, study groups and conferences. I didn't realize at first that most of them were wacky.

Now I think there are maybe five therapists in Dallas I would refer cases to, at most. I've eliminated 90% of the therapists from my referral list. Why? They are wacked.

For instance, the woman who handed me the MKULTRA memo from J. Edgar Hoover to Richard Helms. Her therapist totally believed, without a doubt, that she had been programmed to be an assassin by the government. He thought that the cult was driving by the hospital in a van equipped with special instruments. The cult van was beaming energy at the patient's head that would trigger her to switch to a programmed assassin personality.

This therapist asked me to write an order in her chart for her to wear a plastic hockey helmet. The purpose of the helmet was to block the rays coming from the van, so she would not be triggered to switch to her assassin personality.

My response was, using a pseudonym for the therapist, "Wacky, if there really was such energy being beamed at your patient, a plastic hockey helmet would have no effect on it."

I thought this was a pretty tricky counter-strategy. I didn't have to get entangled in the therapist's delusional system, but I had an irrefutable reason for not writing the order.

This therapist had not stopped to consider the physics of the situation. If this was really happening, the energy beam was passing through the walls of the van and the walls of the hospital to reach the patient. Then it was passing through her skull to get to her brain. Assuming all this to be real, a plastic hockey helmet would be invisible to the beam.

It took me a few months to figure out just how wacked these therapists are. The same man told me that there were 103,000 practicing Satanists in the Dallas-Fort Worth Metroplex area.

What did the cult have to do with the government? Isn't it obvious? The CIA was contracting with Satanists to create dissociative children by abusing them in Satanic cults. The satanic ritual abuse made the children into multiples. The CIA then used children to build really fancy programmed assassins. Manchurian Candidates.

It isn't easy to get rid of these therapists. They have a right to admit their patients to the hospital and do therapy with them there, once they have been credentialed by the hospital. Credentialing is the hospital procedure for checking a doctor or therapist's qualifications and giving them privileges to work at the hospital. A number of wackos were credentialed at Charter before I arrived in Texas. I was never on the Credentialing Committee.

When I finessed the hockey helmet therapist out of Charter, and stopped him from referring patients there or setting foot inside the building, he sued me for $100,000.00. Sued me personally. This was not covered by my malpractice insurance and would have to come out of my pocket. One hundred grand was most of my net worth at the time.

Charter's lawyers had to talk to Wacky's lawyer to get him to drop the suit. They pointed out the facts about Wacky that would come out in court. Wacky's lawyer backed off.

You think it's easy to get rid of these people? Try it yourself.

The wacky therapists moved around from hospital to hospital. They never stayed in one place long. Either they got kicked out, the dissociative disorders program they worked in got canceled, or they just ran out of patients. Some of them are still treating patients at hospitals in Dallas at the start of the new millennium.

I met a lot of therapists who were way, way out into hysteria about Satanic cults. They believed absolutely that their patients had eaten numerous babies as children. There was zero evidence to support any of these beliefs. And the therapists were paranoid. They thought the cult or the CIA was tapping their phones, planting bugs in their lampshades, parking in their office parking lots, and programming their patients against therapy.

Since the patients had nothing better to do with their time, many of them bought into the delusions. It was a Satanic delusion party.

Many therapists wanted to admit patients to the hospital to get them through Satanic holidays. Such as Halloween. Really in-the-know therapists knew about more obscure Satanic holidays such as September 7. Lots of little girls in your neighborhood have been married to Satan in Satanic ceremonies held on September 7, in case you didn't know.

The wacky therapists could not believe that we had no more patients on our Unit over Halloween than at any other time of the year. The facts did not support their delusion. However, we did have lots of patients who made a big deal about Halloween and got all wound up and scared about it. It was hysteria.

What is hysteria? Hysteria is when a mouse comes into the kitchen. The wife jumps up on a chair and starts screaming hysterically. The husband grabs a broom, kills the mouse, slaps the wife in the face to calm her down, and everything goes back to normal.

Shrinks slap hysterics and borderlines in the face to get them to settle down. The procedure is called *crisis stabilization*. It's really no more than a slap in the face. Done in a professional tone of voice and body language.

The therapists needed a slap on the face, badly.

The wacky therapists became completely obsessed with Satanic cults. It was all they talked about. They talked about programming, codes, triggers, cues, all kinds of things nobody had ever heard of, or had the faintest idea how to treat.

In one case at another hospital, a doctor wrote in the chart that a patient was not allowed to go to an outside dentist because the dentist probably belonged to the cult. The dentist might implant a computer chip in the patient's tooth that the cult would activate by remote means in order to trigger her.

I'm not kidding. This was written in the medical record. I read it as an expert witness for the plaintiff in a malpractice lawsuit against the doctors, hospital and therapists. They totally deserved to have their butts sued. What they did to the patient was insane. Kept her in the hospital for eons to protect her from the cult, then kicked her out when her insurance ran out. The hospital collected over $500,000.00 from the insurance company for that one admission.

This was a pretty good scam. It was shut down by managed care in the early 1990's. But it was a sweet deal for a few years. The hospitals made big bucks and the doctors and therapists got fat contracts, fees and perks. The crazy thing was, therapists actually believed all that shit.

When the False Memory Police started attacking the wacky therapists, the therapists thought they were being persecuted by the cult. They didn't get it. Many still don't in Anno Domini 2007.

I got sucked into the vortex. Since I diagnosed and treated multiple personality, I must be a wacky therapist too. I got tarred with the same brush. In the sunny South this is a serious matter. When you get lynched in Texas, it ain't pretty.

For most of the 1990's, and now in the 2000's, the biggest danger to the survival of multiple personality as a diagnosis has been the therapists who believe in it. They have provided the False Memory Police with all the ammunition they need. The Police use shotguns bored out to yield the maximum scatter radius. Which has made me a primary target.

Thanks a lot, wacky therapists.

52

TOP BRAINS IN THE PROFESSION

The top brains in psychiatry can't debate multiple personality at the level of a good high school debating club. Unbelievable? Yes. A fact? Yes. A literal fact. No exaggeration. A pathetic fact about shrinkdom.

In 1992, I was invited to the Annual Meeting of the Canadian Psychiatric Association to debate whether multiple personality is a valid disorder. George Fraser and I were on the "Yes" side, Harold Merskey and Francois Mai were on the "No" side. All shrinks. Annual Meeting of a national shrink organization. Harold Merskey has published his views on MPD in *The British Journal of Psychiatry*, one of the top shrink journals in the world. Harold is a False Memory Policeman.

Top brains in the profession.

Shrinkmeister Mai started off. He said he was going to take an epidemiological approach to the problem. He said he was going to review four major epidemiological studies done in psychiatry, to see how many cases of MPD they found. These were studies in which large samples of people in the general population received standardized interviews to determine which psychiatric disorders they had had in their lifetimes.

Dr. Mai posed as a scientist, academic and mainstream shrink. He took the scientific side of the debate, leaving the personal belief and fringe lunacy side to me and George.

I had to work hard not to drool or twitch during Dr. Mai's talk. I didn't want anyone to catch on to who I really am.

Dr. Mai described each of the four studies briefly. After describing each one, he would pause and ask a rhetorical question. How many cases of MPD were found in the study?

With a resounding and theatrical emphasis, Dr. Mai declared, each time, "Number of cases of multiple personality. None."

He did this without adjusting his tie. His Mai tie. Or was it a Mai Tai? Not sure.

This was heavy science and debate, all right. I almost got pinned to the mat right there. Disgraced. But I thought and thought and thought. Finally I came up with a rebuttal comment. Ready?

The structured interviews used in these four surveys do not inquire about dissociative symptoms or make dissociative diagnoses.

I'm not joking. I'm not playing around. This is what I have to deal with in psychiatry. These people are politically dangerous.

Imagine a debate at the Canadian Medical Association Annual Meeting. The question is whether myocardial infarction is a legitimate medical diagnosis. The "No" debater reviews four general population surveyors that found no cases of heart attack. But the surveyors never asked about chest pain or trips to the ER.

This was not the Special Olympics. This was the Annual Meeting of the Canadian Psychiatric Association. Top brains in the profession. If you made exactly the same argument about myocardial infarction as Francois Mai made about MPD, you would be investigated. People would think you were demented or impaired. You might lose your license. Not in psychiatry. In psychiatry you get applause.

After the debate was over. . . correction, after the non-debate pseudo-debate was over, there were questions from the audience. One shrink who is hostile to MPD in public asked a few questions. This is a man whose grant applications I have reviewed anonymously, and very favorably. For national Canadian grant agencies.

He asked about the DES, a scale for measuring dissociation. He said it was impossible to use a continuous measure to make a categorical diagnosis. What did he mean? Dr. Smarty Pants was pointing out that I am a stupid scientist who doesn't even know research basics. His tone of voice was condescending and dismissive. The audience nodded approval as he spoke.

"Yeah! Great point! Way to go, Smarty Pants. Nailed Colin Ross good that time!"

The DES is a continuous measure. It yields a score that ranges from zero to one hundred. You can score 7, 16, 42, 83, etc., on the DES. This is as opposed to a dichotomous measure, which yields only two scores, such as "Yes/No", "Sick/ Well" or "Shrink/Normal Person."

Dr. Pants, a true wizard, was pointing out that you can't use the DES to diagnose MPD, because it is a continuous measure. There is no cutoff score above which everyone has MPD and below which no one has it.

Was this news to mentally retarded Colin Ross? No.

I pointed out to Dr. Pants that *five minutes earlier* (!!!!!!!!) I had reviewed a paper in press at *The American Journal of Psychiatry* (published in the next year, 1993) on which I was a co-author. In this study, the DES was administered to 1051 patients, of whom 228 had MPD. Of the patients scoring above 30 on the DES, only 17% had MPD. The rest had other diagnoses.

I had described this study, including the 17% figure, not five minutes earlier. This is the most rigorous data proving Dr. Smarty Pants' point ever published. But he was talking like I was using the DES to diagnose MPD. I told the audience that this was an example of willful refusal to listen, and pointed out to them that I had reviewed these data five minutes earlier.

What do you do with people like that? In pre-school, you put them in time out. But these are licensed physicians with ten-plus years of post-graduate education.

Dr. Pants made another comment. He said it was unscientific to diagnose everybody with a sexual abuse history as having MPD. The implication was that I did so.

I pointed out that in the previous year, 1991, I had published the only epidemiological study on the prevalence of MPD in the general population (which Dr. Mai had not read). I said that in my own study, only 20% of subjects who described childhood sexual abuse met criteria for a dissociative disorder of any kind.

No one in the dissociative disorders field has ever endorsed the ridiculous proposition that everyone with a sexual abuse history must have MPD. The False Memory Police do this all the time. They set up a straw man, knock it down, and claim they have defeated Colin Ross & Co. Trouble is, Colin Ross & Co. don't believe in the straw man to start with.

Question is, are the False Memory Police really that dumb? Or are they intellectual fascists? Maybe both. Officer Merskey is an Official Policeman for the False Memory Syndrome Foundation. Dr. Mai is an amateur.

The audience, I'm sure, thought it was a real good debate. Neck and neck. When I said to a colleague that it wasn't a real debate, he didn't get it and disagreed.

Shrinks do not understand the difference between a disagreement and a debate. They just don't get it. Why? Because they are uneducated. They never got a real English nineteenth century liberal arts education. When it comes to real debate, they are functionally illiterate, to use a current illiterate phrase.

Shrinks cannot tell the difference between an insult and an argument. The four epidemiological studies identifying zero cases of MPD is not an argument. If the person who talked like this was a 19-year old blonde female, we would call her a Valley Girl. An airhead. A bimbo. We certainly wouldn't call her, Professor.

In psychiatry, these are the top brains in the profession.

53

THE FALSE MEMORY POLICE

In North America, the KGB doesn't have to come to your door. The False Memory Police can get in through the Internet. If the Police had their way, I would be in Siberia already. They have been trying to send me there since 1992, when the False Memory Syndrome Foundation was formed.

"Boys. And girls. If at first you don't succeed, try, try again."

Want to hear more about how the top brains in the profession operate? Read on.

In grade five I learned about scientific method. We actually did experiments to help us grasp the basic concepts. Here they are, at grade five level.

In science, you make an observation. Step one. We're all done with Step One now. Got it? We make an observation. OK. Onto step two. This science stuff isn't really so hard, once you get into the swing of it.

Step two. You develop a hypothesis to explain your observation. OK. Slow it down. Relax. You can get it. Step one comes first. Then step two. Observation. Hypothesis.

We wrote these headings down on pieces of paper when we wrote up our experiments. In grade five.

Step three. You design an experiment to test your hypothesis. And you do the experiment.

Step four. You analyze your results to see if they support your hypothesis. We wrote this up under the headings, Observation, Hypothesis, Procedure, Results, Discussion. In grade five. Ten years old. Everyone in the class. Children. Prepubertal. Public school. Winnipeg, Manitoba.

That is how science works. Except in psychiatry. Shrinks have their own special science, they are so advanced.

Here's how shrink science works in the debate about multiple personality.

First we have the observation. MPD is diagnosed more often in North America than elsewhere in the world. This is an observation. A fact. It is an accurate observation. No one in the pseudo-debate disputes the observation.

OK. Ready now. Lift your left foot up in the air. High, high, high. Put it down on number two. Number twokins. Good. You're there! Not so hard, was it?

Step two is called, Hypothesis. This is different from Hypotenuse. Don't get confused.

There are two hypotheses to account for the observation. Hypothesis One is by Colin Ross & Co. Hypothesis One: MPD is probably as common in other countries as in North America. Clinicians outside North America don't inquire about its symptoms systematically, or seriously consider MPD as a possibility. Therefore they don't diagnose it.

Restated. Hypothesis One: the difference in rates of diagnosis are due to clinician variables, not true prevalence rates. The majority of North American diagnoses are valid, true and correct.

Hypothesis Two: MPD is rare everywhere. Clinicians in North America way over-diagnose it. Those elsewhere don't.

Great! We have two competing hypotheses! Wait a minute. Wait a minute. I know, I know. Step number three. Oohh. What is it? Oh yeah. I remember! Design an experiment.

Hold it! Not in psychiatry. The False Memory Police use the observation as proof of their hypothesis. In leading shrink journals. In their own Newsletter. At National Conferences. In the media. In the courtroom. They pose as scientists while doing so.

Bong, bong, bong. Poser alert!

You cannot use your observation as proof of your hypothesis. Not in grade five science. But the False Memory Police do. They "argue" that the higher rate of MPD diagnoses in North America proves that MPD is a cultural fad limited to North America.

See what I mean. The shrinks are uneducated. They can't follow the logic of grade five science taught at Robert H. Smith Elementary School, Winnipeg, Manitoba Canada in 1960.

The shrinks make this error of logic repeatedly. They "argue" that the increased rate of diagnoses of MPD in the 1980s and 1990s is evidence that it is a hysterical fad. Same logical error. Using your observation as proof of your hypothesis.

There is a second problem. The False Memory Police set up a closed loop between Step One and Step Two. In logic, this is called a *tautology*. Step One proves Step Two and Step Two proves Step One. What is the second problem?

There are actually data in the literature. These are never discussed. One of the functions of the tautology is to keep the "debate" from ever moving to Step Three.

This Police Maneuver is necessary for several reasons. The Police have not read the literature. If they've read it, they haven't read it. The data support Colin Ross & Co. The Police cannot think scientifically about MPD. They are way too lazy to ever design and carry out any experiments or research themselves.

The Police try to keep the "debate" locked in at the level of personal belief and pseudo-scholarship because that's as far as they can go. They just haven't got it. They have to make Colin Ross & Co. be all about personal belief. Otherwise C.R. might escape the net. This would make the Police look bad. Bummer. Downer.

The Police are obsessed with MPD not being real. Why? What is the big deal? I still can't figure it out. But I have some ideas. It is very important for MPD not to be real for the following reasons. If MPD is real then:

1. The Police are lousy diagnosticians.
2. The Police cannot tell the difference between hysteria and medical brain disease causing psychosis (they misdiagnose MPD as schizophrenia).
3. Childhood trauma is a big deal in psychiatry.
4. Genes are not such a big deal in psychiatry.
5. Drugs are not so important in psychiatry.
6. The Police are just all around ugly idiots.

The stakes are set pretty high. If the Police would just relax and get educated and change their ways, I could be cool. But they would have to work their AA Steps. Make amends and do a fearless inventory of their own bullshit. Which they aren't going to do in the third millennium.

The only strategy, then, is to neutralize them. With real scholarship and science. Plus a little satire. From a little satyr.

"Ye gods! What man is this, that dare challenge Olympus?"

"Didn't I tell you? It's not the Special Intellectual Olympics. It's psychiatry. How could you confuse the two?"

"We're talking about the top brains in the profession, here."

The Police have set up a whole squad of straw men, tautological loops and phony arguments that are too tedious to enumerate. Check the chapter in my book *Dissociative Identity Disorder* for an academic laundry list of bogus Police tactics. With references. Then go to the Appendix to *mon autre livre*, *The Trauma Model:*

A Solution To The Problem Of Comorbidity In Psychiatry. Coffin nails aplenty in those two locations. Also, you can add a third book: *Schizophrenia: Innovations In Diagnosis And Treatment*. Same author.

The Police use another tactic all the time. They make everything be about memory content. Memories are real or false. Satanic cults exist or don't exist. Those are boring simple-minded questions. They never make it be about therapy. They never describe in any detail how they would treat these people. Why? Because they don't treat them.

Whether the memories are real or false is a very minor question in therapy. Very, very, very. Minor, minor, minor. But the Police set up a straw man where decisions about the reality of the memories become the major crux of everything that follows. It's a straw man.

In reality, such decisions cannot be made scientifically and don't affect the tactics, tasks, and strategies of therapy. The Police keep bashing at my door trying to arrest me for crimes I never committed. At times, I affectionately call them the KGB.

These crazy attacks never get made on schizophrenia by Club shrinks. When such attacks get made on schizophrenia, they are called anti-psychiatry. For MPD, *au contraire*, the anti-psychiatry comes from the leaders of psychiatry. On the street, this is called having sexual intercourse with yourself up your rear end. It is a sign of a disturbed individual.

The Club shrinks put both schizophrenia and DID in DSM-IV. It's not my fault they did that. I had zero power and control over DSM-IV. I hadn't even finished medical school when MPD showed upon in DSM-III in 1980. I'm following the rules of the American Psychiatric Association when I diagnose MPD/DID.

Another Police tactic comes in here. The Police attack the trauma theory of the cause of DID to discredit the diagnosis. This confuses etiology with phenomenology, another intro error of logic. The rules of DSM-IV are clear. Theories of etiology (= theories of causation) have nothing to do with diagnostic criteria. Nothing. Ever. Period.

This is true for depression, bulimia, schizophrenia, alcohol abuse, and every other diagnosis made by Club shrinks. There are numerous theories for the cause of every psychiatric disorder. The theories are irrelevant to making the diagnosis. The diagnosis does not depend on any theory for its reliability and validity. DSM-IV diagnostic criteria sets are phenomenological. They are based on signs and symptoms. Not theories. Not schools of thought. Observations.

Oh, oh. We are back at Robert H. Smith Elementary School. The False Memory Police use their Hypothesis to disprove an observation. DID is iatrogenic, they say, therefore it is not legitimate.

The Police use their theory of DID, that it is iatrogenic, to disprove the validity of the diagnosis. This is Hypothesis used to discount Observation. This can't be done in grade five science. And it violates the rules of DSM-IV. The American Psychiatric Association's rules. Namely, that theories of etiology are not relevant to diagnosis.

These rules apply to all DSM-IV diagnoses. Not just DID (MPD). You never hear the Police "arguing" that since someone has a bogus theory about the cause of depression, depression is a bogus diagnosis. Why? Because they haven't got a grudge against depression. They aren't at war against depression.

The Police performance is a psychological warfare campaign. It is not medicine. It is not science. It is not scholarship. It is very tiresome and hurtful.

What about real criticism? Real criticism is the lifeblood of science. I welcome it. I'm not bummed out because I get criticized. I'm bummed out because I never get criticized. I get attacked and slandered. But never criticized. The shrinks can't get there.

"To be or not to be. That is the question. Whether 'tis nobler in the mind to suffer the slings and arrows of outrageous stupidity, or take up arms against a sea of shrinks, and by opposing, end."

54

THE FALSE MEMORY POLICE CIRCA 2004

It is now time to reveal the identity of Dr. Smarty Pants. He usually goes by the name Dr. Joel Paris, Editor-in-Chief (designate) of *The Canadian Journal of Psychiatry*. 'Designate' means he is taking over soon, circa 2004. Done deal in oh seven.

Dr. Intelligent Pants has had it in for multiple personality disorder (dissociative identity disorder) for a long time. This explains why a paper by False Memory Policemen August Piper and Harold Merskey appeared in the September, 2004 issue of *The Canadian Journal of Psychiatry*. Part II was gifted to us in the October, 2004 issue.

The September paper has the scholarly title, "The Persistence of Folly: A Critical Examination of Dissociative Identity Disorder. Part I. The Excesses of an Improbable Concept." The October paper's title is a variation on the same sewer language.

Language like that would not be allowed in a psychiatry journal about any other disorder.

In the first paragraph, Officers Piper and Merskey state that the dissociative disorders have "suffered some significant wounds" of late. Their evidence?

1. Between 1993 and 1998, the International Society for the Study of Dissociation lost half its membership.
2. In 1998, the journal *Dissociation* ceased publication.
3. Several dissociative disorders units closed
4. Several dissociative disorders therapists were sued.

Always ready to tell a good joke, Piper and Merskey cite papers by themselves and other False Memory Policemen and hangers-on as evidence in favor of their proposition that dissociative identity disorder is a bogus diagnosis.

Wait a minute! The validity of a psychiatric disorder can be decided by membership figures for professional organizations? A journal ceasing publication is *scientific* evidence about the validity of a diagnosis?

Oh, I get it. Between 1993 and 1998, Charter Medical Corporation went from operating 100 psychiatric hospitals in the United States to operating zero. That proves that depression and schizophrenia are bogus diagnoses.

It is absolutely impossible to get that "argument" about schizophrenia and depression published in any psychiatry journal. But hey, MPD can get fucked over any day of the week.

Piper and Merskey failed to mention that the journal, *Dissociation*, ceased publication because the International Society for the Study of Dissociation wanted to take over full control of its official journal. *Dissociation* was replaced by *The Journal of Trauma and Dissociation*, which is published by the Haworth Press, a large academic publisher, and the first issue was published in 2000.

So that's it, I just proved that MPD (DID) is real because *The Journal of Trauma and Dissociation* exists.

"Basil, this man needs help. Existence of *The Journal of Trauma and Dissociation* proves that the ardent defenders are still perpetrating their folly on society."

That's what Piper and Merskey call Colin Ross & Co: "ardent defenders" of DID.

Those are the rules in psychiatry. If a journal stops, DID is bogus. If a journal starts, we don't mention it. If membership in the ISSD goes down, DID is history. If it went up, we wouldn't mention that. Dissociative disorders units close, DID is dead. One hundred hospitals close: no other psychiatric disorder is dead.

The beat goes on.

Piper and Merskey "argue" yet again, circa 2004, that since DID is diagnosed more inside North America than out, this proves it is bogus. Ditto for the fact that it has been diagnosed more recently than previously.

That science stuff is hard to grasp. Observation, Hypothesis. All so confusing.

Note to logicians: zero cases of schizophrenia were diagnosed before Bleuler coined the term in 1908. Zero cases of bipolar mood disorder were diagnosed before the twentieth century. Zero cases of posttraumatic stress disorder were diagnosed before World War II. Zero cases of anaphylactic shock caused by penicillin were diagnosed prior to the invention of penicillin. Zero cases of. . . OK, I don't want to overdo it.

Fortunately, Officers Piper and Merskey reveal what it is all about in their paper. No need for further rebuttal. In a section on the trauma histories of people with multiple personality, the Officers claim that the definition of childhood sexual abuse is too vague in the dissociative disorders literature.

Does this question from my Dissociative Disorders Interview Schedule (DDIS) sound vague to you? The DDIS has been used in lots of studies, some of which the Officers reference. The person being interviewed is asked:

> *"Were you sexually abused as a child or adolescent? Sexual abuse includes rape, or any type of unwanted sexual touching or fondling you may have experienced."*

If the person answers 'Yes,' the interviewer then says:

> *"The following questions concern detailed examples of the types of sexual abuse you may or may not have experienced. Because of the explicit nature of these questions, you have the option not to answer any or all of them. The reason I am asking these questions is to try to determine the severity of the abuse that you experienced. You may answer Yes, No, Unsure or not give an answer to each question."*

The interviewer then asks,

> *"If you were sexually abused was it by: a) father b) mother c) stepfather d) stepmother e) brother f) sister g) male relative h) female relative i) other male j) other female."*
>
> *Possible responses are Yes, No or Unsure."*

The person being interviewed is then asked about specific types of sexual abuse. There is one list for males and one for females.

The list of possible acts for females respondents is: a) hand to genital touching b) other types of fondling c) intercourse with a male d) simulated intercourse with a female e) you performing oral sex on a male f) you performing oral sex on a female g) oral sex done to you by a male h) oral sex done to you by a female i) anal intercourse with a male j) enforced sex with animals k) pornographic photography l) other.

This doesn't seem like too vague a list to me.

The respondent is also asked his or her age when the sexual abuse started and stopped and how many separate incidents he or she experienced before age 18, and in a separate question, after age 18. Possible responses to these two questions are: 1-5, 6-10, 11-50, >50, and Unsure.

I remember reading an article in the *Journal of the Canadian Medical Association* in which the authors reported the results of a survey of sexual behavior by gay men in Vancouver. One of the response categories for lifetime number of sexual partners was 'over 500.'

Doesn't seem like the DDIS is overdoing it.

Of course, Piper and Merskey did reference my paper on abuse histories of 102 patients with MPD interviewed with the DDIS, which was published in *The Canadian Journal of Psychiatry* in 1991. Of these 102 people with MPD, 39.2% reported sexual abuse by their fathers, 46.1% by a male relative and 62.7% by an 'other male.'

Concerning acts perpetrated on them prior to age 18, 77.5% reported hand-genital contact, 54.9% intercourse, 52.9% performing oral sex on a male, 37.3% anal intercourse performed on them, 20.6% pornographic photography, 19.6% oral sex performed on them by a female. . .

The average duration of childhood sexual abuse was 11.7 years.

In criticizing the vagueness of the literature on childhood sexual abuse, Piper and Merskey reveal their true natures:

> *. . . Briere and Runtz define sexual abuse as any sexual contact, even kissing, between a female under age 15 years and someone at least 5 years older. The authors apparently do not consider whether the young woman desired, initiated, or willingly participated in the activity or whether she actually found it traumatic. Conversely, the term sexual abuse is also applied to children much more severely victimized. Other studies do not define the term at all. Finally, several authors discuss intergenerational sexual activity that might be considered to involve abuse.*

OK, I get it. A girl under 15 can be involved in "intergenerational sexual activity" and that may not be abuse.

This is a pedophile's argument. That's what this is all about. It's an apologist position for pedophilia masquerading as a scientific critique of a psychiatric disorder. MPD/DID can't be real – it can't be caused by real childhood trauma – the trauma can't involve real sexual abuse. Why?

Because if MPD is real and is caused by childhood sexual abuse, then "intergenerational sexual activity" isn't OK, even if a girl under 15 desires, initiates or willingly participates in it. That's the problem posed by MPD. It makes childhood sexual abuse look bad.

Better get rid of MPD, then.

55

ALCOHOLISM, THE DISEASE YOU CAN DECIDE NOT TO HAVE

I listened to a woman in cognitive therapy group explain to me how her "disease" had gotten out of control. Alcohol and cocaine. The solution? She knew she had to work her steps harder.

This woman didn't know that by DSM-IV rules, she has two diseases, since she abuses two separate substances. That is the first absurdity in the shrink system. The idea that you have separate diagnoses, disorders or diseases if you abuse different substances. Alcoholism disease. Cocaine disease. LSD disease. Separate diagnoses. People on the street know this is a ludicrous idea.

The idea that alcoholism is a disease is dumb for several reasons. See my chapter in *Pseudoscience in Biological Psychiatry*. Psychiatry is obsessed with the idea of single disorders. Schizophrenia. Bipolar mood disorder. Obsessive-compulsive disorder. Separate single disorders. Single disorders with separate causes. Equals separate genes, since genes are the most revered causes in shrinkdom currently.

The gene fad has lasted about twenty years. With any luck, it will have died out within another twenty years. Eventually, the public will get tired of funding research that yields no real results.

Alcoholism cannot be a genetic disease like Cystic Fibrosis or Huntington's Chorea. These are caused by single genes. The inheritance patterns are different but crystal clear for each.

Why can't alcoholism be a genetic disease driven from within by biology? Because it depends on the existence of alcohol. Before alcohol was discovered, there were no alcoholics. If alcohol didn't exist, there would be no AA, no alcoholics, and no DSM-IV diagnosis.

What kind of genetic disease depends absolutely on the existence of a cultural invention? Sure, alcohol and fermentation occur in nature. Did so before man evolved. But the drinking of alcohol is a human cultural behavior that depends absolutely on the deliberate brewing of booze. Without this cultural behavior, there would be no alcohol to consume.

Right away, it is obvious that alcoholism cannot be a genetic disease. Not like Cystic Fibrosis. If you have the genetic defect that causes Cystic Fibrosis, you will have the disease no matter what. It is unavoidable. Not so with alcoholism.

Let's assume there is a gene for alcoholism. In the absence of alcohol, the gene would be biologically meaningless. The DNA would be the same. But there would be no gene for alcoholism because there was no alcohol. Invent alcohol, brew it up, and party. All of a sudden, the same sequence of DNA has become a gene for alcoholism. But the DNA didn't change. The environment changed.

The gene for alcoholism can't be a gene for alcoholism in the absence of alcohol. The meaning and function of that section of DNA depend absolutely on environmental conditions. This is totally different from real genetic diseases like Cystic Fibrosis. It doesn't matter if you move to Katmandu. If you've got Cystic Fibrosis, you've got it.

OK. There may not be a gene for alcoholism as such. But there is a gene for substance abuse in general. Fine. In that case, alcoholism and cocaine abuse are not separate diseases. There should not be separate DSM-IV diagnoses. There should be only one generic substance abuse diagnosis.

Fine. But what if *none* of those substances existed? There would be no substance abusers of any kind on a space station that lacked substances of abuse. The supposed gene would be biologically inert. It would have no biological function. It would not be a gene. Just because you have a sequence of DNA, doesn't mean you have a gene, or even part of a gene.

OK. There is no gene for substance abuse. There is a gene for addictive and thrill-seeking behavior in general. Fine. Let's look at the data. Such behavior simply does not follow a genetic pattern. Any possible genetic effects are swamped out by environmental variables like your parents and culture.

Are people born with different temperaments? Sure. That's obvious to everyone. But temperaments are not medical psychiatric disorders. People with certain temperaments may be at higher risk for certain disorders. That's fine. But a higher risk is not a specific gene for a specific disorder.

The AA people, the patients, the shrinks, the media, the politicians. You hear about the disease of alcoholism from all of them. Except the far right. They don't buy the disease excuse at all.

In the next paragraph, after the disease explanation, in the *Textbook of Conventional Thinking About Psychiatry*, you hear that the treatment is working your steps. How can you turn off a gene by going to AA meetings? Is this what the shrinks are proposing? If so, what kind of a gene is that? It's not a Cystic Fibrosis-type gene. You can't turn the Cystic Fibrosis gene off no matter who you talk to, what you say or think, or what therapy groups you attend.

But AA does affect the rates of sobriety. Shrinks recommend it. Insurance companies applaud it. Mostly because it's free. Stop. Think for a minute.

Let's go back to the assumption that there is a gene for alcoholism. Let's agree that AA works for many alcoholics. Wait a minute. We just agreed to a conceptual revolution in psychiatric genetics. If there is a gene for alcoholism, the environment can both turn it on and turn it off.

Now we're cookin'.

Let's drop back to the gene for general substance abuse. Same conclusion. The AA model can turn it off. The unavoidable conclusions from the efficacy of AA are: 1) alcoholism is not a disease, or 2) therapy can modulate gene expression.

I'm a personal believer in 2. No matter what, the Cystic Fibrosis model of psychiatric genetics is completely bogus. The genetics of mental illness are far, far, far, far more environmentally interactive than the primitive, reductionistic, unidirectional, pseudo-medical models that dominate shrinkdom today.

Alcoholism. The disease you can decide not to have.

Can you believe the shrinks have sold that scam successfully? Amazing. Typical.

56

GETTING SUED, THAT'S FUN

In the movies, Clint Eastwood or Bruce Willis or Sylvester Stallone can be counted on to say, with studied *sang froid*, through however many takes are required, "Now it's personal."

It's personal with me. Two lawsuits were filed against me in Canada, in 1994 and 1995. Both were stirred up by the False Memory Police, who had direct involvement. I have documentation of the Police involvement.

The first case was a woman I actually treated. She sued me for the usual implantation of false memories of Satanic ritual abuse and creation of iatrogenic multiple personality. The Police have applauded and supported her in public. She claimed that 100% of her abuse memories were caused by me. I have a copy of her own description in her own handwriting of twenty or so rapes by family members and others. Written and dated by her six weeks before I met her.

The patient claims that I told her I did not believe her story of being impregnated by aliens, who later came back to remove the fetus. These were charitable aliens. Seven years later they re-appeared in her apartment to show her her Star Child. It is true that I did not believe her and told her so. She complains in her journal that I did not believe her. But she accuses me of implanting the memory of alien abduction in her lawsuit.

There were so many lies and fantasies in this woman's account of therapy that I can't even remember them all. In and of herself, she's harmless. She's very mixed up. But the Police championed her cause.

They shit all over me in an affidavit for prescribing her high doses of triazolam. This is a sleeping pill in the class of drugs called benzodiazepines, to which Valium belongs. I prescribed the ultra high doses only in the controlled hospital setting. The purpose was to reduce the hostile, irritable, abusive behavior she showed on previous admissions. All of this is documented in great detail in the records.

The Police got all over me for prescribing doses of triazolam far above the recommended maximum. When the lawyer deposed me in 1996, he made a lot of hay about how the doses were 100 times above the recommended dose. The experts clamored for my head for such flagrant malpractice.

The problem? The expert who accused me of malpractice in an affidavit had himself published a paper in which he gave 80 milligrams a day of another benzodiazepine, lorazepam, to his own patients. The recommended daily maximum in the same book the lawyer used to beat me up for triazolam is under five milligrams a day.

The Police are challenging the world record for hypocrisy.

This woman alleged that I prescribed her tons of triazolam as an inpatient. It is true that I did. There is a large literature on the proper usage of mega-doses of all classes of psychiatric medication. Written by Club members in Club journals. The high doses harmed her, she said. She also complained that I abused her by making her go to the pharmacy every day to pick up one day's supply, as I tapered her dose down post-discharge. And she complained that I kept her addicted to triazolam for another two or three years, because she kept taking the inpatient tablets she had secretly stock piled.

Which was it? She took the high doses as an inpatient and was harmed? Or didn't take them and was harmed later? Her story shifts with the wind. The therapy ended in 1990. The lawsuit was filed in 1994. I was deposed in Winnipeg in 1996. As of 2005, nothing else had happened, except she complained to the Manitoba Bar Association about her lawyer, and had to get another one. Then the case was finally dismissed.

The case has no foundation. A couple of years ago this woman told a Winnipeg reporter that I was being investigated by the RCMP. The Reporter phoned Charter Hospital and said I was being investigated by the RCMP. I could have lost my contract with Charter and 90% of my income because of this false accusation. I had to talk to the RCMP and get them to confirm there was no such investigation.

Charter Corporate could have ditched me just because I was a PR liability. Even though I had done nothing and there was no investigation. The woman also complained about me to the Manitoba College of Physicians and Surgeons and the Texas State Board of Medical Examiners. Now the False Memory Police were after my license.

Both Manitoba and Texas dismissed the complaints after investigating them. Then she complained to the Texas State Board of Medical Examiners a second time. This time she complained on behalf of herself and several other patients. Three of them I had never met. One was the borderline woman who was murdered by sadistic counter-transference before I left Canada.

In this complaint it was alleged that I had violated professional standards by spreading hysteria about Satanism. This complaint was also dismissed.

These complaints are very stressful. They are part of an organized campaign of harassment. They are fascist. The Police applaud them.

The second lawsuit was by a friend of the woman who filed the first suit. I was sued by a man I had never met on behalf of his ex-wife and deceased sister-in-law, neither of whom I had ever met. The sister-in-law committed suicide in Winnipeg in July, 1986. I never met her. Never met her therapist. Never had any involvement of any kind, direct or indirect in her treatment.

I never got to see this woman's medical record, but supposedly it was my fault she had MPD and memories of involvement in a Satanic cult, both present by the fall of 1985. The first time I ever heard of Satanism was in 1986. The first time I talked in public about MPD was the autumn of 1985. I finished my psychiatry residency in June, 1985.

The ex-wife never got any psychiatric treatment of any kind till after I left Winnipeg in 1991. She never had an MPD diagnosis or memories of Satanism. I never met her or had anything to do with her. The lawsuit was ridiculous. It was dismissed by the Court. As well as me, he had sued the University of Manitoba and the Government of Manitoba.

These lawsuits were reported in the Police Newsletter. I got bugged by the Winnipeg media about them. They fuel ongoing rumors that I am a kook. An article blaming me for the 1986 suicide appeared in *The Winnipeg Sun* in September, 2000.

As far as I am concerned, I'm a stalking victim. Many of my colleagues applaud the stalkers. The plan is to wear you down and make you quit. The patients are pawns in the game. The Police don't give a shit about the patients, reality or justice. They are abortion clinic bombers.

God is on their side. They are right. They will use whatever tactics it takes. The cash register is ringing.

"Expert witness fees, baby."

One Policeman made $100,000.00 in expert witness fees off a single case. The case resulted in a hung jury and was not retried. It was a totally bogus case. But the Policeman got paid. And scored a few more points with God. Or the downstairs guy. I forget which. Talk about Satanic ritual abuse!

57

THE DEPARTMENT OF SILLY GENETICS, GODOT UNIVERSITY

The Island of Godot is difficult to find on a map of the Caribbean. But it's there. The Island was settled by British immigrants who had failed their O Level exams at the end of the nineteenth century. Before these academically challenged Brits arrived, the Island was uninhabited.

Godot University opened in 1924. The Medical School opened in 1973. It is still a bit small. There are only two Departments in the Godot Medical School. The Department of Psychiatry and the Department of Silly Genetics. The Department of Silly Genetics derives its name from an old British institution, the Ministry of Silly Walks. I believe the current Minister in England is the Honourable John Cleese.

You won't believe what they believe in the Department of Silly Genetics. But I'll tell you anyway. In a joint project with the Department of Psychiatry, the Department of Silly Genetics has been studying a unique psychiatric disorder that occurs only on the Island of Godot.

The researchers believe that this disorder is caused by a gene peculiar to the Island. It was brought over by one of the first immigrants, a man who couldn't pass any O Level exams no matter how hard he tried.

The disorder is called Silly Walk Syndrome. It is well described in the Godot medical literature. The University publishes its own medical journal, the Godot Medical Journal. It is difficult to find in medical school libraries on the mainland.

The onset of the symptoms in Silly Walk Syndrome is usually in the late teens or twenties, although cases have been described in children. The only known treatment is antisillywalkotropic medication, manufactured by Godot Pharmaceuticals.

Symptoms include: a compulsion to walk down the street in a silly goose step; excessive, rapid and excited speech; poor taste in comedy; paranoid ideation; and a belief that the BBC is controlled by Americans. Silly Walk Syndrome was at first thought to be a variant of mania, but it has been proven to be a separate and distinct syndrome. This was proven by a vote of the Faculty Members of the Departments of Psychiatry and Silly Genetics at Godot University.

Quite a bit is known about the inheritance patterns of Silly Walk Syndrome. It affects 1% of the population. Because Silly Walk Syndrome causes such bad responses in other Islanders, sufferers marry and reproduce at 20% the rate of other Islanders. Overall, Silly Walk Syndrome victims only have 20% as many children as everyone else on the Island.

The rate of Silly Walk Syndrome on the Island has remained constant at 1% of each generation for the last one hundred years.

If a person has Silly Walk Syndrome, the chances that his parents have it are 3%. The chances for his children or siblings to have it are 10%.

The researchers in the Department of Silly Genetics have done twin studies to investigate the genetics of Silly Walk Syndrome. They have looked at concordance rates in monozygotic and dizygotic twins. Monozygotic twins are identical. Dizygotic twins are fraternal or non-identical. Monozygotic twins come from the same egg. Dizygotic twins come from two different eggs. Monozygotic twins are always the same gender. Dizygotic twins may be the same or different genders.

Concordance means if one twin has a disease, then the other twin does too. Discordance means that one twin has a disease, but the other does not. For diseases like Cystic Fibrosis, the concordance rate in monozygotic twins is 100%. There is never an exception to this rule, in Cystic Fibrosis.

Cystic Fibrosis is what is called a recessive disorder. There are two copies of each gene in your DNA. One comes from your mother and one from your father. To have the disease of Cystic Fibrosis, you have to inherit the abnormal gene from both your mother and your father. If you get an abnormal recessive copy from one parent, but a normal copy from the other, the normal copy over-rides and you don't get the disease. The normal gene is dominant.

In genetics, genes are described with abbreviations. The gene for Cystic Fibrosis might be called *cf*. The normal gene would then be *CF*. To get Cystic Fibrosis, both your parents have to be carriers. They have to have one cf copy and one CF copy each. Neither has the disease of Cystic Fibrosis. The parents are described as cfCF.

By chance, the combinations of genes in the children of these parents can be: cf from mom, cf from dad; cf from mom, CF from dad; CF from mom, cf from dad; and CF from mom, CF from dad. The combinations are: cfcf; cfCF; CFcf; and CFCF.

If both parents are carriers, by chance half their children will be carriers, one quarter will be genetically normal, and one quarter will have Cystic Fibrosis. In any given family, the pattern will vary by chance. But if you look at hundreds of Cystic Fibrosis families, things will average out to half carriers, one quarter normal and one quarter affected by the disease.

For Silly Walk Syndrome, the concordance rate in monozygotic twins is 28%.

The concordance rate in dizygotic twins is 10%. Dizygotic twins have the same concordance rates as regular siblings. If a parent has Silly Walk Syndrome, the chance his child will have it is 10%.

But it doesn't work the other way around. If a person has Silly Walk Syndrome, the chances for a parent to have it are only 3%.

What have the researchers at the Department of Silly Genetics concluded about Silly Walk Syndrome? In a recent paper, they described a review of all the twins ever born on the Island. They keep very thorough records there. As I said, they found a concordance rate of 28% in identical twins, 10% in non-identical.

The Godot researchers used a fancy statistical analysis of their data to find out what percentage of the cause of Silly Walk Syndrome is genetic. The answer: 83%.

What? Are we sure this is a real Medical School? Maybe Godot University is just a figment of some fevered imagination. Maybe it doesn't exist in reality. Surely no real geneticists at a real Medical School would be so ridiculous.

Look at the facts. When one identical twin has Silly Walk Syndrome, the other twin has it less than one third of the time. How could the cause be 83% genetic? It's obvious that the cause of Silly Walk Syndrome is less than half genetic, at most.

Lots of research on the mainland, published in North American journals, has shown that identical twins are treated the same, and have the same experiences, much more than non-identical twins. This is also common sense. Identical twins more often: wear the same clothes; have the same hair styles; sleep in the same rooms; are put in the same classrooms; are mistaken for each other; are given names that start with the same letter; are treated as a unit rather than as two individuals; and so on.

The environments of identical twins are much more similar than the environments of fraternal twins. Especially if the fraternal twins are a girl and a boy. Therefore, if identical twins end up the same in some way, more often than fraternal twins, it is hard to tell for sure if this is due to more similar genes or more similar environment.

In genetics, there is a concept called *the equal environments assumption*. The equal environments assumption states that the environments of identical twins are no more identical than the environments of fraternal twins. This must be true for different concordance rates to be due solely to genetics.

The problem is, all the data, not to mention common sense, refute the equal environments assumption. Identical twins are clearly treated the same much more than are fraternal twins.

It doesn't matter what you are looking at. Could be favorite television shows. Could be Silly Walk Syndrome. If identical twins are concordant for favorite television show more often than fraternal twins, you can only say this is caused by genes if the equal environments assumption holds. It never does.

Therefore, when the concordance rate for Silly Walk Syndrome in identical twins is only 28%, we can conclude that it would be even less if the equal environments assumption held. Some of the concordance is likely due to shared environment, not shared genes. There is no way to know scientifically, based on the Godot studies, but the concordance rate for monozygotic twins separated at birth and raised in separate homes might only be 15% or 20%.

There is no way to know because there aren't enough monozygotic twin pairs separated at birth to answer the question. To really know the concordance due to shared genes, you'd have to have thousands of monozygotic twin pairs separated at birth. This is because Silly Walk Syndrome only affects 1% of the population.

So where do the Godot geneticists get their conclusion from? That 83% of the cause of Silly Walk Syndrome is genetic? From science? No. From data? No. They get their conclusion from themselves. They reach that conclusion simply because they want to, not because the data lead them there. The data lead directly to the conclusion that the cause of Silly Walk Syndrome is mostly environmental.

What can you expect from researchers who spend most of their day on the beach?

Let's look at the data a bit more. If 10% of children and siblings get Silly Walk Syndrome, why do only 3% of parents have it? This doesn't make any genetic sense. Your odds of having Silly Walk Syndrome are lower if your child has it than if your parent has it. By two thirds.

The meaning of the data are clear. Having a child with Silly Walk Syndrome is only one third as upsetting as having a parent with it. The Syndrome is passed on through the environment, and learned from the parent, in two thirds of cases.

What about the reproduction rates of people with Silly Walk Syndrome? Overall, they only have 20% as many children as the other Islanders. They are social misfits and no one wants to have sex with them.

But the rate of Silly Walk Syndrome on Godot Island remains constant at 1% of each generation. How is that?

Look at the numbers. Look at the great-grandparents' generation. One per cent of people in that generation have Silly Walk Syndrome. They only produce 20% as many children as everyone else on the Island. Therefore in the grandparents' generation, the gene has been diluted out by 80%.

There should only be 20% as many cases of Silly Walk Syndrome in the grandparents' generation as there were in the great-grandparents' generation.

In the parents, there should be a further dilution of 80%. In the parents' generation, there should only be 4% as many cases as there were in the great-grandparents. In the children, the rate should have dropped to under 1% of what it was in the great-grandparents.

But the rate remains constant at 1% generation after generation. From this analysis, I conclude that 99% of the cause of Silly Walk Syndrome is not inherited through the genome. The cause could still be genetic. But the genetic defect would have to have an environmental cause, like radiation, chemicals, viruses, or something in the diet. It wouldn't be an inherited genetic defect. The defect and the Syndrome would tend to run in families because of shared family environment. Not shared genes.

Consider the generational numbers in reverse. One per cent of current adults have Silly Walk Syndrome. Given the 20% reproduction rate, 5% of their parents must have had it. This means that 25% of their grandparents had Silly Walk Syndrome. Which means that over 100% of the great grandparents had it.

Does this sound like a scientific possibility to you?

Another way to look at the problem is what are called *cross-fostering studies*. In such studies, the researchers look at adoptions. They look at kids born into families with cases of Silly Walk Syndrome who have been adopted at birth into unaffected families. And vice versa. If Silly Walk Syndrome is a genetic disorder, the risk should not change because of adoption. This is true for Cystic Fibrosis, Tay-Sachs Disease, Huntington's Chorea and other truly genetic diseases.

But not for Silly Walk Syndrome. The cross-fostering data show that if you are born from biological parents, one of whom has Silly Walk Syndrome, but adopted at birth into a normal family, your risk of developing Silly Walk Syndrome drops by over half. From 10% to under 5%.

The data the other way around are not so clear. It seems that if you are born from normal parents but adopted at birth into a family with a Silly Walk parent, your risk goes up. But the data are fuzzy on that point. They are clear the other way around.

The cross-fostering and twin concordance data for Silly Walk Syndrome prove a large environmental component to the disease. The genetic component is possible but unproven.

There is another strange thing about Silly Walk Syndrome. Ninety per cent of people who have it do not have any affected relatives. Only 10% of people with Silly Walk Syndrome have a single relative with the problem.

This is a pain in the butt for researchers. They have to study thousands of families to find examples of families with two or more affected members.

Genetic, huh? I don't think so.

One more thing about Silly Walk Syndrome. It does not *breed true*. Breeding true is true for truly genetic diseases. Take Cystic Fibrosis and Huntington's Chorea, for instance. These are two purely genetic diseases. And they are completely distinct and separate. They breed true.

This means that if someone has Cystic Fibrosis, there is an increased risk for Cystic Fibrosis in their relatives, but not for Huntington's Chorea. Vice versa, the relatives of people with Huntington's have an increased risk for Huntington's, but not for Cystic Fibrosis.

Silly Walk Syndrome does not breed true. The relatives of people with Silly Walk have increased rates of both Silly Walk and Bulimia, on the Island of Godot. Inversely, the relatives of people with Bulimia have increased rates of Silly Walk, compared to the relatives of people with neither condition.

Having Silly Walk increases your aunt's risk of having bulimia. The two conditions are connected somehow and do not breed true. This means they are not separate disorders and cannot have separate genetic causes. The situation is messy and muddy, not clear and scientific like it is with Huntington's Chorea and Cystic Fibrosis.

Intellectual, scholarly and scientific standards are very low at Godot University. The Departments of Psychiatry and Silly Genetics have accepted the conclusion that Silly Walk Syndrome is a genetic disease. Completely, 100% accepted it. The environment has minimal if any role in causing the disease. It could have a minor affect on the symptoms at most. This is the accepted dogma at Godot University. No one questions it.

The shrinks on Godot Island have done a great job of selling the genetic basis of Silly Walk Syndrome to the public. The public has bought it hook, line and sinker. So have the politicians.

The exciting discoveries in the genetics of Silly Walk Syndrome are used to hype the importance of psychiatry and psychiatric research on the Island. Funding for shrinks is up. The shrinks think they are real doctors now. Real medical scientists. They feel good about themselves.

The shrinks at Godot University are pretty sure surgeons respect them as real doctors now, because they treat genetic diseases like Silly Walk Syndrome. Unfortunately, there are no surgeons at Godot University. The shrinks are so isolated in their own little world at Godot University, they might as well be on a different planet. One where there is no real medicine.

Of course, the Department of Silly Genetics is happy. Their turf just expanded. Now they can be bosses of a new field called *behavioral genetics*. I'm sure their mothers are proud of them.

Sorry to waste your time with the situation on Godot Island. Really, the Islanders are nice people. Make great Mai Tai's. The shrinks may have had a couple too many. But what can you do? It's the Caribbean.

58

THE SCHIZOPHRENIA GENE SCAM

The biggest scam going on in psychiatry today is the schizophrenia gene scam. Similar cons are being run for bipolar mood disorder, unipolar depression, obsessive-compulsive disorder, panic disorder, and alcoholism. Plus maybe cocaine abuse. But the big money is on schizophrenia.

The highest-ranking research journal in psychiatry, in the world, is called the *Archives of General Psychiatry*. The *Archives* recently published a paper on the genetics of schizophrenia. Researchers in Finland studied concordance rates for schizophrenia in a large sample of monozygotic and dizygotic twin pairs.

They found a concordance rate in the monozygotic twins of 45% and in the dizygotic twins, 9%. They did a statistical analysis of their data and concluded that 83% of the cause of schizophrenia is genetic.

At a recent talk at the American College of Psychiatrists Annual Meeting, schizophrenia researcher, Dr. Kendler received an award for his work on the genetics of schizophrenia. In his acceptance speech he stated that, "Most if not all the reason why schizophrenia runs in families is due to shared genes and not to shared environment."

In the same talk, Dr. Kendler presented data from his own study of 16,000 twin pairs. He found concordance rates for schizophrenia of 31% in monozygotic twins and 6% in dizygotic twins. No one questioned his conclusion. Overall, pooling the well-designed studies, concordance for schizophrenia in monozygotic twins is 28%.

Schizophrenia affects 1% of the population. The rate is constant across generations but schizophrenics only reproduce at 20% the rate of the rest of the population. Only 10% of schizophrenics have even one relative with schizophrenia.

If an individual has schizophrenia, the risk of his child getting it is 10% but the chance of his parent having it is 3%. Cross-fostering studies show that the risk of schizophrenia drops substantially if you are adopted out of a schizophrenic family into a normal one.

Schizophrenia does not breed true. Relatives of people with schizophrenia have increased rates of both schizophrenia and depression, compared to the relatives of people with neither schizophrenia nor depression. Vice versa, relatives of people with depression have increased rates of both depression and schizophrenia. Depression and schizophrenia are not distinct separate disorders and cannot be caused by distinct separate genes.

The claim that psychiatry has gotten more scientific in the last twenty years is a scam. It is a posture of science. The big selling point is the genetics of schizophrenia and other mental illnesses. The thought patterns are no more scientific than those of Sigmund Fraud and colleagues.

Psychiatry has not gone from Fraudian superstition to real science in twenty years. No way. It's the same people. Shrinks used to know that 99% of incest memories were Oedipal fantasies. Now they know that 83% of the cause of schizophrenia is genetic. It's all a scam.

Before they were selling Fraud. Now they're selling genetics. The content has changed, but nothing else.

By the way, if you want to talk about a polygenetic predisposition to psychopathology in general that contributes 50% or less of the causation of serious mental health problems, I am with you. Specific genes or sets of genes for specific psychiatric disorders as defined in DSM-IV? Forget it. It's a scam.

A scam to get research dollars, power and prestige. Like all scams, it will have its day, then fail.

Tick, tick, tick, tick.

59

THEM CRAZY PILLS SURE DON'T WORK TOO GOOD

I remember, as a psychiatry resident, reading *The Comprehensive Textbook of Psychiatry, Third Edition, 1980.* According to that learned tome, incest occurs in one family out of a million in North America.

I encountered many other anecdotes, myths, folklore beliefs, superstitions, and lies in that book, but not much science. One of the superstitions that was taught, taught and re-taught to me, in my textbooks, in my lectures, and in my clinical supervision, was the idea that antipsychotic medications are effective.

The scientific fact is they barely work at all. The myth that these drugs are effective is a close relative of another main figure in the family tree of psychiatry, the Schizophrenia Gene Scam.

"Ya sure kin tell it's a brain disease cause them pills work so good! Gosh durn it, perfessor, ya know it's true."

In response to this analysis, the Professor of Psychiatry nods his head in agreement.

Let's take a look at the data. Data. Data, data.

Take Seroquel, for instance. It's a new antipsychotic medication that doesn't have too many side effects. Came on the market in the 1990's. It really is better than the old drugs because of the lower neurological side effects (I promise I won't talk about the diabetes and obesity it causes). But how effective is it, how well does it work, really?

The main study that got Seroquel approved by the Federal Drug Administration in the United States involved 361 people with schizophrenia recruited from 26 different research centers. Some got placebo, some 75 milligrams of Seroquel, some 150, some 300 and some 600 milligrams. It turned out that 150 milligrams was the most effective dose.

To get into the study, the subjects had to have schizophrenia with a current flare-up of their disorder and they had to score above 27 on the Brief Psychiatric Rating Scale (BPRS), a widely used measure of psychotic symptoms. A score above 27 means you are really sick.

"Wait a minute! Hold your horses, here. Why were 26 different research centers required to round up 361 schizophrenics?"

That's because of what are called *exclusion criteria* in drug studies. Exclusion criteria are the things that get you kicked out of a drug study. In the Seroquel study, subjects were not allowed into the study if they had any other psychiatric disorders like depression or substance abuse going along with the schizophrenia. They couldn't have serious medical problems, be pregnant or have received injectable antipsychotic medications recently.

"Goodbye most schizophrenics."

The reason 26 different research centers were required is because it is very hard to find such squeaky-clean, pure, straight-forward schizophrenics. But that's OK because the subjects in the drug studies are so clean and simple, they are easy to treat, which makes the drugs look real good. In the messy world of real psychiatry, you rarely find a schizophrenic without depression, substance abuse, suicidal ideation, medical problems or other exclusion criteria. But hey, it's the ivory tower.

So how good is Seroquel for the easiest, cleanest patients in the world? Ready? Here come the data.

The subjects on 150 milligrams of Seroquel had an average BPRS score of 47.2 at the start of the study. At the end of the study, the average score was 38.3. This was a symptom reduction of 18.6%, which is barely noticeable. At the end of the study, the average patient on the most effective dosage of Seroquel was still 11 points above the cutoff score required to get into the study. In other words, still really, really psychotic.

Another way the data were analyzed was to look at the number of people who could be classified as "responders" to Seroquel. Sure, the average person only had the edge taken off his or her symptoms, but how many people got a big benefit?

In the study, a "responder" was defined as someone whose BPRS score fell by 40% or more. This, according to the psychiatrists doing the study, the drug company, the Food and Drug Administration, the editor of the journal in which the results were published, and shrinks in general, is a good, solid response.

The percentage of subjects who were "responders" to the most effective dose of Seroquel (150 milligrams) was 29.2%. Less than one third of subjects!

"Wait another second. Hold those horses again. If you start at an average score of 47.2 on the BPRS and have a score reduction of 40%, your score is now 28.3 – still high enough to get into the study. We call such a person a "responder"?"

It turns out that only about 25% of subjects on the most effective dose of Seroquel ended up with scores below 27 on the BPRS – 75% were still sick enough to get into the study again. This means that, scientifically, medically, antipsychotic medications only work for a small percentage of people. For most people, they only take the edge off the symptoms, or do nothing.

In another paper summarizing the data on Seroquel, the authors compare the data on Seroquel to data on another new antipsychotic, Zyprexa. The idea was to demonstrate that Seroquel is as effective as Zyprexa, which it is, as proven by the data.

Additional factoid: in this paper, there is a bar graph showing the percentage of subjects who were responders to Seroquel and the percentage who were responders to Zyprexa in a separate study of Zyprexa. The percentage of subjects who responded to placebo in the Zyprexa study was greater than the percentage who responded to Seroquel in the Seroquel study!

This is not an odd or unusual finding. It is typical. To repeat: the scientific fact is that antipsychotic medications barely work. They aren't useless, but they only help a little bit. From the behavior and verbal utterances of psychiatrists, you would think these drugs are pretty powerful. They aren't. Scam alert! Case closed. Chapter closed.

60

ST. JOHN'S WART, OR WORT

There are a couple of things I don't understand about this guy, John. How did he get to be a saint? And why is everybody so interested in his wart?

Maybe I'm misreading the literature on St. John's Wart. All these smart Professors of Psychiatry couldn't be that out to lunch. Maybe, maybe, maybe. . .

"Anybody hear an echo in here?"

"Not me, gov. Wort yer hearin'?"

"Sounds like some kind of obsessive rumination combined with dyslexia."

"Well, gov, I'll see if we's got somat fer dat."

"Oh, I say, Jeeves, sounds like you have a tectonic plate problem there."

"Say what?"

"Continental drift, old boy. Shifting continents."

"Yessir, massah, whatevah ya'll say, massah."

"Oh, I say, Basil, could you help Jeeves with his dentures? I do believe they've slipped again."

"Dentures? Don't you mean his plate, Cecil?"

"Quite, Basil, quite."

The April 10, 2002 issue of *JAMA, The Journal of the American Medical Association* was a hoot. In case you missed it, let me fill you in. There was an article about St. John's Wart, two about use of placebo in drug studies of depression, one about declining student interest in psychiatry, one about misperceptions behind mental health policy, one about psychiatry and stigmatization, one about overcoming pessimism about treatment of addiction, and one about chlorpromazine and the psychopharmacologic revolution.

It was a heavy propaganda issue.

The author of the article on overcoming pessimism about treatment of addiction pointed out that treatments for addiction are actually pretty effective. Problem, he said, is the dumb-heads in Washington don't get that.

The author of the article on declining student interest in psychiatry blamed the problem on managed care and was mystified about why medical student attitudes towards psychiatry get worse the more exposure they have to psychiatry.

The misperceptions behind mental health policy author stated that psychiatric treatments are quite effective and the problem is the dumb-heads in Washington don't get that.

The psychiatry and stigmatization author lamented the fact that the public doesn't buy the biological disease model of mental illness. He said that scientific research "has not been successful in fully convincing the public or physicians that tangible biological disturbances underpin diseases of the mind as well as the body."

The chlorpromazine revolution author told the same story about the wonderful, effective antipsychotic medications we hear on every street corner. Well, at least on every street corner where a psychiatrist is standing on a soap box.

The authors of the article on placebo response in studies of depression reviewed all placebo-controlled drug trials for depression published in the English literature between 1981 and 2000. After kicking out a bunch of studies that had bad methodology, they then analyzed the data from 75 drug studies.

The overall results?

"Take a breath, take a breath. Sit down. You can handle this."

"Response" to medication or placebo was defined as a 50% or greater drop in depression scores during the study.

Based on this criterion, the overall results from the 75 studies were:

Percentage of subjects responding to placebo – 30.0%

Percentage of subjects responding to medication – 50.1%.

Hmm.

Medical students are not impressed by the power of psychiatric medications.

Hmm.

I wonder why?

Then there was the study of St. John's Wart. It was even funnier. You've got to give these doctors credit for being good comedians.

The study involved 340 depressed patients who got either placebo, St. John's Wart or the antidepressant, sertraline (Zoloft).

The conclusion of the study?

The doctors wrote that, "This study fails to support the efficacy of [St. John's Wart] in moderately severe depression."

The doctors made this point a bunch of times in their paper. They concluded by saying that, "According to available data, [St. John's Wart] should not be substituted for standard clinical care of proven efficacy, including antidepressant medications and specific psychotherapies, for the treatment of major depression of moderate severity."

Goodbye St. John's Wart. It just doesn't work.

The evidence?

The percentage of subjects who had a full response to placebo – 37.0%

The percentage of subjects who had a full response to St. John's Wart – 27.0%

The percentage of subjects who had a partial response to placebo – 13.0%

The percentage of subjects who had a partial response to St. John's Wart – 16.0%.

There you have it. Statistically, St. John's Wart is no better than placebo. Goodbye health food nuts. Science just kicked your butts.

You can't argue with science.

By the way, who manufactures sertraline? Answer – Pfizer.

There are six authors on this paper. In tiny print at the end of the article is a long list of items under the heading, "Financial Disclosures."

The first author holds stock in Pfizer, has received speaker fees from Pfizer, has been a scientific advisor to Pfizer, has received research support from Pfizer, and has received drugs for studies from Pfizer. The Zoloft for the study was donated by Pfizer.

Every other author has also received money from Pfizer.

But, hey, you can't argue with science. The data clearly show that St. John's Wart is no better than placebo for moderate depression. Fact. Proven. End of discussion.

It follows, scientifically, that, based on this and another similar study, in which St. John's Wart also was no better than placebo, psychiatrists should prescribe proven, effective drugs like Zoloft. The authors of the study point this out many times over.

You with me? We know this, scientifically, because of the data from the study.

The funeral for St. John's Wart is tomorrow.

Oh. Whoops. I forgot to tell you one thing. The Zoloft data.

How did Zoloft do in the study? We used the data to prove that St. John's Wart is no better than placebo. Right? Right. Therefore we have to go with Zoloft and other antidepressant drugs, like Effexor. I know Effexor is good because a two-page ad in the April 10, 2002 issue of *JAMA* tells me so.

But back to the data:

Full response to placebo – 37.0%

Full response to St. John's Wart – 27.0%

Full response to Zoloft – 27.0%

Partial response to placebo – 13.0%

Partial response to St. John's Wart – 16.0%

Partial response to Zoloft – 26.0%.

Way to go, colleagues! Way to go, objective scientists.

Maybe, maybe, maybe. . . maybe the funeral for St. John's Wart is part of The Great Psychiatry Scam.

Why aren't we having a funeral for Zoloft? If the study proves that St. John's Wart is no better than placebo, it equally proves that Zoloft is no better than placebo. But the shrinks execute St. John's Wart and go back to the bank laughing. Sorry, I mean the drug company.

Of course the shrinks have a scientific answer. There are lots of studies in which Zoloft, Effexor and other antidepressants are better than placebo.

Uh huh. Are there also lots of studies where there is no difference between shrink drug and placebo? For antidepressants? Yep. Antipsychotics? Yep. Anxiolytics (anti-anxiety drugs)? Yep? Mood stabilizers? Yep. Every shrink drug on the market? Yep.

But we are ready for the funeral here at Godot Medical School. St. John's Wart has got to come off. It's a blemish on the face of psychiatry. There ain't much dough in it, either.

Two studies, and John's Wart is cured. Wow! Those Professors of Psychiatry are sure good scientists! Wonder why real doctors and medical students don't get it?

Hmm.

Can I get back to you on that?

61

SAY AGAIN, HOW MANY SYNAPSES?

Some Senior Professors in the Department of Psychiatry have proposed that the brain is a biological machine. The structure of the brain is controlled by the DNA, they say, and "the mind" is merely a sloppy, subjective, unscientific word for brain output. DNA controls the brain, the brain controls the mind, and psychiatrists treat genetic brain diseases.

How far off of reality is this core belief of biological psychiatry? By a factor of one billion.

How many genes are there in the human genome? The final, final word isn't in, but ballpark it's about 30,000. Maybe about 60% of these genes code for brain proteins.

How many synapses are there in the human brain? The final word is not in here, either, but the range is 100 trillion to 1000 trillion. This means that there are about a billion synapses for every gene. This means that the synaptic design, structure and function of the brain is completely out of the control of the DNA. It is not biologically determined in any "biology is destiny" kind of fashion.

What really happens, medically, biologically and scientifically, is a profusion of synaptic growth that is completely random and uncontrolled from a genetic perspective. There is also intensive pruning or trimming of synapses going on all the time. All of this growing and trimming is highly responsive to input from the environment. A motto of neuroscience is: *neurons that fire together, wire together.*

Which neurons fire together is highly responsive to the environment - to learning, experience, perception, social context, meaning and reinforcement.

How fast are synapses created? If there are 100 trillion synapses, this means that during a nine-month pregnancy, about ten million synapses are created per second, on average. TEN MILLION PER SECOND!!

Attention, boys and girls: TEN MILLION PER SECOND AND ONLY 30,000 GENES.

This is how preposterous, unscientific, un-biological, and off of reality current biological psychiatry is, with its "genetic" model of mental disorders. Literally off by a factor of one billion. Psychiatry was a lot closer on rates of incest - there it was only off by a factor of 10,000.

What *is* biologically true, then? DNA certainly controls the macroscopic structure of the brain, such as the existence of a right and left hemisphere, the location of the cerebellum, and where the major nerve tracts run. But that is not where the action is in psychiatry. There is no consistent macroscopic, structural brain abnormality in any psychiatric disorder. The action is all at the microscopic level, even according to biological psychiatry - at the level of synapses and neurotransmitters.

It is scientifically impossible to have a "genetic" mental disorder at this level because there is only one gene per billion synapses. The structure and function of synapses cannot be under direct genetic control. Therefore abnormal genes cannot cause mental disorders in any direct causal fashion.

"What was that noise, Basil?"

"Not sure , not sure. Sounded like a house of cards collapsing."

"Not to worry, old chap. Plenty of sherry left."

"Quite."

62

VACUUM BABY VACUUM

In case you are uncertain where all this ends up, let me enlighten you. I'm talking about the Great Psychiatry Scam. I'm talking about the drugs-genes-biological psychiatry package.

Behind the mask of pleasant smiling liberal humanitarian is a Nazi eugenics doctor. Nothing has changed. It's the same bogus package that psychiatrists marketed to Hitler in the last millennium. Back then, the German psychiatrists told Hitler that mental disease is caused by bad genes and they, the psychiatrists, could identity who has the bad genes.

There were three lies then and there are three lies now: 1) psychiatry has established scientifically that bad genes cause mental disease 2) psychiatrists can identify who has the bad genes through clinical interviews, and 3) killing the mentally ill will erase the bad genes from the gene pool, thereby eradicating mental disease. In order to identify the mentally ill for the Final Solution, the Nazi psychiatrists made "diagnoses."

How does the eugenics plan sound when an American psychiatrist states it in the current millennium? Like this:

> *If we learn as much as it looks like we might about the genetics of major mental illness, I predicted in the Archives just a couple of months ago, major mental illnesses may be very rare diseases in a hundred years. Because our ability to detect them in utero may be so trivially easy that the majority of our citizens may decide to stamp them out, as we have with, for example, Tay-Sachs disease.*

This was not an isolated kook psychiatrist talking. This was Dr. Robert Michels, Past President of the American College of Psychiatrists, 1998 candidate for President of the American Psychiatric Association (he lost the election) and Deputy Editor of *The American Journal of Psychiatry* addressing the crowd at the Annual Meeting of the American College of Psychiatrists in Vancouver on February 26, 2003.

It's exactly the same bogus eugenics plan. What it means is abortion of genetic mutants, thereby cleansing the gene pool. The humanitarian advance is that properly educated citizens will "choose" to abort their children, instead of the Third Reich doing it for them when the fetuses are adults. The American Final Solution is more efficient than the Nazi Final Solution.

God Bless America.

And God Bless the Drug Companies - they paid for 63 pages of full-color ads in the April, 2003 issue of *The American Journal of Psychiatry*. That helped keep the American Psychiatric Association and its eugenics plan afloat financially. I chose the April, 2003 edition at random - it's the same cash flow from drug companies to psychiatry every month.

63

SCHIZOPHRENICS DON'T HAVE SPLIT PERSONALITIES

Thank God there's one thing you can count on from shrinks. They know the difference between schizophrenia and multiple personality disorder. The general public, however, is confused on that point, as the shrinks repeatedly note with amused condescension.

"I've read it here. I've read it there. He's a well-respected shrink about town, doing the best things so conservatively. And he's oh so good, and he's oh so fine. He's. . ."

"Shaddup down there! I'm trying to sleep!"

Returning to the point at hand, in North American psychiatry there is a very clear conceptual system in place. Schizophrenia is an inherited biological brain disease. It is treated with medication just like any other medical disease.

"Ain't no use analyzing a schizophrenic," I was taught in my psychiatry residency.

Schizophrenia is a psychosis. Psychosis is a heavy-duty brain disturbance where you get crazy and lose touch with reality and start hallucinating and thinking the Martians are monitoring you through a listening device implanted in your living room lamp. Psychiatrists are the medical experts on this kind of brain disease. Cardiologists specialize in the heart, gastroenterologists specialize in the gut, and psychiatrists specialize in the brain. All doctors. All in the club.

This Scam is milked for grant money, prestige, high salaries, political power, and the right to prescribe drugs.

There is a completely separate category called the neuroses. Now we are talking about neurotic reactions to the environment. These are not real medical diseases. They are forms of *hysteria*. Pretty well only women suffer from hysteria, except for a few guys of questionable virility.

Take multiple personality disorder, for instance. Now there is a classic example of hysteria! Best thing for women who think they have too many people in their heads is to get them away from their crazy therapists. Then everything settles down pretty quick. That's what the shrinks know for sure. Just ask Officer McHugh. He wrote it down so nobody would get mixed up anymore.

"Thanks, Paul."

At this point you're probably thinking, "Who is Eugen Bleuler, anyway?"

"Hold on a minute. I'm getting to him."

Let's get it straight. Schizophrenia is a brain disease caused by bad genes. It's medical. Shrinks are experts on it. You treat it with meds, not therapy. Multiple personality is hysteria. It's not a real disease. If you ignore it and sue the therapists into the ground, multiple personality will go away.

"Yep. We sure got that straight here in Shrinkville, dad gum!"

OK. Question. Why is schizophrenia called schizophrenia? What does schizophrenia mean, anyway? Answer. It is a Greek term invented by Eugen Bleuler in 1908 to replace the previous name for schizophrenia, *dementia praecox*. Schizophrenia means *split mind*.

An uneducated person with a low I.Q. might ask, "If schizophrenia means split mind disorder, then why am I an idiot for thinking that people with schizophrenia have split personalities?"

The common folk are always asking dumb questions like this. Thankfully, psychiatrists are available to make correct diagnoses. Bleuler helped them get it straight. He is one of the top few experts on schizophrenia of the entire twentieth century.

No shrink textbook questions Bleuler's top-of-the-totem-pole status on schizophrenia. The shrinks are working hard to correct popular myths about mental illness, such as the myth that people with schizophrenia have split personalities. This was reported, for instance, in the December 7, 2001 issue of *Psychiatric News*, the trade paper of the American Psychiatric Association.

The National Alliance for Research on Schizophrenia and Depression, which is a major league grant agency, conducted a survey on myths about mental illness, the results of which were reported in the *Psychiatric News* article. One such myth is the misunderstanding that schizophrenics have split personalities. The shrinks are just about unanimous that schizophrenia and multiple personality are in two completely separate, distinct categories.

Doesn't matter if you talk to a shrink who believes in multiple personality, or one who doesn't. Believer and nonbeliever both agree on the two categories, neurosis and psychosis, reaction to the environment and inherited brain disease, multiple personality in Box One, schizophrenia in Box Two.

Believers think multiple personality occurs naturally in childhood as a reaction to an abusive, traumatic environment. Nonbelievers think it occurs in adulthood as a reaction to a toxic therapy. But both agree it belongs in Box One.

"Thank God we got one thing straight."

There remained a nagging question, when I was learning about schizophrenia in my psychiatry residency. "Why did Bleuler call schizophrenia *split mind* if it has nothing to do with split personality, which is a synonym for dual personality, multiple personality and, now, dissociative identity disorder?"

Of course, my shrink Professors had an answer: "He thought that a split between thought and feeling was the core of the disorder."

Once that answer is given, there are no more questions to ask. It is another example of MCQ thinking. The schizophrenia-split mind disorder problem is wrapped up, investigated, analyzed, categorized and done for, and anyway, everyone's beeper just went off. No time for academic questions. Patients to see.

I'm a little slow upstairs. I don't get it. "A split between thought and feeling?"

If Bleuler is one of the top experts on schizophrenia in the history of psychiatry, and the shrink who named the disorder, and if he thought a split between thought and feeling is the core of the disorder, then why is there not a single word in the recent schizophrenia literature about a split between thought and feeling, or a split of any kind? Why is there no mention of a split in the mind of a schizophrenic in DSM-IV? Why is there no mention of a split in the entire literature on antipsychotic medication?

One more annoying question. "Why doesn't anyone actually read Bleuler?"

I can answer that question. Because Bleuler's description of schizophrenia is EXACTLY IDENTICAL TO THE DSM-IV DESCRIPTION OF DISSOCIATIVE IDENTITY DISORDER.

"Hello? Anybody home?"

If you read Bleuler, you realize the Emperor has no clothes. Solution? Don't read him. Cover the problem with a revisionist MCQ answer.

"Oh, oh. Beeper went off."

Here are some quotes from the 1950 English translation of Bleuler's classic textbook on schizophrenia, as reprinted in a Synopsis of the text published in 1966:

> *Single emotionally charged ideas or drives attain a certain degree of autonomy so that the personality falls to pieces. These fragments can then exist side by side and alternately dominate the main part of the*

> *personality, the conscious part of the person.*
>
> *Patient knows what he has formerly experienced but ascribes it to another person.*
>
> *When patient is split into two or more personalities they may operate alternately or simultaneously and tend to speak of themselves in the third person.*
>
> *A part of the personality may detach itself and be attributed to another person.*
>
> *Another person may be incorporated by the patient.*

I remember a consult I did on a black woman in her thirties who had an alter personality named J.R. Ewing, who believed he was the character from the TV show *Dallas*. When I asked J.R. Ewing how he explained the fact that he was living inside the body of a black woman, he became incensed, stormed out of the room, and never returned to the consultation room. The staff at the hospital I was consulting to continued to treat the woman for schizophrenia.

This woman was no more psychotic than the field of psychiatry.

The biggest expert on schizophrenia of the twentieth century called schizophrenia *split mind*. He described schizophrenia in exactly the same way that DSM-IV describes dissociative identity disorder.

It is absolutely impossible, logically, scientifically, and medically to endorse the following three propositions simultaneously: "I don't believe in multiple personality - I do believe in schizophrenia - Bleuler is a great expert on schizophrenia."

Or wait a minute. . . No, it isn't. Where? You got it. At the Mad Hatter's Tea Party.

This completes my report from Planet Earth.

Signed, Colin of Altair.

P.S. Look for a book by Colin A. Ross, M.D. on this conceptual mess, available in bookstores on that planet. Title: *Schizophrenia: Innovations in Diagnosis and Treatment*. The author goes into the Scam about Box One and Box Two and destroys the two boxes.

Shrinks on Planet Earth are expected to attack with full fangs.

64

BIPOLAR MOOT DISORDER

It's a moot point whether you have bipolar mood disorder or not because if you have been to a psychiatrist recently, you do, in fact you don't even have to go because you could be certain you have bipolar mood disorder even when you're still on the way to your first appointment so there's no need to go because everyone and his dog has bipolar mood disorder these days which your shrink knows is a genetic brain disease resulting in a chemical imbalance even though concordance in monozygotic twins is only 40% but then you don't have to let the facts interfere with your happiness when you're manic so what the hey eh?

Bipolar mood disorder should not be confused with bipolar moat disorder - no cases of the latter have been diagnosed since the Middle Ages.

One of my proposed to myself in my head but now on paper future books has the title, *Bipolar Mood Disorder: The Bad Little Girl Who Decided To Be Good*. The title pretty well sums up everything I have to say on the subject.

Until that book is out you'll just have to take it on faith that bipolar mood disorder is the most overused diagnosis in psychiatry currently. It therefore has honored status within the Great Psychiatry Scam.

65

BANG, BANG, YOU'RE DEAD

Now here's a crazy conspiracy theory. Let's say that the Government of the United States of America adopted the official position that antidepressants increase the risk of suicidal thinking, suicidal behavior, completed suicide, homicidal thinking and completed homicide in children and adolescents. Increase it compared to placebo in children who are being treated for depression.

This could be science fiction. Or it could be the official position of the Food and Drug Administration. It could be that the Food and Drug Adminstration did a thorough scientific analysis of the drug company data and then ordered drug companies to place a BLACK BOX WARNING on SSRI antidepressant labels stating this very exact same conspiratorial science fiction scientific fact.

But let's just say that happened on some other planet. On that planet - but not on our planet, of course - where would we look for examples of children and adolescents who had committed murder while on antidepressants? How about school shooters?

Back to planet earth. Fortunately, here on earth, the tobacco companies assured us for decades that cigarettes do not cause lung cancer. We have those good corporate citizens to thank for that. And drugs companies through their shrink spokesdealers assure us there is nothing to worry about concerning SSRI's. Meanwhile dozens of school shooters have been on antidepressants.

Thanks, colleagues, for the safety endorsements!

66

THE DSM-IV COMMITTEE

My name appears in DSM-IV. Don't hold that against me.

I was on the DSM-IV dissociative disorders committee. Our job was to review the five dissociative disorders and make changes to the text and the diagnostic criteria. The diagnostic criteria are the rules for making the diagnoses. We tinkered around and made a few changes, nothing major. As far as the diagnostic criteria are concerned.

There were a few clods on the committee, but mostly it was a reasonable and intelligent group of people. There wasn't a lot of posturing or political maneuvering. We just did the work. The best part of the experience was getting to attend a committee meeting held on the Presidio in San Francisco, just before the American Psychiatric Association Annual Meeting. That was cool.

We did make quite a few changes in the text, updating it based on research published since DSM-III-R came out in 1987.

The biggee was we changed the name of multiple personality disorder to dissociative identity disorder. MPD to DID. This was like eradicating smallpox. What a rush! Suddenly, all cases of multiple personality were cured. Strangely, the next day, each one of these people came down with dissociative identity disorder.

I had experienced the hypocrisy of semantic changes as a victim of the Manitoba Unified Family Court, less than a decade earlier. My relationship with my children was restricted and devalued on the grounds that I was male. This was supposed to hurt less if they called it joint custody, rather than sole custody.

The idea was that people would buy MPD better if we called it DID. I voted against the name change. Since the committee was only advisory, the vote didn't carry much weight. Suddenly, I was treating DID.

Everyone on the committee agreed that MPD was a bad name for the disorder. Everyone agreed that these people don't really have more than one personality. But we couldn't decide what new name to choose. DID was pulled out of a hat late in the process.

I voted against the name change because I am against semantic card tricks. MPD had a century of history and everyone knew what it meant. PMS had been renamed *late luteal phase dysphoric disorder* in DSM-III-R. That seemed ridiculous to me. There was no way LLPDD would ever become part of the

English language. Do not confuse LLPDD with the LAPD.

We thought the blockheads might stop disbelieving in MPD if we made it clear we don't believe these are literally separate people or personalities. I was pessimistic about the desired effect accruing. But I understood the motivation and the strategy.

As it turned out, I have warmed up to DID. I use it in my professional writing for journals. I renamed my textbook in its second edition. It is now called *Dissociative Identity Disorder: Diagnosis, Clinical Features and Treatment of Multiple Personality (Second Edition)*. I talk about DID to my patients. But I am still bilingual. I use MPD and DID interchangeably.

DID really is a better name. It's more neutral and takes the emphasis off the alter personalities. Which is good. I agree with my colleague who says these people don't have multiple personalities. Their problem is that they have less than one personality. They have no unified, coherent identity.

The False Memory Police are beating us over the head for changing the name. You can't win with them. They used to beat us over the head for the previous name, now they beat us for changing it.

When psychologists treat experimental lab animals this way, the animals are said to have been subjected to *inescapable shock*. Inescapable shock induces *learned helplessness*, which is a withdrawn apathetic state. Otherwise known as giving up. The alternative response strategy is homicidal rage. In animals.

Fortunately, Cro-Magnon man has other response strategies available to him. Or her. To them. At them. Them, the Invaders From Mars. The False Memory Police.

Speaking of aliens, the interesting question is not whether they do or do not exist.

There is one and only one interesting thing about aliens and UFOs. That is the physics of their propulsion systems.

Here is an interesting problem.

"Now hear this."

An aircraft carrying biological passengers makes right angle turns at many times the speed of sound within the earth's atmosphere. Assume for a minute that this is really happening. The physics of the craft's propulsion system cannot be Newtonian. The biological passenger cannot be experiencing conventional Newtonian forces of motion. Otherwise he would be splattered against the inside wall of the UFO during the right-angle turn.

A physicist who figured out how to solve this problem would be up there with Einstein. While the non-believers are scoffing, let the research begin.

Same thing with DID. The scoffers are irrelevant. Scientifically.

We did not talk about aliens on the DSM-IV Dissociative Disorders Committee.

There are quite a few psychiatric syndromes that should be added to DSM-V. Parental Alienation Syndrome. Alien Abduction Syndrome. Twentieth Century Syndrome. Or no, that last one has been cured. The aliens do have a right to be recognized, I believe. We have animal rights. Why not alien rights? Shouldn't aliens have inalienable rights?

I'm asking that question as a psychiatrist. A medical professional. A scientifically trained specialist in the mind and brain.

While I'm on the subject, another amazing aspect of The Great Psychiatry Scam is popular superstitions about what psychiatrists know. People think I "know" all kinds of stuff I haven't a clue about.

Someone will say, "My son prefers Superman cartoons to Batman cartoons. What does that *mean*?"

My answer is usually something like, "That means he will grow up to be a serial killer."

I try to joke it off. But people think I really know. I used to think this was evidence of ignorance and superstition in the general population. It is. But I figured out it is also part of The Great Psychiatry Scam.

You don't see any psychiatrists standing up to expose the Naked Emperor. No way. The shrinks like the superstition that they have X-ray vision. Good for their income. No group of shrinks ever got together to run The Scam as a coordinated marketing plan. It just kind of happens. Lemmings. Shrinks. Ants.

The shrinks slide the superstition about X-ray vision out into the culture, on the sly, they being sly. Like a virus. A sexually transmitted disease. Shrinks have been fornicating with the planet for over one hundred years.

The shrinks should be quarantined. I've got to clean up the planet. It's not like I have a choice. It's my job description. Planetary shaman. I retired from shrinkdom part way through this book. Psychiatry is now my patient.

"Oh, oh. Megalomania. Get Ross some haldol, quick."

"Right away, Basil. Right away. Nurse! Twenty milligrams I.M. Stat!"

What would be the correct DSM-IV diagnosis? Maybe Disagreement with the

Big Boys Syndrome. I know the shrinks will come up with some DSM-IV-based slander for me, when *The Great Psychiatry Scam* comes out. I helped put DSM-IV together. I belong to the American Psychiatric Association. I know The Scam from the inside.

67

EXPERT WITNESS GAMES

I might write a separate book about my experiences as an expert witness. Many amazing stories.

One reason I decided to do expert witness work was to desensitize myself to the courtroom and legal procedures. In case I ever got sued. That turned out to be a good plan. I know how the game works, in detail. I know the lingo, from Bates stamp to consulting expert to Frye-Daubert hearing.

I have testified for both the defense and the plaintiff in malpractice lawsuits. I was an expert witness in a legal malpractice suit against a law firm. Previously, I was an expert witness for that law firm in a medical malpractice lawsuit. Being an expert witness is like going on rides at the carnival, except you get paid and you don't have to stand in line.

There are many things I like about lawyers. They are a lot smarter than shrinks. They are more normal and have better mental health. They have a far, far better grasp of evidence and argument. Tactics? Way ahead of shrinks.

Just look at how society is organized. Politicians run the government. They're mostly lawyers. See any shrinks there? Nobody in his right mind would vote for the average shrink. See any shrinks sitting on the bench as judges? See any shrinks earning seven figures as corporate executives? See shrinks being in control of any aspect of the social system?

Hardly. The shrinks have completely lost control of the health care system. How many lawyers get sued for malpractice, compared to doctors? The lawyers have got it pretty good. They make the laws. But they construct the laws so that lawyers have to earn lots more money debating them and revising them. All the way to the Supreme Court.

The money in the legal system is way above the levels in the mental health system. One conference table in a big law firm's office is worth more than all my office furniture put together.

Take the costs of death row in Texas. At any time there are about 350 people on death row in Texas. This was the entire population of Norman Wells when I lived there in the seventies. The average time a person spends on death row is nine years. Then they get the big injection.

The average cost of a death row inmate from conviction to execution is $2,200,000.00. This is for all the appeals and legal hearings. The average cost of keeping these people in jail for the rest of their lives with no chance of parole would be $700,000.00. The State of Texas is spending an extra $1,500,000.00 per death row inmate per decade to execute them, compared to giving them life without parole. Multiplied by 350 people that is about half a billion dollars per decade.

Where does this money go? Into the criminal justice system. The death penalty is a cash cow for lawyers. You don't see shrinks getting a deal like that from the State. Half a billion dollars!

It makes me really angry when I think what I could do with that money in the mental health system. I can't get my hands on it because the lawyers are way smarter, better organized and in control of the social system. Way ahead of the shrinks.

Thanks again, colleagues.

Another thing about lawyers is they don't take things personally. Shrinks do. Big time. But lawyers can insult the hell out of each other in the courtroom, then go to lunch together. Shrinks get all bent out of shape and hold grudges for years. Careers. Lawyers go to work but take time off at lunch.

Lawyers also keep much better records. Of course they get paid more the more paper they generate, so this is not surprising. But you can actually tell what a lawyer is doing and why he is doing it from the paperwork. Not so with shrinks. The average shrinkiatric medical record is extremely vague. I know this from reading lots of them, as a clinician and as an expert witness.

Another thing about being an expert witness is, you get to find out what people are actually doing. I have testified against a number of colleagues in malpractice suits. People I have published with and sat on committees with at the International Society for the Study of Dissociation. People I have chatted to at conferences, had lunch with, and been driven around by in their hometowns.

I've taken political heat about this. But I don't care if they are Dissociation Club Members. I don't play by those rules. In fact, the opposite. I feel I have a duty to police the zany malpractice that goes on in the dissociative disorders field. The patients need to be protected from my colleagues. The field needs to be protected from the field.

Not everyone in the mental health field is nuts. But many are. There are people I know who seemed pretty with it and sensible at meetings. You can't tell by having lunch with them what they are actually doing with their patients. Then when you read their charts, holy cow! You find out what is really going on.

I have testified in cases where I'm not allowed to know the settlement figure. Testified against Dissociation Club Members. All I know is we're talking seven figures. Big cases. I learned a ton about my colleagues by doing expert witness work.

The main thing I have noticed reading dozens of depositions by defendants, defense experts and plaintiff's experts, is how full of shit most shrinks and therapists are. How vague. They do an incredible amount of waffling and they can't explain anything clearly.

I've read dozens of professionals giving incredibly vague explanations of all kinds of things in psychiatry. Everything from the definition of counter-transference to the DSM-IV criteria for borderline personality to the causes of depression. One shrink, a Professor at the Medical School, claimed to be able to diagnose over thirty chemically distinct types of depression. She claimed she would choose which antidepressant to prescribe based on such distinctions.

I'm not lying. Or exaggerating. Or kidding. The shrink was talking complete bullshit, while bashing the defendant for being unscientific.

I have read numerous examples of shrink expert witnesses stating conclusions with complete dogmatic certainty. Then when the lawyer asks them the foundation of the conclusion, they can't give a single piece of evidence or data to support it.

What about ability to quote the literature? Unbelievable! Not one expert witness in ten can give a coherent, referenced account of the literature on the point under discussion. Some can't name a single publication correctly on a disorder they have diagnosed in the case.

Top brains in the profession.

In expert witness work, the fascists really show their true colors. There you get hypocrisy to the max. Pretending they know stuff they don't. Having complete certainty about something when they in fact don't know the relevant literature. Crucifying people for not doing things they themselves don't do. Or doing things they themselves do do. It's doo doo.

When I went into psychiatry, I had a good attitude towards shrinks. And psychiatry. My respect for shrinks started off high. It has been whittled down and down and down by experience. Reading depositions of brain dead colleagues has been a major cause of scorn.

You think I am bitter? Negative? Projecting? Sorry. I'm not. I'm just telling it like it is. The purpose of this book is to get the negative energy of my colleagues puked back up. I don't want it inside me anymore. This book is a cleansing. Holy water.

Om.

68

DUMPED BY CHARTER

I worked for Charter Medical Corporation from late 1991 to August, 1997. From November, 1991 to May, 1996, I was on what is called a stipend. I was an independent contractor. Charter paid me a monthly fee to run the Dissociative Disorders Unit.

From May, 1996 to August, 1997 I had what is called a *management services contract*. I still ran the Unit, but during this period I employed about a dozen people to run the Unit for me. They had previously been Charter employees, now they were employees of The Colin A. Ross Institute for Psychological Trauma, P.A.

The Unit was always highly profitable for Charter. The CEO at Dallas transferred down to Atlanta in 1995. She then tried to recruit me to move to Atlanta. The upshot of these negotiations was an agreement to start up a second Unit in Atlanta under a management services contract.

The contract was reviewed and approved by the CEO of the Atlanta hospital, Charter Peachford of Atlanta, the woman who had moved from Dallas. It was approved by the CFO of the Hospital and the Corporate Financial Officer for that region. It was approved by the Corporate VP for that region. And by Corporate legal.

In June, 1996, I flew down to Atlanta a couple of times to interview personnel. The Unit was scheduled to open in August, 1996. I went away on vacation for a few weeks in July, expecting to complete the initial hiring when I returned.

Then a shrink got his hands in the pie. Charter Corporate had a token VP Medical because that is the right thing to do. You have to be able to tell managed care companies, insurers and government that you have shrinks involved at top levels. It was strictly token.

But the shrink was maneuvering. He went to the head honcho at Corporate and jockeyed for more real power in the system. The head honcho gave him some. The shrink told the head honcho to cancel my Unit at Atlanta Peachford. The Unit was dead in the water. This all happened during the couple of weeks I was away on vacation.

It took a shrink.

Mere business people would never have canceled the second Unit. It made perfect business, legal and risk management sense to them. I would have made lots of money for Charter and myself. And I was poised to start a third Unit in Phoenix in late 1996.

The shrink was against me. Once he had veto power in the system, I was sunk. Within less than a year, Charter had canceled my contract in Dallas, giving me the required ninety days notice. At the time I left Charter Dallas, I accounted for one third of their revenue. Charter Dallas closed in late 1999. Charter Medical Corporation went bankrupt and ceased to exist shortly thereafter.

The CEO who moved to Atlanta from Dallas got the plum job in Atlanta (Peachford was the flagship hospital in the Charter system) because of me. The incremental revenue generated by me pushed her from an average performer in the system to the fifth most profitable hospital in the system.

Charter was an amazing place to work. The personnel turnover was incredible. I had four different CEOs at Charter Dallas in six years. This was typical of the entire system. After a while, I just couldn't connect with another new Director of Marketing, or Intake, or Social Work, or Medical Records. They all kept changing, annually. There was zero continuity.

The thing that troubled me the most, was listening to each new arrival. Each new person was pumped and positive. Each would talk about the good of the hospital, how census was going to be increased, how we were going to improve this and that. It was like listening to people with end-stage cancer talk about what they plan to be doing ten years from now.

It was 100% certain these people would be gone in a year or two. Quit or fired. People got fired at a really ugly, hurtful, stupid rate. It didn't even make business sense. There were no customer relations. You couldn't form a network. There was zero loyalty. But the new hires pretended they had loyalty.

I can't count the number of times I listened to people explain why someone had to be fired for the good of the hospital. We all had to pull together. Six months later, the person who gave the speech was fired. To be replaced by someone else who gave the same speech. Then got fired.

In Canada, it was not unusual for nurses to receive ten and twenty year pins from St. Boniface Hospital. Shrinks practiced their entire careers at the same hospital. This is called stagnation. But Dallas is at the opposite extreme. Everyone is a transient in everyone else's lives.

The same is true in the yuppie neighborhoods. The old timers have been there five years. People move in and out all the time. It's very difficult to form relationships. Especially if you're a compensated extreme introvert like me.

I arrived in Texas in the same month the Attorney General was starting to prosecute private for-profit hospitals in Texas. A bunch of hospitals and doctors committed major fraud. I never saw outright fraud at Charter Dallas. But I saw lots of shaving clinical services to the bone.

From the time I arrived in November, 1991 to the time I left in August, 1997, I bet Charter Dallas' revenue declined by 75%. The mental health industry has been gutted. This has had a huge impact on clinical services. It's depressing working in an impoverished system in the midst of plenty. There is obscene wealth everywhere in Plano and North Dallas. Business opportunities out the ying yang.

Not in the mental health system. The cash flow through the clinical sector of the mental health system dwindled dramatically in the 1990's. You bet this has affected morale and the quality of clinical care. Humongously. It's close to the point now where it's simply not going to be possible to deliver quality care. There just isn't enough money.

The average quality of care in inpatient psychiatry today in North America is pathetic. There is hardly any real treatment of any kind. There is no real therapy. Group or individual. Lengths of stay are too short for the drugs to start working. It's just warehousing and processing of charts. The satisfaction for the clinical staff is in the basement. Salaries stink and burnout is really high.

I don't know what the future holds for mental health. If the shrinks don't destroy psychiatry, managed care will.

People rotate around from hospital to hospital and company to company so fast in the mental health system, it's like one big company with revolving internal transfers. Except everybody is competing with each other.

It's too stressful. If I could afford to retire, I don't think I would do this work. It's just too much. The shit from colleagues, the pressure from managed care, the indifference of the culture at large. I discourage anyone from going into psychiatry or clinical psychology. Psychiatry is a dying field. There's very little positive energy in it. The positive hype about biology is illusory. There's no real substance in it.

When I first arrived in Dallas, insurance companies paid for psychological testing. We used to get wonderful, thorough, lengthy psychological reports from Ph.D.s. Slashed. Cut. Burned.

Psychiatry just isn't a happy field to work in. Not because of the patients. Because of the system. If it wasn't for the rewards of direct clinical work, it just wouldn't be worth it. That, and my intellectual, research interests.

I think I might choose to have a mid-life crisis soon.

69

ON BECOMING A MIND CONTROL NUT

I have taken quite a bit of abuse because of my study of CIA mind control. I have been made fun of in *Esquire, The New Yorker, The British Journal of Psychiatry, The Journal of the American Medical Association*, several books, on the web, in the Newsletter of the False Memory Syndrome Foundation, in testimony in legal cases, and in several other sewers. Speaking hypothetically, it would cause job stress to find out that two former Directors of Covert Operations for the CIA are mad at you. Mad at you for things you said in a draft of *BLUEBIRD: Deliberate Creation Of Multiple Personality By Psychiatrists*.

Oh well. We all have our crosses to bear.

I undertook the necessary revisions. By the way, I do have in my possession a copy of a 1960 Memo from J. Edgar Hoover to the Director of Naval Intelligence. The subject of the memo is Lee Harvey Oswald. 1960. Hoover wanted the Director of Naval Intelligence to look into Marguerite Oswald's concern that someone was using her son's identity. 1960.

Lee Harvey Oswald was a subject of personal concern to J. Edgar Hoover over three years before JFK was shot.

I am the only physician in world history who has been ridiculed in medical journals as a CIA conspiracy nut.

It feels good.

None of these writers ever interviewed me or asked me what I really think. The propaganda is based entirely on a CBC television program where I was set up to look like a nut, and a leaked book proposal.

It is curious that those who bring the conspiracy nut charge against me are themselves conspiracy nuts. They have nutty conspiracy theories about my being a conspiracy theory nut. This brings us to the nut of the matter. Or the tea party of the Mad Hatter. Whichever. What does it matter? They're all nuts anyway. The pecans, the pistachios, the hazelnuts, the shrinknuts.

What do I mean?

"I meant what I said and I said what I meant. An elephant's word is one hundred per cent."

Was that me who said that? No. It was Horton. Horton who laid an egg. In the

Dr. Seuss book. Dr. Seuss, not Dr. Ross. This is the Dr. Ross book. I'm no nut. But, but, but, but.

"Basil, Basil. He's perseverating now. Get some more haldol."

Back to the subject matter. CIA conspiracy nuts. Like Colin Ross. Conspiracy nuts have characteristic thought patterns. They take little bits of unverified evidence from unreliable sources, and weave them together into a certainty. When patients do this, we call it delusional thinking.

This is what has happened to me. I am the victim of delusions in my colleagues. Which is very pitiful. For them, not me. My status as CIA conspiracy nut is based entirely on a trash job done by the CBC and a leaked book proposal. Or did I say that already?

These pitiable shreds of "evidence" are the proof that I'm loco. In *The British Journal of Psychiatry* and the *Journal of the American Medical Association*. Actually, I'm flattered. I too get mentioned in the tabloids. This makes me a celebrity. My tabloids are two of the leading medical journals in the world. Talk about prestige!

I was interviewed once by a man who identified himself as a freelance science reporter. Back in Canada. He asked me about depersonalization. A while later an article about depersonalization by this writer appeared in a publication called *The National Inquirer*. The article included several paragraphs of direct quotation from me, telling a story about a patient. It was completely made up. I never said one of those words.

But my name appeared. It turns out that the standards of thought about Colin Ross are standardized. Which makes sense, since they are standards. Standardized across *The National Inquirer*, *The British Journal of Psychiatry* and the *Journal of the American Medical Association*.

According to the nuts, my nutty theory is that tens of thousands of children have been turned into Manchurian Candidates by the CIA. The nuts are right. It is a nutty theory. Only problem is, I don't hold it. Never did. Never will.

I do know some facts however. I know these facts to be facts because they are in the documents. CIA documents I obtained through the Freedom of Information Act, 15,000 pages worth. And papers I photocopied from medical and psychiatric journals. None of this, zero, one goose egg, nada, niente, zip, has anything to do with my personal opinions, beliefs or theories. We are talking facts and documents.

Sample tidbits anyone?

Dr. Jose Delgado, a neurosurgeon at Yale University, implanted brain electrodes in children as young as eleven years of age for non-therapeutic purposes on contract to the Office of Naval Research. The experiments and funding are documented in his published papers. You can find them at any medical school library.

The American Psychological Association received funding for mind control research through the CIA's MKULTRA program. The clearance level for the psychologists receiving this money was TOP SECRET.

Dr. Robert Heath at Tulane University tried to cure a 19-year old man's homosexuality by putting electrodes in his brain. The electrodes were stimulated electrically to make him have orgasms while he watched heterosexual pornography. As part of his treatment, the man had intercourse with a female prostitute hired by Dr. Heath. During the intercourse, Dr. Heath studied the man's brain waves. Dr. Heath had contracts with the Army and the CIA. This is all described in Dr. Heath's published papers.

MKULTRA documents describe beaming various kinds of energy at the heads of human beings and animals to make them amnesic or unconscious.

BLUEBIRD and ARTICHOKE documents describe operations to create amnesia in political prisoners prior to their release. An ARTICHOKE Team that included physicians performed interrogations on U.S. soil using sodium amytal and other drugs to create amnesia and false memories.

Children as young as five years of age received LSD for months at a time at Creedmore State Hospital in New York. Their candy man was Dr. Lauretta Bender, revered psychiatrist who received a full-page obituary in *The American Journal of Psychiatry*.

G.H. Estabrooks was the man. Get all the details in my book, *The CIA Doctors*. Given the state of psychiatry, it is not surprising that I get raked over the coals for bringing this dirty history to light. Not the dirty history of the CIA. The dirty history of psychiatry.

I am not a critic of the CIA. Exactly the opposite. The Cold Warriors were the only people who stood between me and Gulag. I am a great admirer of William Donovan, grandfather of the CIA.

What has psychiatry's strategy been to date? For dealing with my study of psychiatric participation in CIA and military mind control? Negative propaganda. A smear campaign. Ridicule.

That's typical.

I am still waiting to hear a voice of reason. From a shrink. In public. In writing. A voice of medicine. Science. Honor. Integrity. Maybe even an apology.

"What's that? What's that? No, can't hear anything," quoth Colin Ross.

All I need is a few good men.

You think I'm a paranoid conspiracy nut? I don't notice one other psychiatrist on the planet having the guts to write *The CIA Doctors*. They're all too paranoid. Or android. Or humanoid. Or just plain annoyed. Or annoying.

Quoth the raven, "Nevermore."

Never more will that negative energy enter my soul. This book is my shield and my sword. You cannot touch me, head shrinkers, with your head-shrinking death rays. Mantra rays. Mantras. Om.

70

BURNING OUT, FLAMING OUT

Why I am experiencing burnout? It isn't the patients. It's the colleagues and the insanity of the mental health system. That's where the stress comes from.

There are many things I was never told in medical school. For instance, how to write prescription orders in medical charts. If the patient is supposed to get his meds once a day, you write o.d.; twice a day, b.i.d.; three times a day, t.i.d.; and four times a day, q.i.d. At bedtime is q.h.s. and take as needed is p.r.n. These are all based on Latin words no doctor actually knows.

When I first went on the wards in med school, I had to learn these abbreviations from the nurses. I had learned that Lesch-Nyan Syndrome is caused by an inherited deficiency of a specific enzyme, and affects a couple of dozen people in the world. Hypoxanthine-guanine phosphoribosyl transferase, if I remember right. But I had not learned the basics of writing med orders.

From the M.D.'s, I learned nothing about the behavior of physicians and why it stresses everybody out, from nurses to physiotherapists to patients. Not a word on that topic, from the docs. That lesson too I learned on the job.

They didn't tell me in med school that I would end up on the outside looking in. Why did I end up there? Club rules. Of those, I broke many. I questioned the dogma of the day, such as the genetic basis of schizophrenia. I took childhood trauma seriously. I diagnosed and treated multiple personality. These were minor crimes.

Worse, I worked hard at delivering intensive, complex psychotherapy to psychiatric inpatients. This was a big no-no in the 1990's and continues to be early in the third millennium. Makes the other shrinks look lazy and bad. While the other shrinks are claiming that managed care prevents them from doing inpatient psychotherapy, it continues alive and well in my Trauma Programs. On the same budget as everyone else has.

For this I get ex-communication. I give up. Psychiatry is going to continue down its present blind alley for at least another two decades. Futile searches for specific genes and specific biological defects for the different DSM-IV disorders. Sorry, boys, it ain't there in nature.

It is not inspiring or energy-enhancing to see your profession in a dead end. Whistle blowers get blackballed.

"Run to the hills!"

I like being a guerilla. The health insurance and dental plan are great.

71

OK, I'LL MAKE MOVIES

Over the last few years I have decided to become a producer of motion pictures. Don't look for my first release for a few months yet. Why have I decided on this career move? I'll concede it's a long shot.

Actually, it isn't a career move. It is a career expansion. There are several reasons for it. First and foremost, moolah. Second and second-most, have lots of fun. Third, and foremost, I decided it is necessary to do an end run around psychiatry. I could talk and write about multiple personality and trauma in academic journals for another twenty years. Which I intend to do. But I am worried about the thickness of the calluses on my forehead. I want to hurry up the process.

So I plan to go to the real world. What better pipeline than movies? The resistance to accepting the Trauma Model, within psychiatry, is really big. I am tired of fighting it. I'm not talking about academic skepticism, scientific caution, or reasonable criticism. I'm talking about ugly, hostile, close-minded stonewalling. It's just really, really tiring.

I thought if I could educate the public, then I could get pressure back on psychiatry from the outside. This is how the recognition of child abuse has happened. Academic psychiatry has bucked and fought first the reality and then the relevance of child abuse every step of the way. The pressure and motivation has come entirely from outside the medical schools and outside psychiatry.

At the beginning of the third millennium A.D., psychiatry is still in the dark ages on trauma. So it's off to Hollywood. I'm thinking that there I could find healthy people who are interested in reality.

"Whoops. Maybe not."

One of the pathologies of our culture is a disconnection, a cultural dissociation. Hollywood is entertaining and creative, but superficial and empty. Academia is serious but boring. Where in our culture can you be both entertaining and profound at the same time? Not in hackademic prose. Not in Hollywood. Not on network TV.

The challenge is to combine the seriousness of academia with the entertainment and creativity of Hollywood. This is not a new idea. Shakespeare did it. And who was he? He didn't even have a Ph.D. And he was never invited to give Grand Rounds at Harvard. So he and I have two things in common.

Little Colin and Big Bill. I'm fine being grandiose with respect to twentieth century psychiatry. Shakespeare? Nuh, uh. I'm not that far gone.

72

KISSING THE BUTT OF MANAGED CARE

Psychiatry is in a very undignified position with respect to managed care. Kissing its butt. I remember in med school, I did one rigid sigmoidoscopy. Under the supervision of a surgeon. A rigid sigmoidoscope is a tube about an inch in diameter and maybe eighteen inches long. It has a light that shines out the bottom. You stick the sigmoidoscope up the patient's butt and look around at his rectum and sigmoid colon.

First, the patient lies face down on the sigmoidoscopy table. Then buttons are pushed so the table lifts up in the center. This leaves the patient with his butt up in the air, his legs hanging down the near side, and the top half of him hanging down the far side.

The next step is to throw back the patient's hospital gown. Which was already half open anyway. Then you stick the sigmoidoscope in a couple of inches and turn on the light. Then you open the little window. It is important to step back at this point in the procedure to allow for pressure equalization between the inside of the rectum and the outside air in the room.

If you forget to step back, you can get a silent one right in the nose. Then you push the tube up and look around. This is the most embarrassing, undignified procedure in medicine. It is nothing compared to the performance going on between shrinks and managed care.

I have heard approximately seventeen thousand shrinks moan and groan about managed care. They have forgotten to ask one important question.

"Why do we have managed care?"

We have managed care because the doctors were out of control. They were billing the hell out of the system and weren't going to stop till the country was bankrupt. Psychiatry is a small-bucks part of medicine. Doctors as a whole were out of control.

I was actively, repeatedly taught to order absurd numbers of lab tests in medical school. Whenever I questioned the thousands and thousands of wasted dollars, I was met with a decisive counter-argument. One which silenced all discussion.

"If it was your grandmother, would you want any stone left unturned?"

That was all the teaching on medical economics I got at medical school. I was taught to ignore medical economics. Somewhere in Ottawa there were some evil bureaucrats who wanted to interfere with the doctor-patient relationship. It was our ethical and moral duty to resist such interference with the doctor-patient relationship.

It was really all about the doctor-wallet relationship.

My duty was to my individual patient. Coincidentally, fee-for-service was also my teachers' income source. I should never, ever let cost stand in the way of doing the best for my patient.

The problem was, doing the best translated into a ridiculous waste of resources - expensive, obscure tests that never told us anything. This was called *chasing canaries*. Chasing canaries was not the right thing to do, supposedly. But in fact we spent half our day chasing canaries. We were a group of morally righteous canary chasers. Or technically, Wilson's warblers chasers, since there are no wild canaries in Canada.

We have managed care because the doctors would not manage themselves. That pisses me off. I have to deal with the bullshit of managed care because my teachers and Professors were out of control. They taught me to be out of control. I resisted.

I remember at the Department of Shrinkiatry at St. Boniface Hospital, the neurologists were pissed because the shrinks were always ordering EEGs and CT scans of patients' heads. They were being doctors. Real doctors. Or so they thought. The neurologists were pissed because they were tired of reading all the normal EEGs. The shrinks never found anything. It was a waste of time and money.

I was with the neurologists. The shrinks needed to stop ordering EEGs and CT scans. But the noise that went up! I never heard so much whining, bleating and defensive posturing in my life. The shrinks were incensed that they couldn't get no respect.

"We is real dockers too, ya knows."

"Dad gum it."

In fact, the shrinks were just pathetic. It was a pathetic attempt to pass for real doctors. Later, I published a study. The shrinks also wasted a fortune on thyroid tests. I did an analysis of the yield from twenty grand of thyroid tests. Zero. Complete waste of blood and money. I showed that you could perform a systematic screen on everybody for $6,000.00.

Instead, the shrinks were ordering a chaotic mess of different combinations of thyroid tests on a hit-and-miss basis. On half the patients at random. It had nothing to do with medicine or science. A license to order lab tests is a dangerous thing. If you have no medical sense and no fiscal responsibility, you need to be controlled from the outside.

Welcome to managed care. I did the thyroid study in Canada in the 1980's. Had a hell of a time getting it published because of bogus objections by the shrinks who reviewed it for journal editors. There was no way the shrinks were going down without a fight. They rationalized ordering useless tests and wasting money big time. All dressed up as science and cutting edge biological psychiatry. What a farce.

Doctors have lost control of the health care system. It's their own fault. The pose as victims of managed care is another part of The Great Psychiatry Scam. The shrinks and doctors pose as protectors of patients. It's about wallets, not patients.

If we let up on managed care for one month, doctors would be right back to where they were ten years ago. Pushing health care expenditures upward on a curve that would intersect with Gross National Product in the first half of the twenty-first century. Driving the culture bankrupt. The freight train had to be stopped.

The political posturing of doctors is the most sickening and hypocritical thing they do. The only reason we have managed care is that doctors were looking after their wallets, not patients. The doctors are not the victims of managed care. They are the cause of it.

Is managed care totally insane? Yes. We can thank the doctors for that curse. And if they keep on whining, you know what's going to happen. The screws will get turned tighter.

Managed care is out of control. We have gone from one curse to another. What is the solution? Managed care for managed care? That sounds good. Let's introduce another layer of costs and bureaucracy. Soon we will have managed managed care.

Some day maybe, we could just have managed. We could dispense with the care part altogether. We're almost there already.

I still hear shrinks wax nostalgic for the good old days when you could keep patients in the hospital for months. Bill for them seven days a week and see them three times for five minutes. And never have anyone question your divine wisdom or review your chart.

I could have made millions of dollars if I came to the U.S. in the seventies. Setting up programs in different hospitals. Millions. Per year. Oh, well. I missed out on the good old days. Which is handy. I am less depressed than my colleagues who are still grieving that loss.

It was tough for the shrinks, when managed care came in. All of a sudden, society rejected a major component of The Great Psychiatry Scam. There was no stock market crash. But there was a shrink income crash. Sad, huh?

“Anybody got a kleenex?”

73

THE STATE OF THE CARPETS

What's wrong with psychiatry today? Normally, to answer a question like that, you'd have to set up a big Committee, allocate a few million dollars, and issue a fat report with lots of Appendices. All that time and energy can be saved. To understand what is wrong with psychiatry today, requires only a couple of minutes.

All you have to do is take a walk down the hallways in a private for-profit psychiatric hospital. Check out the carpets. What have I seen? Cheap carpets that are worn out and have lots of stains. Supplemented with cheap, uncomfortable, mismatched, ugly, worn-out furniture. Drapes, blinds, bed sheets, wall decorations and sundry furniture are ditto.

There just isn't enough money in the system. Revenues are way too low and margins are way too tight. Staff are badly paid, burned out and frequently replaced. Since training is minimal, replacing humans is cheap compared to replacing carpets or furniture.

Then there are the bed linens. No middle class person would stay in a hotel that was as dirty and ugly as a psychiatric hospital. The physical facility of my hospital in Dallas is equivalent to a $29.95 a night motel. If you took your dry cleaning to a dry cleaner, and saw carpets like those at psychiatric hospitals, you would turn around and walk out.

What about the computers? The computer systems are in the dark ages. Both the hardware and the software are way, way behind the average for other industries. Third world, really.

Psychiatric health care in North America is funded at the third world level. If we funded NASA this way, we would have no satellites in orbit. We get what we pay for. Nineteenth century psychiatry, with drugs. It isn't the fault of the psychiatric hospital corporations. They would be happy to increase their revenues and margins. People, society, the culture, just don't care.

The problem can't be solved by giving psychiatry more money. The psychiatrists are incapable of using the money effectively. They are lost in their delusional system about genes and biological psychiatry. It is such Mickey Mouse biology. The ones who support psychotherapy are lost in the delusional system of psychoanalytic psychotherapy. With too few exceptions to make a difference.

The solution? The Trauma Model. Psychiatry needs to be re-conceptualized as a branch of public health. Public health problems, mostly diet and infectious diseases, cause far more morbidity and mortality on the planet than fancy, high-tech diseases. Even in North America, most of the action is due to street drugs, alcohol, tobacco, lack of exercise and bad diet.

Same with psychiatry. Sure there are people with single, distinct psychiatric disorders, of whom some may have distinct genetic abnormalities. But these people are a drop in the bucket. The epidemic of horrendous bad mental health in North America today is overwhelmingly an environmental problem. Distinct genes for distinct mental illnesses account for maybe 2% of the serious mental illness in our culture. Or 2.4%.

Instead of viruses, bacteria, high-fat diets, drugs, alcohol and cigarettes, in psychiatry we have abuse, neglect, family violence and other forms of psychological trauma. Which the shrinks ignore. The shrinks are wrong. Biologically, medically and scientifically. It doesn't work by specific genes for specific DSM-IV disorders. Or specific Fraudian mechanisms inside individual human beings. It's the polluted drinking water.

You can tell how much serious energy, resources and expertise are being put into the problem of mental illness by looking at the carpets. Psychiatry in its current form isn't worth investing in, beyond a token minimum. Everyone knows that. Psychiatry just isn't there. Hasn't got it. Can't do it. The state of the carpets is a direct measure of the value of psychiatry to the human race early in the twenty-first century. Psychiatry is less valued than dry cleaning.

74

THE TRAUMA MODEL

Why do I keep referring to my other books in this book? Because my books are a unified body of thought. Including the present one. Including *The Trauma Model: A Solution to the Problem of Comorbidity in Psychiatry*.

Book-length, unified, scientifically testable theories of psychopathology do not come down the pike every week in psychiatry. In fact, *The Trauma Model* is the first one. The Trauma Model is my fundamental gift to psychiatry. It is a comprehensive theory of mental illness. I have formulated the Trauma Model very carefully. To be scientific.

To be scientific, a theory does not have to be correct. It only has to be testable. The Trauma Model leads to literally hundreds of specific research projects in psychiatry and psychology. It re-organizes and re-conceptualizes the existing literature. I've called it a Model, but it is full-bodied, intricate, deep and original. It meets the criteria for a Theory.

The basic idea of the Trauma Model is pretty simple. The hyperbolic of the parabolic curvilinear is to the asymptote of the exponential as the corpus callosum is to the hippocampus, given the necessary corrections for biomolecular noise at the messenger RNA level.

What a minute. Let me try that again. The basic idea of the Trauma Model is pretty simple. Trauma is a big deal in psychiatry. Much bigger than genes.

"Want a little more? OK."

The Trauma Model is set up so that every one of its assumptions is specified and every one of its predictions is testable. For example, people with multiple personality never have just multiple personality. MPD/DID never exists in isolation. At least not among psychiatric inpatients. Multiples always have tons of comorbidity. Which means lots of other psychiatric problems.

Anxiety, depression, substance abuse, eating disorders, personality disorders. . . the list goes on. Why?

From within the conceptual model of twentieth century psychiatry, which is unchanged at the dawn of the new millennium, the comorbidity of DID doesn't make any sense. You can do a little calculation. Let's say that undiagnosed DID affects 5% of general adult psychiatric inpatients. In Charter hospitals in the United States alone, this meant 6000 admissions per year, when I was in the Charter system, before Charter closed. That's a big problem just by itself.

Then look at the levels of comorbidity in these patients. On average, over their lifetimes, they have met DSM-IV criteria for 12-15 different psychiatric disorders. It is absurd to suggest that so many people could have so many independent disorders. It is also statistically impossible. Why?

Take the baseline rate of these disorders in the general population. Just for example, using round numbers, let's say 10% of people will get clinically depressed sometime in their lives. Two percent will have panic disorder. Two per cent will have posttraumatic stress disorder.

If these are separate disorders, as shrinkdom claims, the number of people who will have all three is easy to calculate. It is 0.02 x 0.02 x 0.1 = 0.00004 of the population. If there are a quarter of a billion people in the US of A, then 10,000 people should have all three disorders.

My patients average 10 - 12 different psychiatric disorders each. Six thousand of them were admitted to the Charter system alone per year. This doesn't add up.

What percentage of the population should have that many different, independent disorders? There are over ten zeros after the decimal place. Which means that less than one person in a trillion should have that many disorders in one lifetime. Which means nobody on the planet. But 6000 got admitted to the Charter system alone per year, before Charter went out of business.

By a very long shot, it doesn't add up. Psychiatry's solution to this problem has been to ignore it. Or laugh at it. What does the Trauma Model have to say?

According to the Trauma Model, all this comorbidity is the normal, typical, expected human reaction to chronic childhood trauma. Chronic childhood abuse and neglect don't cause just anxiety, or just depression, or just dissociative symptoms. They cause a whole bunch of different symptoms. The exact picture varies from person to person for numerous researchable reasons specified by the Model.

The psychiatric disorders are not independent diseases. They are different elements of the trauma response.

Here's a prediction that would never arise from conventional psychiatry.

The hierarchy of comorbidity in DID predicts the percentage of each diagnostic category that will report chronic childhood trauma in the general population. What does that mean? Simple. But elegant. And never dreamed of in the sleep of regular shrinkdom.

All you do is list the frequency of the different disorders that go along with DID. Based on standardized diagnostic interviews given to DID patients. Depression will be most common, then panic disorder, then substance abuse, then eating disorders, then schizophrenia. I've left a lot of disorders out of the hierarchy in order to make the previous sentence shorter. But you get the idea.

The next step is to go out in the general population and give the same diagnostic interviews to 20,000 people. The more, the merrier. Also, you have to make a standardized inquiry about childhood trauma. Then you convert this to a trauma dose number. Then you figure out the average trauma dose score for each diagnosis. Or you simply calculate the percentage of each diagnostic group that reports serious, chronic childhood trauma. There are different wrinkles on the methodology.

The prediction? The hierarchy in the general population will be the same as that in the DID comorbidity study. The most common comorbid diagnosis in DID will be the one with the highest trauma rate in the general population. Number two in DID will be number two in the general population, et cetera. Et ceteree. Et cetero. O cicero. Cicero, Cicero, Cicero.

"I am the Barber of Seville. I shave the heads of shrinks at will."

Why will the study work out like this? Because DID patients teach us the logic and structure of the normal human response to chronic childhood trauma. Ridiculous? Maybe. A scientific hypothesis? You bet. Refutable using the tactics of psychological warfare? You bet. Politically. In science? No. But then science ain't got much to do with shrinkdom. And vice versa.

The shrinks claim that they are doctors and scientists. No way. The Emperor has no lab coat. And no stethoscope. It is all a scam. The Great Psychiatry Scam. One of the tests of my theory about the Scam, will be the reception given to the Trauma Model.

It is easy to predict. Silence. Chill. A few stabs.

The Trauma Model finally brings some real biology to psychiatry. The biology of the normal human response to psychological trauma. Forget specific genes for specific diagnoses. Forget Sigmund Dr. Fraud. The biology of trauma. That's where the gold is, in them thar hills. The trauma hills. Where the guerillas are hiding.

I will close with a dream. Last night I dreamt that research had proven fact number one. Fact number one: chronic trauma raises the levels of cortisol in the blood. Cortisol is the mammalian stress response hormone *par excellence*, as we say in Italy.

Also, fact number two. Fact number two. In chronically stressed mammals, elevated cortisol affects one part of the brain in a specific way. The hippocampus. The high levels of cortisol affect gating mechanisms in the walls of brain cells in the hippocampus. But not elsewhere in the brain. At least not to the same degree.

Fact three: the altered gates allow more toxins to enter the hippocampal neurons, resulting in cell damage and death.

Fact four: the hippocampus has the job of integrating perception and memory into a unified whole.

Five: the hippocampus is damaged in chronically traumatized mammals in two ways. It is shrunken, and it doesn't function as well. The shrinking can be detected on MRI scan, the low function on PET scan.

Six: the clinical presentation of DID patients is exactly what one would expect to see in individuals with damaged hippocampi.

Seven: the clinical picture of the DID patient treated to stable integration is profoundly improved, profoundly *repaired*, compared to the picture at the start of therapy. In terms of symptoms, diagnoses, health care utilization, employment, and life satisfaction. The improvement can be measured in dollars.

Eight: the hippocampi of the successfully integrated DID patient will normalize on MRI and PET scan.

Nine: once this finding is replicated and accepted, something will have been demonstrated for the first time in the history of western medicine.

The regeneration of central nervous system tissue through a specific medical intervention. One possible only in mammals with complex verbal languages. The intervention? Psychotherapy.

I dreamt that psychiatry didn't want to hear about it. Why? Because shrinks are not real doctors, or real scientists. They are too busy running The Great Psychiatry Scam.

I'm not sure if I have woken up yet. Or maybe I didn't have that dream. Maybe I am just a frog on another planet in another galaxy dreaming that I'm dreaming about psychiatry on earth. I hope so. Because then I could wake up and become a Prince. Assuming there are beautiful Grant Agencies on that planet to kiss me.

Maybe a psychiatrist could help me understand my dream. For under twenty grand. In less than ten years.

"Zzzzzzzz."

"Huh? What? Where am I? Oh. Earth. I still haven't been abducted by aliens."

"These guys are sure taking their sweet time. They're starting to piss me off."

"Excuse me, Dr. Ross, I say, do be quiet."

"Sorry, Basil. Sorry."

"It's so confusing trying to decide what Club I am in. All I know is, it ain't shrinkiatry. I ain't gonna be part of that Scam. No siree."

But the Club is a good place to sleep. So quiet. Nothing going on. No noisy thinking or research. Nothing like that. Not at the Psychiatry Club.

Good night.